PENGUIN

THE ILIAD

The Greeks attributed both the *Iliad* and the *Odyssey* to a single poet whom they named Homer. Nothing is known of his life, though the main ancient tradition made him a native of the island of Chios, in the east Aegean. His date too is uncertain: most modern scholars place the composition of the *Iliad* in the second half of the eighth century B.C.

MARTIN HAMMOND was born in 1944 and educated at Winchester College and Balliol College, Oxford, from where he graduated in 1966 in Literae Humaniores. Since leaving Oxford, he has taught in England and in Greece. On his return from Greece, he became Assistant Master at Harrow School and in 1974 moved to Eton College, where he was Head of Classics for six years before becoming Master in College. He was appointed Headmaster of the City of London School in 1984, and Headmaster of Tonbridge School in 1990. He is married with two children.

HOMER

THE ILIAD

TRANSLATED WITH AN INTRODUCTION
BY MARTIN HAMMOND

PENGUIN BOOKS

PENGUIN BOOKS

Published by the Penguin Group
Penguin Books Ltd, 27 Wrights Lane, London W8 5TZ, England
Penguin Books USA Inc., 375 Hudson Street, New York, New York 10014, USA
Penguin Books Australia Ltd, Ringwood, Victoria, Australia
Penguin Books Canada Ltd, 10 Alcorn Avenue, Toronto, Ontario, Canada M4V 3B2
Penguin Books (NZ) Ltd, 182–190 Wairau Road, Auckland 10, New Zealand

Penguin Books Ltd, Registered Offices: Harmondsworth, Middlesex, England

First published 1987
9 10

Copyright © Martin Hammond, 1987
All rights reserved

Printed in England by Clays Ltd, St Ives plc
Filmset in 9 on 10½ Ehrhardt

Except in the United States of America, this book is sold subject
to the condition that it shall not, by way of trade or otherwise, be lent,
re-sold, hired out, or otherwise circulated without the publisher's
prior consent in any form of binding or cover other than that in
which it is published and without a similar condition including this
condition being imposed on the subsequent purchaser

CONTENTS

INTRODUCTION

The *Iliad* is the first substantial work of European literature, and has fair claim to be the greatest. The influence of the *Iliad* determined much in subsequent Greek literature, thought, and art, and thereby much that is central to the European tradition: it may fairly be described as the cornerstone of Western civilisation.

This is an astonishing achievement. And yet of the circumstances of the *Iliad*'s creation – date, provenance, authorship – little can be said with certainty. The Greeks attributed both the *Iliad* and the other great early epic poem, the *Odyssey* (which is clearly set in a deliberate relation to the *Iliad*), to a single poet whom they named Homer, and located variously in the Ionian cities of the Asia Minor coast or the east Aegean islands, the main tradition setting Homer in the island of Chios. It is likely that the composer of the *Iliad* was indeed an Ionian, and that the poem was composed in the latter part of the eighth century B.C. Whether the poet of the *Iliad* also composed the *Odyssey* is quite uncertain, and proof is hardly possible one way or the other. The *Odyssey* presupposes the *Iliad*, and may have been composed in conscious emulation of the greater poem. A variety of evidence suggests that the *Odyssey* was composed perhaps about a generation later than the *Iliad*, and it is by no means impossible that the same poet created the two epics, the *Odyssey* as the work of his old age.

THE BACKGROUND TO THE *ILIAD*

THE EPICS AS ORAL POETRY

What is certain, and important, is that the two Homeric epics stand at the end of a long and rich tradition of *oral* poetry, and form, perhaps consciously, its triumphant culmination. Behind the achievement of the *Iliad* and the *Odyssey* lies the work of generations of highly skilled and professional oral poets, illiterate singers in an illiterate age who composed and transmitted their repertoire of songs without the aid of writing. 'Composition' in the context of oral poetry includes not only the creation of original material but also the adaptation, elaboration, or conflation of songs learnt from other performers. Composition and performance are one and the same act: and extemporisation, controlled and guided by a complex inheritance of forms of expression and narrative themes, is an essential feature of the oral poet's skill. The subject-matter of these songs is the doings of gods and men in a semi-legendary heroic past. The occasions for their performance will have been gatherings of men with the time and desire to hear them, ranging from aristocratic feasts in the halls of noblemen to the ancient equivalents of the popular festivals, fairs, and markets which are a characteristic feature of social life in modern rural Greece.

There is literary reflection of these singers and their songs in the Homeric poems themselves. The *Odyssey* introduces two court poets, presented as inspired artists held in high respect, whose function is to provide entertainment after the feast for the delight of the nobles gathered in the king's palace. Phemios, the poet of Odysseus' household in Ithaka, is obliged to sing for the suitors who have taken over the palace in the absence of his master. We are told the subject of one of his songs – the story of the Achaians' painful homecoming from Troy (in the literary context of the *Odyssey* this is of course recent history, not a song of the heroic past). Phemios has an extensive repertoire, and Penelope asks him to choose a less distressing subject (this story sets her weeping for her husband): 'Phemios, you know many other ways to charm men's ears – deeds of men and gods that poets celebrate. Sing one of these to the suitors here, and they can drink their wine in silence as they listen' (*Od.* 1. 337f.). Her young son Telemachos defends the choice on the grounds of novelty – 'men always praise the most the song which comes freshest to their ears' – and his observation is doubtless true of the conditions under which Homer himself and his immediate predecessors worked. In a parallel passage later in the *Odyssey* Odysseus himself asks Demodokos, the blind poet at the court of King Alkinoös in Phaiacia, to sing the story of the Wooden Horse, and is overcome by emotion as he listens to it. Shortly before, Demodokos had sung a different sort of song for the amusement of the company – a light and sophisticated tale of Olympian adultery between Ares and Aphrodite, and the revenge of her husband Hephaistos. There are no such singers in the sterner world of the *Iliad* – only the keeners set beside the bodies of the dead – but the tradition of heroic song finds pointed reference in Homer's treatment of the two most complex and self-aware characters of the *Iliad*, Achilleus and Helen.

When the embassy of leading Achaians comes to Achilleus' hut to beg his return to the fighting, they find him 'giving pleasure to his heart with a clear-voiced lyre . . . and singing tales of men's glory' (9. 186ff.). And Helen, whose sharp sensibility of her guilt is contrasted with her abductor's insouciance, so that she loads herself with the contempt that others feel for Paris, sees them both in the perspective of history: 'On us two Zeus has set a doom of misery, so that in time to come we can be themes of song for men of future generations' (6. 357ff.).

Such 'themes of song' were Homer's inheritance – a wealth of stories of gods and men, fanciful or semi-historical, or a mixture of both, created and transmitted in a multiplicity of versions by generations of oral poets, whose performances would vary with the nature and demands of their audience, and doubtless with their own skill in re-working, elaborating, or conflating elements of a fluid tradition.

THE *ILIAD* AS HISTORY

A particularly rich source of material for this tradition was the accretion of history and saga surrounding the Trojan War – the preliminaries, the war itself, and the varied fortunes of the victorious Achaians on their return from Troy. There is a substantial element of historical truth in the tradition, in that the city of Troy, in the north-west corner of Asia Minor, was indeed destroyed, after what appears to have been a prolonged siege, towards the end of the thirteenth century B.C., when the kings of golden Mykenai held a loose hegemony over the rest of mainland Greece in the late Bronze Age – all this some five hundred years before the composition of the *Iliad*.

Achaian civilisation declined and collapsed within a century of the Trojan War, and it is likely enough that stories of the great expedition to Troy and the long battle there were circulating in song within a generation or two of the events. Certainly the violent overthrow of the centres of Mycenaean power and culture in the late twelfth century, and the beginning of the so-called Dark Age, will have encouraged the growth of the tradition of a heroic age, a time when great men lived and great deeds were done. The half-remembered glories of Mycenaean civilisation in the Bronze Age provided a semi-historical basis for this poetic tradition, though with a compression characteristic of such traditions the Greeks confined their heroic age to a span of three or four generations, and centred it on two great wars in succeeding generations, the campaign against Thebes led by the fathers of the heroes of the Trojan War (the 'Seven against Thebes'), and the Trojan expedition itself. In the *Iliad* the engaging figure of Nestor provides a constant link with the earlier generation of heroes, and his reminiscences frequently contain the notion of a decline from a greater and more glorious past – a standard element in traditions of a heroic age which appears in the poet's own reflections on the contrast between his characters and 'the folk that live now'.

The transmission and elaboration of the repertoire of songs concerning the Trojan War in the five centuries that separate the actual war from the time of Homer is largely a matter of speculation. As poet learnt from poet, and added his own elaborations or variants, the element of historical or cultural accuracy (perhaps not very strong even at the beginning) would inevitably weaken, and various accretions would extend and dilute the tradition (for example the introduction of mythological figures, perhaps including Achilleus himself, who had no original connection with the Trojan saga). The result of centuries of such fluid adaptation and accretion is evident in the Homeric poems. Elements of historical fidelity to the late Bronze Age remain – notably the political geography of the Achaian world, the almost universal predominance of bronze (as opposed to iron) as the metal for weapons and tools, and certain features of arms and armour – but the poems are in general a linguistic, cultural, and material amalgam, combining elements which reflect every stage of the transmission of Trojan War poetry. No Greek ever spoke quite the language of Homer – it is a literary construct, a strong Ionic base overlaid with other dialects and specifically 'epic' forms – and no society combined quite the range of practice and material culture displayed in the Homeric poems.

THE ORAL TRADITION AND HOMER

A characteristic and essential feature of orally composed and transmitted poetry is the dominant part played in composition by the variety of repetitions, standard phrases, and verbal or thematic templates conventionally known as 'formulas'. Obvious examples in the *Iliad* are recurrent combinations of noun and epithet ('swift-footed godlike Achilleus', 'sacred Ilios', 'long-shadowed spear'), lines introducing speech or answer, descriptions of attack, wounding, and death ('he fell with a crash, and his armour clattered about him', 'over his eyes came the surge of death and strong fate took him'), and more extended descriptions of important or ritual processes (arming, sacrifice, preparation of food). The reading of only a few hundred lines of the *Iliad* will reveal the extent of this principle of composition. Within larger narrative blocks (indeed within the whole sweep of the entire *Iliad*) the attentive reader will become aware of the poet's use of *thematic* 'formulas' – repeated situations, with or without variants, repeated sequences of events, parallel narrative structures. Such a system, developed to a greater or less degree of elaboration, is an essential aid to the oral poet, enabling him at one level (the verbal template) to meet the demands of his metrical unit (the Greek hexameter being a particularly sophisticated and flexible medium), and at another level (the thematic template) to control the architecture of his narrative. The poet has at his disposal an inherited store of building-blocks, in a huge variety of sizes and shapes, ranging from single short phrases to whole passages of several lines, and also a considerable set of architectural themes or designs of varying compass to help him shape his structure – and of course he will pass on the inheritance adapted or enriched with elements of his own personal style and invention. The success and quality of a singer's creation will depend on the richness of the tradition within which he works and his own skill, experience, and originality in handling his material. The Greek epic tradition was exceptionally rich, in both matter and manner, and highly skilled (as comparison with other oral traditions of poetry quickly demonstrates), and by the time of Homer centuries of selection, rejection, and refinement had created a formulaic system of astonishing complexity, flexibility, and economy.

Such was the necessary groundwork – a rich and finely-tilled seedbed – for Homer's achievement. The Homeric poems are in one sense the creation and final flowering of a long and distinguished tradition, and could not have taken shape independently of that tradition. Even so, it is clear that Homer was a poetic genius of quite exceptional power and range, who far excelled his predecessors (and his few successors) in technical skill, breadth of vision, quality of imagination, and sheer ambition. In the language of philosophy, the pre-existing epic tradition was a necessary cause of the phenomenon of Homer, but not a sufficient cause. The pure scale of the Homeric poems signals their uniqueness (the *Iliad* contains over 15,000 lines, the *Odyssey* some 12,000). It is a reasonable guess that the *Iliad* is at least ten times longer than the longest song that a poet would normally present to his audience, whatever the nature of the gathering. The creation of the *Iliad*, then, demands a poet with the confidence, ambition, and originality to compose a poem on a quite unprecedented scale, and the reputation to command an audience and determine an occasion or occasions for its performance (and its performance as a whole: the *Iliad* is not a bolted-together accumulation of separable stories or incidents, but a clearly and elaborately structured unity). We can only speculate on the conditions of performance of the *Iliad*. What is clear and important is that Homer did have the authority to impose his radically new concept of the monumental epic on the audience of his time: and that quite rapidly (to judge by the artistic and literary evidence) the Homeric poems became widely known throughout the Greek world, and recognised as without question the definitive voice of epic poetry, and the major influence on all subsequent Greek literature – so that the Greeks could refer to Homer simply as 'the poet'.

The practical need of a formulaic framework for the oral poet is readily intelligible: the literary effect is a function of the quality of the tradition and the poet's skill. In less skilled hands, or within an impoverished tradition, the effect may be dull, mechanical, and repetitive (such is often the impression given by the modern Yugoslavian oral poets, much studied in recent years for the light they might shed on the Greek tradition, though the illumination is generally oblique and remote). Most readers' experience of Homer is quite different. The traditional features of expression and structure in the composition of the poems, and Homer's consummate skill in the control of this traditional medium, are rightly regarded as one of the chief and distinctive glories of Homeric art. The general effect of the pervasive formulaic expression – repeated epithets and descriptive phrases for gods, people, and things, standard lines for regular actions and events, unvaried descriptions of ritual or semi-ritual processes – is to shed a rich dignity over the Homeric world, and to invest the elements of that world with universal significance. This universalising effect of the traditional poetic style, expressive of an ordered and stable world in which all things have their proper excellence and beauty, stands throughout the *Iliad* in moving contrast with the narrative action, whose tone is set in the opening lines. These speak of pitiable doings. The story will be one of pain, discord, destruction, desecration – of a world gone awry, in which fine men die before their time and their bodies lie unburied, torn by dogs and carrion birds. This constant tension intensifies the tragic quality of the poem – the *Iliad* is the first, and the greatest, of the Greek tragedies. Only in the last book of the *Iliad*, which is set in a conscious and elaborate relation to the first, is disorder set to rights, and a perverted world restored, albeit only for a short while, to proper order.

The general effect of the traditional features of epic style is readily felt, even in translation, and contributes greatly to our enjoyment of the poem. Less immediately apparent is Homer's skill and subtlety in turning elements of *practical* technique (especially repetition) to the achievement of *literary* effects – effects of emphasis, contrast, irony, pathos, cumulation. Particularly skilful, because dependent on sensitive and highly selective control throughout the whole length of the *Iliad*, is his use of repeated lines or repeated narrative patterns to establish and emphasise significant points of structure, including elaborate forward and backward references within the poem which set or suggest a relation – parallel, contrasting, or ironic – between characters or events. A striking example lies in the sequence of major encounters, resulting in the death of a great hero, which dominates the structure of the final third of the *Iliad* – Patroklos and Sarpedon, Hektor and Patroklos, Achilleus and Hektor. The narrative implications establish this as a significant sequence, but the particular and tragic relation between the death of Patroklos and the death of Hektor is further emphasised by forms of words, descriptions of death, and narrative structures which are common to both episodes but not used elsewhere in the *Iliad*, and so reserved specifically for these two important and importantly linked deaths. Both episodes include the notion of the gods calling the hero to his death (an identical half-line, 16. 693 = 22. 297, which does not recur elsewhere). Common to these two episodes alone is the fine passage describing the moment of death (16. 855ff. = 22. 361ff.):

As he spoke the end of death enfolded him: and his spirit flitted from his body and went on the way to Hades, weeping for its fate, and the youth and manhood it must leave.

Both episodes contain an otherwise unparalleled sequence of verbal exchanges between victor and victim, in which the dying hero warns that the killer will himself be killed. These verbal and thematic repetitions, specific and exclusive to the deaths of Patroklos and Hektor, serve to link the two in necessary sequence in the tragic movement of the whole poem, and point forward to that still greater death which, though lying outside the *Iliad*, is yet part of its focus – the death of Achilleus. This cross-referencing use of repetition to point the structure of the poem can be seen at its most extended range in the close and elaborate relation which Homer has set between the first book of the *Iliad* and the last – a vast frame which unites the action of the *Iliad*. The *Iliad* opens with the old man Chryses appealing to Agamemnon for the return of his captive daughter, and his appeal is rudely rejected. In the great closing scene of the *Iliad* Priam visits Achilleus to beg for the body of Hektor. There has intervened all the suffering and death of the *Iliad*, all partly determined by that first act of rejection. Once more an old man, a father, and a suppliant appeals to a proud, unstable, violent king for the return of his child, and this time his appeal is accepted. The relation between the two scenes is pointed by a number of clear parallels of structure and linguistic detail. Both suppliants, for example, are threatened with rough words and frightened into submission. The same line, 'So he spoke, and the old man was afraid and did as he was ordered', is used of Chryses' response to Agamemnon (1. 33), and then once again of Priam's response to Achilleus (24. 571). The second use recalls the first context, and serves both to emphasise the parallel and to point to the contrast between the two related scenes. Such cross-references, of varying degrees of elaboration, abound throughout the *Iliad*, giving structure and significance to the narrative sequence, and revealing the unity of conception which runs through the whole length of the poem.

It is important for the reader of Homer to understand something of the tradition within which the poet worked, and the techniques of composition which that tradition had evolved, if only because the Greek oral tradition is a particularly interesting part of literary history, and accounts for some immediately noticeable features of the texture of the Homeric poems. Equally important, once that understanding is gained, is for the reader to dismiss it largely from his mind, and not allow it to distort his intuitive response to Homer's poetry. The poems could not have been composed without the traditional technique of verbal and thematic formulas, but Homer's extraordinarily skilful control of the technique allows him all the sophistication and subtlety of more 'literary' epic poets (Virgil, say, or Milton), and perhaps some additional virtues beyond their scope. The traditional technique, in Homer's hands, is no bar to variety and flexibility of style, or to subtle use of language and reference, or to the control and direction of narrative within an overall structure of conscious unity, or to the coherent presentation of a particular tragic vision of man's place within the divine governance of the world. Awareness of the poem's oral composition may rightly affect some points of detailed interpretation: but generally the *Iliad* deserves, and will repay, the approach that would be natural to any other great work of literature.

THE THEME OF THE *ILIAD*

The *Iliad* announces its subject in the first line. The poem will tell of the anger of Achilleus and its consequences – consequences for the Achaians, the Trojans, and Achilleus himself. Achilleus' anger does indeed dominate the story of the *Iliad*. All the major events of the poem – near-defeat of the Achaian army, the entry of Achilleus' friend Patroklos into the fighting, the death of Patroklos, the death of Hektor – spring in unbroken sequence from the anger that entered Achilleus as a result of the quarrel with Agamemnon described in the brilliant opening scenes of the first book.

This was not an obvious choice of theme for a large-scale epic concerned with the Trojan War, and as the poem progresses it becomes clear that Homer's conception of theme and treatment is bold, sophisticated, and highly original. He chose to concentrate on a very short period in the tenth and final year of a long war. The whole story of the *Iliad* is contained within the span of fifty-two days. The bulk of this time is accounted for by the parallel intervals of inactivity (dramatically speaking) set at the very beginning and the very end of the poem, which serve to frame and insulate the main action of the *Iliad*. This main action, running from Book 2 to Book 23, occupies only four full days. These four days determine the fate of Troy, and of Achilleus. The death of Achilleus and the fall of Troy lie outside the narrative of the *Iliad*, but are clearly seen, both by the poet and by his characters, as inevitable further events in the causal sequence started by Achilleus' anger. The death of Hektor symbolises the destruction of Troy, and the laments at Hektor's burial with which the poem ends are also laments for Troy. It was open to the poet to deal explicitly with these final events implied by his story (and indeed to extend the story's range to encompass the entire war). His allusive reticence contributes powerfully to the tragic intensity of the poem, and the chosen ending brings a particular sense of completion, as anger turns to pity and respect, and with suffering has come fellow-suffering and understanding, set in the context of the universal fate of mortals in the divine scheme. Homer's choice of theme for the *Iliad*, rigorously limited in time and place, creates an intensity and clarity of focus which invests the surface narrative with emotion and significance beyond the mere events, and constantly turns action and character into archetypes or symbols. The astonishing compression of immediate reference to a particular fragment of a major war, and that before its conclusion, allows the poem's scope to expand to the presentation of a universal and tragic view of the world, of human life lived under the shadow of death, against a vast and largely unpitying divine background. War is not the main subject of the *Iliad*, nor heroism, but human suffering and death. The young men, for all their godlike greatness, die: the old men, the women and children suffer and grieve: the gods, exempt from pain, look on.

The manner of the *Odyssey* is in striking, and probably deliberate, contrast to that of the *Iliad*. The *Iliad* is intensive, the *Odyssey* extensive. The action of the *Odyssey* ranges widely over time and place, encompassing the limits of the known and the unknown world, and exposing Odysseus to all imaginable forms of experience on or beneath the earth. The *Iliad* is a tragedy, the *Odyssey* a romance: between them these two great epic poems have determined much of the course of Western literature, and it is tempting to think of them as successive products of a single poetic intelligence.

A CRITICAL SUMMARY OF THE *ILIAD*

BOOK I AS INTRODUCTION

The *Iliad* opens with the Trojan War in its tenth year. The scene is the Achaian camp on the shore of the Troad, where the ships that brought the army to Troy are drawn up on land. Almost all the human action in the *Iliad* is set either in this camp, or in the beleaguered city of Troy, or in the plain between Troy and the camp, the scene of most of the fighting. (Homer's regular name for the Greeks is Achaians, and he also refers to them indifferently as Danaans and Argives.)

The cause of the war was the seduction and abduction of Helen, the wife of Menelaos king of Sparta, by the Trojan Paris (also known as Alexandros), one of the sons of Priam king of Troy. Menelaos and his brother Agamemnon, the king of Mykenai, raised an army from all over Greece, which gathered at Aulis and then sailed to Troy with the purpose of recovering Helen and punishing the Trojans for Paris' crime (which was also a breach of the laws of hospitality, as at the time of the abduction Paris was being entertained in Menelaos' house). By the beginning of the *Iliad* the war has lasted for a very long time, but it is clear that the Achaians have been generally superior to the Trojans and their allies, if only because Achilleus, the leading Achaian fighter, is a much more formidable warrior than the champion of the Trojan side, Hektor son of Priam. Major Trojan success only comes when Achilleus is withdrawn from the fighting.

The *Iliad* opens directly, without any elaborate scene-setting or story-so-far retrospect. Some perspective – the setting of the immediate events in the wider context of the whole war – comes from forward references or narrative implications, increasingly significant in the latter part of the poem as the inevitability of the death of Achilleus and the fall of Troy grows sharper, and from backward references to much earlier events. In particular Books 2 to 4 function partly as a sort of reprise of the beginning of the war, either directly (as in the account of Kalchas' prophecy at Aulis in 2. 300ff.), or more often indirectly, in the 'anachronistic' presentation of events more suitable to the first than the tenth year of the war.

The brilliant first book of the *Iliad* describes the disastrous quarrel between Achilleus and Agamemnon which determines all subsequent action in the poem, and introduces elements both human and divine which will have major significance in the direction of events – the characters of Agamemnon and Achilleus, the role of Achilleus' divine mother Thetis and her knowledge of Achilleus' fate, the power of the gods and the nature of their involvement in human affairs. And it is established at the very start that the story will be one of suffering and death, as part of the divine will.

The old man Chryses comes to the Achaian camp to seek the release of his daughter Chryseïs, captured in an earlier attack on a Trojan town and allocated to Agamemnon as his concubine. Already in this first scene the poet has presented archetypes which will have central thematic importance in the poem as a whole. Chryses is the type of the old man, the innocent whose life is ruined by the war, through loss of son or daughter: a figure of dignity and pathos, for which the *Iliad* has a particular sympathy. His daughter represents that other class of pathetic innocents, 'the Trojans' wives and their little children' (6. 95 etc.). Chryses and Chryseïs contain in outline what will be fully developed in Priam and Andromache: and this early scene lays preparation for the parallel and contrasted scene in the final book, when Priam himself comes to the Achaian camp and appeals to Achilleus for the return of his son's body.

Chryses is a priest of Apollo, he brings fully adequate ransom, and his claim is upheld by all the other Achaians: but Agamemnon rejects his appeal and dismisses him with deliberate cruelty. Apollo's vengeance is swift and terrible – a plague which ravages the Achaian army. In the assembly called to consider this crisis, Agamemnon rounds on the seer who reveals the true reason for Apollo's anger, and a quarrel quickly flares between Agamemnon and Achilleus as Agamemnon insists on the provision of another 'prize' to compensate for the loss of Chryseïs, and then threatens to replace her by taking the girl who is Achilleus' own prize of honour, Briseïs. This threat is carried out immediately after the assembly. The quarrel is handled in a dramatic style of great brilliance, and again preparation is made for later parallels and contrasts. Agamemnon is presented as a stage-tyrant – insensitive, irrational, self-obsessed. He is clearly in the wrong: the Achaians think so, his own heralds are reluctant to carry out their orders to take Briseïs, Briseïs herself goes reluctantly with them. The roles are reversed later on. When Agamemnon offers full reparation, and sends an embassy of Achilleus' closest friends to plead with him to relent, it is then Achilleus who remains obdurate and self-obsessed, helpless at the mercy of a ruinous pride which beats down reason. Then Achilleus is in the wrong: the other Achaians think so, his own Myrmidons and Patroklos think so, and Achilleus knows it himself.

After Briseïs is taken from him, Achilleus calls on his mother, the sea-goddess Thetis. The scenes between Achilleus and his mother are the most poignant in the *Iliad*. Thetis, an immortal with a doomed mortal son, for whom she feels all the agony of mortal motherhood (see especially 18. 54ff.), is set at the painful edge of the gulf between god and man, and of all the gods is the only one whose nature is touched by tragedy. Tragedy is otherwise the reserve of the human actors – they can die. Achilleus is the son of a goddess: but it is characteristic of the *Iliad*'s austere humanity that this confers no invulnerability or freedom from pain – the result is to draw the mother into the world of mortality, rather than exempt the son.

Thetis tells Achilleus to withdraw completely from the fighting, and promises to secure Zeus' agreement to show honour to Achilleus by granting such success to the Trojans as will make Agamemnon realise his folly in slighting the best of the Achaian fighters. Zeus nods his head in agreement, but Hera had seen Thetis' visit to Olympos, and starts a domestic wrangle with Zeus which leads him to threaten physical violence. The quarrel subsides and turns to general laughter as a result of the intervention of Hera's son Hephaistos. There is of course an ironic and chilling contrast between the deeply serious human quarrel which begins this first book and the frivolous divine squabble which closes it. The first will achieve resolution only after untold suffering: the second is easily turned to feasting, bed, and beatitude by Hephaistos' observation that it is not worth quarrelling over humans. This contrast is essential to the *Iliad*. The care-free frivolity of 'the gods who live at their ease' (6. 138) gives definition and a sort of dignity to the pain and suffering of humankind. 'This is the fate', says Achilleus to Priam in their final fellowship of grief, 'this is the fate the gods have spun for poor mortal men, that we should live in misery, but they themselves have no sorrows' (24. 525ff.). Homer's vision is that of Sophocles also, that man is both great and insignificant. There is no comfort in the *Iliad*, but there is nobility.

The first book of the *Iliad* is grandly conceived as an introduction to the whole. There is introduced the world of men, and the world of gods, and the relation between these two worlds, symbolised in the tragic figure of Thetis. As throughout the *Iliad*, divine and human causation work in parallel, and major events are doubly determined. The quarrel is divinely caused, but splendidly imagined and evolved in purely human terms: there is careful exploration of Agamemnon and Achilleus, such that much of the subsequent human action of the *Iliad* flows intelligibly from their characters. This duality is set at the head of the poem, in the first five lines. The story is both the anger of Achilleus and the fulfilment of the will of Zeus. The divine will or whim completely interfuses human action, and is understood to do so by the actors. Human causation has its own coherence and logic, but behind all events necessarily lies the will of Zeus, inscrutable, inexplicable, and inevitable. This cardinal and comfortless fact is put in the forefront of the *Iliad*. The gods frame the action of the first book, and are revealed in all the aspects that will be fully explored in the *Iliad* – overall control, effortless intervention, passionate involvement in the world of men combined with ease of detachment, majestic grandeur, and sublime frivolity.

Achilleus is withdrawn from the fighting, and Zeus has promised major Trojan success and the discomfiture of the Achaians, so that the need of Achilleus can be felt by all. Zeus ultimately fulfils his promise to Thetis, and awareness of his solemn and irrevocable assent underlies all the intervening narrative. But the decisive Trojan breakthrough which causes Patroklos' fatally successful appeal to Achilleus is delayed for two-thirds of the length of the poem by a series of retardations, as the fighting swings this way and that, influenced by the presence or absence of divine involvement, but tending always to greater Trojan triumph. The Trojans bivouac in the plain for the first time in Book 8 (this spurs the fruitless appeal to Achilleus in Book 9): intense fighting on the following day sees the wounding of major Achaian heroes

(Agamemnon, Diomedes, Odysseus) and the breach of the Achaian wall by Sarpedon and Hektor (Books 11 and 12): later that day, despite the intervention of Poseidon on the Achaian side and the temporary distraction of Zeus by Hera (Books 13 and 14), the Trojans break the Achaian resistance and are ready to fire the ships (Book 15). Book 16 begins with Patroklos' tearful appeal to Achilleus, and there is set in train the inevitable and tragic sequence of the last third of the *Iliad*. When Thetis revisits her son in response to his cries of grief for the loss of Patroklos, her question echoes that of their first meeting in Book 1: 'Child, why are you crying? What pain has touched your heart? Tell me, do not hide it' (18. 73f. = 1. 362f.). The first question leads to the promise of Zeus. The second follows the disastrous and unforeseen consequence of the fulfilment of that promise, and leads to the certainty that both Hektor and Achilleus must die. 'Then, child', says Thetis, 'I must lose you to an early death, for what you are saying: since directly after Hektor dies your own doom is certain.' 'Then let me die directly', replies Achilleus, 'since I was not to help my friend at his killing' (18. 95ff.).

BOOK 2

Book 2 begins with Zeus' chosen method of giving effect to his promise – the sending of a false dream to Agamemnon. His intention is to provoke a full-scale encounter between the Achilleus-less Achaians and the Trojans by deluding Agamemnon into the hope of capturing Troy on that very day. The scenes that follow – Agamemnon's near-disastrous attempt to test his troops' morale, the rebellious outburst of the commoner Thersites, Odysseus' virtual assumption of command (symbolised by his use of Agamemnon's sceptre) – serve to exemplify the criticisms of Agamemnon's leadership voiced by Achilleus (and repeated by Thersites), and further reveal his weaknesses: he is impetuous, unstable, querulous, subject to violent swings of mood, and capable of wholly misconceived action. Later scenes will give evidence of his strengths. Resolution for the fight is restored by reminders from Odysseus and Nestor of the favourable omens that accompanied the start of the expedition at Aulis (these are in ironic contrast to Zeus' present intentions, but have important truth for the ultimate fate of Troy). The Achaians then mass for war, and the second half of the book, introduced by an unparalleled sequence of similes and an invocation to the Muses, contains the famous 'Catalogue of Ships', a list of all the Achaian contingents, their leaders, the towns of each area, and the number of the ships that carried them to Troy. This is followed by a much shorter catalogue of the Trojans and their allies, as they too issue forth for battle.

BOOK 3

We expect a general engagement of the two armies, but this is delayed until near the end of Book 4 (later in the single day which occupies the narrative from Book 2 to Book 7). Before the armies can clash, Paris issues a challenge to a duel, which is joyfully accepted by Menelaos. The duel is to determine possession of Helen and her goods, and to be accompanied by a general truce and the end of hostilities. Helen comes to the wall to watch the impending combat between her two 'husbands', and at Priam's request identifies for him the leading Achaians that can be seen on the plain below. After elaborate preliminaries and the solemn ratification of the truce, the duel is fought and results in effective victory for Menelaos: but Aphrodite rescues Paris and sets him down in his bedroom. Then, in a scene disturbingly expressive of Aphrodite's power and Helen's helplessness under its influence, Aphrodite summons Helen and forces her to bed with Paris.

The book is superbly constructed to introduce the world of Troy, and the attitudes and behaviour which typify important characters on the Trojan side – Paris, Hektor, Priam, and most especially Helen. There is an immediate contrast between the manner of the Trojans and the Achaians as they advance to war: the Trojans are noisy and ill-disciplined, the Achaians silent and full of grim resolve (3. 1ff.), a contrast which reappears when the two sides clash later that day for the first time in full battle (4. 422ff.). And Paris, the first Trojan we meet, is not a fully heroic figure. He begins the book with empty bravado, dressed in flashy clothes quite inappropriate for real fighting, and ends the book resplendent in his scented bedroom, like one who has just come from the dance (3. 394), apparently unconcerned by the huge issues threatening his city for which he is wholly responsible. It is no accidental juxtaposition which ends Book 2 with the vignette of the Trojan ally Nastes, who 'went into battle wearing gold like a girl, poor fool'. Achilleus killed him, and took the gold (2. 872ff.). In Book 3 we can see the nature of the man, and the power of the goddess, that led to the cause of war. Divine power chooses suitable human channels, just as Athene selects the vain and foolish Pandaros for the breaking of the truce in Book 4. The scene in which Aphrodite forces Helen to respond to the sexual appeal of Paris prefigures the seduction of Zeus by Hera in Book 14. One point is that the power of Aphrodite works on gods and humans alike: the other is that the divine world mirrors the world of men, but without real pain or consequence. Helen's contempt for Paris is mixed with self-contempt, and her misery lies in the constant tension between feelings of repulsion and attraction. Paris is hated by all the Trojans, and the burden of this is felt most strongly by his brother Hektor, who must bear the major responsibility for protecting Troy against the consequences of Paris' criminal folly. Hektor's manner to his brother in Book 3 is typically bitter and critical: and Paris' response to criticism is typically that of a charmer, to accept the blame and turn away anger. We shall see more of this in Book 6.

Helen is the visible symbol of Paris' guilt which implicates all Troy, and the Trojans' attitude to her is ambivalent. As the old men sitting round Priam see Helen approaching the wall, they whisper to each other, 'No shame that the Trojans and the well-greaved Achaians should suffer agonies for long years over a woman like this – she is fearfully like the immortal goddesses to look at. But even so, for all her beauty, let her go back in the ships, and not be left here a curse to us and our children' (3. 156ff.). Only Priam and Hektor are consistently kind to her. Helen is deeply conscious of her guilt, and given to extremes of self-criticism (for example 3. 173ff. and 6. 344ff.). She is also conscious of herself as manipulated by forces she cannot control – as part of some predetermined historical design, and at the mercy of a divine power whose imperative she hates but cannot resist. And, like Thetis, Helen suffers at the edge between two worlds, her present and her past. The scene in which she identifies the Achaian heroes for Priam brings out both her revulsion at her present state and a sort of painful nostalgia for her past life, which the poet turns to exquisite pathos at the close of the scene. Helen looks in vain among the Achaian leaders for her own two brothers, Kastor and Polydeukes. Perhaps they did not join the expedition, she says, or perhaps they have come to Troy but will not show themselves in shame for their sister. 'So she spoke, but the life-giving earth already held them under, there in Lakedaimon, in their dear native land' (3. 243ff.). Helen's pathetic ignorance prefigures that of Andromache later, when Hektor lies dead and she is busy at home preparing the bath for his return from battle (22. 437ff.).

In Book 3 the old man Priam is established in the character maintained throughout the poem – a figure of dignity and pathos, worn by the long war which afflicts his family and his people. Homer's masterly use of ironic foreshadowing is seen as Priam leaves the field before the duel between Paris and Menelaos takes place. 'I shall go back to windy Ilios', he says, 'because I will not yet bear to look with my own eyes on my dear son fighting against the warrior Menelaos' (3. 305ff.). He will not look on his lesser son fighting Menelaos: yet he will see with his own eyes his greater son killed by Achilleus.

Book 3, by concentrating on the natures of Paris and Helen and the agency of Aphrodite, and presenting a single combat between the main parties to the dispute, sets the war in the context of its cause. The emphasis is on Trojan guilt (and, by implication, deserts), and we see how divine and human causation work inextricably towards the same end ('It is not you I blame', says Priam to Helen, 'I blame the gods, who brought on me the misery of war with the Achaians' (3. 164ff.)). Hektor and Paris are seen like the two sons in a fable, the good son and the ne'er-do-well, an apparently simple antithesis which is deepened and turned to tragedy as the poem progresses. The picture of Troy and the Trojans in Book 3 is balanced by that in Book 6. The exploration of the relation between Paris and Helen in Book 3 is complemented by the exploration of the relation between Hektor and Andromache in Book 6: and the second picture, drawn in terms of responsibility and pity, emphasises the human cost of a disastrous war.

BOOK 4

Book 4 opens with an Olympian scene – the gods at their ease in Zeus' golden courtyard, drinking, and looking out over the human spectacle at Troy. Zeus provokes Hera with the suggestion that they might now end the war: but Hera and Athene are insistent on pressing on to Troy's destruction. There follows a chilling agreement, a formalisation of Hephaistos' argument at the end of Book 1. Dissent over the fate of Troy cannot be allowed to disturb the gods' peace. Hera may have her will with Troy, but on the understanding that Zeus in turn may, when he wishes, destroy human cities which are particularly favoured by Hera: and Hera offers a trio, Argos, Sparta, and Mykenai. Then Athene is dispatched to induce the breaking of the truce by the Trojans. She easily persuades Pandaros to shoot an arrow at Menelaos. The wound is trivial, but decisive. Agamemnon declares his conviction that this perfidy will mean the destruction of Troy and its people: it is significant that his solemn words are echoed, with equal certainty, by Hektor to Andromache in Book 6 (4. 163ff. = 6. 447ff.). Then as the

Trojans advance Agamemnon reviews his troops and their commanders
– a scene which reestablishes Agamemnon's claims to leadership, and
extends the survey of leading figures on the Achaian side which was
begun in Helen's responses to Priam.

The two sides clash, gods driving them on, and the book ends with a
brilliant account of the first full-scale fighting in the poem. First the
massed encounter:

When they had advanced together to meet on common ground, then there was
the clash of shields, of spears and the fury of men cased in bronze: bossed
shields met each other, and the din rose loud. Then there were mingled the
groaning and the crowing of men killed and killing, and the ground ran with
blood. As when two winter-swollen streams coursing down from the mountains
hurl together the mass of their waters where the valleys meet, joining in the
gash of a ravine from the great well-heads above, and a shepherd hears their
thunder from far in the mountains: such was the noise and the violence of the
armies' meeting. (4. 446ff.)

Then, in what will become a familiar mode of description, a series of
individual encounters, enlivened by an intensity of detail, with an
elaborate variety of circumstance, wound, and personal history. The
arrangement of the encounters, and the summary which follows them
('on that day many of the Trojans and Achaians lay stretched side by
side, face down in the dust' (4. 543ff.)), suggest an evenness of initial
fortune, soon to be disturbed by Diomedes' overwhelming career in
Book 5. Characteristic of Homer's manner in his battle-poetry is his
description of the death of the young Trojan Simoeisios, brought
down by Aias (4. 473ff.). The detailed treatment creates and illumi-
nates an individual who is also a symbol of the pathos of war: and
every detail speaks of sympathy for the young who must die, and the
parents who must grieve.

Then Telamonian Aias struck the son of Anthemion, Simoeisios, a strong
young man not married. His mother had given birth to him by the banks of the
Simoeis, coming down from Ida where she had gone with her parents to watch
over their flocks: and so they called him Simoeisios. But he could not repay his
dear parents for the care of his rearing, but his life was cut short, brought down
by the spear at the hands of great-hearted Aias. As he came through the front
line Aias struck him in the chest, by the right nipple, and the bronze spear
pushed straight on through his shoulder. He fell to the ground in the dust like a
poplar, which grows in the grassy flat of a great water-meadow, smooth-
trunked, with branches springing at its very top: then a wainwright fells it with
the gleaming iron, to bend its wood into a felloe for a chariot of finest make,

and it lies there seasoning along the bank of the river. Such was Anthemion's son Simoeisios, killed by royal Aias.

The elaborate simile which ennobles Simoeisios' death links it in sadness to the happy circumstances of his birth, and expresses both his beauty and his value. There will be many such doomed young men in the *Iliad*.

BOOK 5

The fighting continues throughout Book 5, dominated by the Athene-inspired supremacy of Diomedes and the involvement of gods on both sides. The narrative structure of this long book of fighting is handled with sustained vigour and brilliance – there is constant variety of pace, scene, and circumstance, and an astonishing richness of visual detail and of poetic invention in vignettes and similes.

Diomedes is encouraged by Athene to attack the gods themselves: he wounds both Aphrodite and Ares, and even makes repeated attempts on Apollo, a much more formidable god. Diomedes reaches the height of human prowess under divine inspiration: but these encounters with the gods serve to emphasise the unbridgeable gulf between man and god. The same point is made in the partly comic episode with Aphrodite and again in the more solemn encounter with Apollo. Aphrodite, trivially wounded, sits in her mother's lap and is comforted. Dione ends her comfort with the threat that mortals who fight the gods, like Diomedes, will never return from battle to sit their own children in their lap. This point is then reinforced in chilling and imperious form by Apollo's shout of final warning, as Diomedes attempts him for the fourth time: 'Think, son of Tydeus, and shrink back! Never think yourself gods' equal – since there can be no likeness ever between the make of immortal gods and of men who walk on the ground' (5. 440ff.). This sequence, of three attacks followed by Apollo's final rebuff, foreshadows that which leads to the death of Patroklos (16. 784ff.).

BOOK 6

With the gods now out of the fighting, the Achaians break the Trojan line and drive them back towards the city. Hektor is urged by his brother Helenos to rally the Trojans and then go into the city and arrange for the women to offer appeasement to Athene, in the hope that she will hold back Diomedes. As Hektor goes towards Troy there is the famous meeting between Diomedes and the Lycian Glaukos. We expect a major combat, but as Glaukos tells the story of his ancestry Diomedes realises that their families are linked in guest-friendship, and the encounter ends in joy and the exchange of armour (of widely differing value – a splendidly mordant tailpiece, 6. 234ff.).

The rest of the book is set in Troy, and contrasts eloquently with the scenes involving Paris and Helen in Book 3. This Trojan interlude is carefully structured in three linked scenes between Hektor and the women of Troy (his mother Hekabe, Helen, and his wife Andromache), interwoven with a running contrast between Hektor and Paris. With superb economy the scenes explore the effects of war on the non-combatants – women and children – and the relation between a fighting man and those strong ties that would hold him in time of peace. The scenes define, both directly and symbolically, the proper spheres of men and women, and of war and peace. Paris is discovered out of his proper sphere, lounging in the women's quarters and fussing over his armour, while the women get on with their tasks around him. When Hektor goes to visit his wife – the third and most important of the triptych of encounters with women, marked by its length and intensity – it is significant that Andromache is not at home when Hektor comes. She too is out of her proper sphere (and even presumes to advise on tactics, in a desperate attempt to keep her husband in Troy): and at the end of the scene Hektor returns her to her sphere ('Go back to the house and see to your own work, the loom and the distaff, and tell your maids to set about their tasks', 6. 490ff.). Hektor and Andromache meet at the exact point which forms the boundary, both physical and symbolic, between the spheres of war and peace, between the realm of men and the realm of women and family – the Skaian gates. The tension between a man's duty to fight and his duty to his family is marvellously expressed when Hektor's great nodding helmet terrifies his own baby son, and he removes it for a moment of domestic tenderness – the formulaic phrase 'Hektor of the glinting helmet' here invades the narrative, just as 'swift-footed Achilleus' takes tragic meaning when Achilleus chases Hektor to his death. At their parting, when Hektor has refused Andromache's tearful invitation to put family above country, they separate to their spheres. Hektor, taking up his by now symbolic helmet, goes out to the plain of war and danger. Andromache returns, reluctantly, to the home, the sphere of family and security and women's tasks (she will be there, properly engaged in her wifely duties, when Hektor is killed). The moment marks Hektor's choice, and Andromache recognises it as such (this choice foreshadows the fatal decision in Book 22, when once again Hektor chooses to stay outside Troy and reject his family's appeals). Andromache follows Hektor's instruction and tells her maids to set about their tasks – but the task she gives them is lamentation for Hektor, in his own house, while he still lives (6. 499ff.). The scene ends on a note of impending tragedy: it is now certain that Hektor will die.

Paris comes running through the city (his eager speed described in a splendid simile) to catch Hektor just as he is turning to leave, and the two brothers return to the fighting.

BOOK 7

The reappearance of Hektor and Paris leads to some immediate Trojan success, but Athene and Apollo agree that the fighting should stop for a duel between Hektor and an Achaian champion. Hektor issues the challenge, and his concern to establish that the victor should return the loser's body for burial (7. 76ff.) prefigures his own treatment when killed by Achilleus. This is an altogether more serious affair than Paris' challenge which began this long day. Menelaos again accepts, but is dissuaded by Agamemnon – he would certainly have been killed by Hektor. Aias is chosen by lot to face Hektor, and it is now Hektor's turn to feel fear. Aias has the better of the contest, but heralds from both sides stop the the fight on the grounds that darkness is coming on, and the combatants part with the exchange of gifts. It is clear that Hektor is lucky to come out alive. The following morning the Trojans propose the return of Helen's possessions and others besides – which is rejected – and a truce for the gathering and cremation of the dead, which is agreed. A day is spent in tendance of the dead of both sides, and on the next day the Achaians build a defensive wall and ditch around their ships and encampment. The first phase of the fighting is over, the first dead buried, and Zeus' plan is so far ineffective – the Achaians have generally had the upper hand.

BOOK 8

The desired Trojan victory comes in the next day's fighting, wholly contained within Book 8. The day, and the book, begins with a scene on Olympos in which Zeus forbids the gods to intervene in the war, and threatens them with the consequences if they do. General fighting resumes, and fortunes are even until noon, when Zeus holds out his golden scales and the Achaians' fate sinks down – foreshadowing of the critical moment in Book 22 when those same golden scales weigh the fates of Achilleus and Hektor, and Hektor's fate sinks down into Hades (22. 209ff.). The Achaians give way, and despite brief reversals by Diomedes (ultimately turned back by a thunderbolt from Zeus) and Teukros (disabled by Hektor) they are driven back behind their new defences by a Zeus-inspired Hektor. Athene and Hera plan help for the Achaians, and disobedience to Zeus, but Zeus warns them back, and they agree between themselves that it is not worth fighting Zeus for the sake of mortals (8. 427ff.).

For the first time the Trojans bivouac out in the plain (instead of returning to the protection of the city), and Hektor is confident of victory over the Achaians on the following day. The book ends quietly, with a night-picture of the innumerable Trojan watch-fires burning in the plain. The wonderful simile which describes the sight of these fires (8. 555ff.) is set in contrast with that at the beginning of Book 9 describing the Achaians' emotional reaction (9. 4ff.). The first speaks of clarity, order, and untroubled silence: the second of turmoil and confusion. Such 'pairing' of similes is seen quite frequently in the *Iliad*.

BOOK 9

Agamemnon reacts to this Trojan threat with characteristic despair. He repeats his suggestion of Book 2, that the Achaians should sail home, but this time the danger is real and he is in earnest. His suggestion meets with a characteristically forceful response from Diomedes. At a meeting of the council Nestor tactfully blames Agamemnon for his folly in insulting Achilleus, and suggests an attempt to win him over with gifts and persuasion. Agamemnon accepts his responsibility and lists the spectacular range of gifts which Achilleus will receive from him if he abandons his anger. An embassy is selected to convey this offer to Achilleus – Odysseus, Aias, and the old man Phoinix, who stands in a special relation to Achilleus, as his tutor from the earliest years. Each member of the embassy speaks to Achilleus, and Achilleus replies to each: three long speeches (Odysseus, Achilleus, Phoinix) are followed by three much shorter (Achilleus, Aias, Achilleus).

Odysseus begins, with a carefully presented moral and material appeal. He sets out the great extent of the danger facing the Achaians, reminds Achilleus of his father's instruction to control his anger and keep away from quarrels, lists the gifts that Agamemnon is offering, and ends with an appeal to Achilleus' sense of pity and loyalty to his comrades, and to his desire for glory ('Now you could kill Hektor'). It is a powerful case, and the 'heroic code' – the set of individual and social values revealed in the *Iliad* which ordinarily govern a hero's responses, either urging or prohibiting action – would normally determine its acceptance. It is made explicitly clear by Phoinix in his speech (9. 515ff.) that Achilleus' maintenance of his anger is right and justified up to the offer of compensation and the sending of the embassy, but wrong and perverse thereafter: and Phoinix, as an old man, may be taken (like Nestor) as an authority. Odysseus' presentation of the case is characteristically subtle and comprehensive (that is why he was chosen for the embassy), but its centrepiece is the unparalleled magnificence of Agamemnon's offer of material and honorific compensation (the strength and importance of this offer is underlined by the full-scale repetition of Agamemnon's catalogue of gifts). The function of gifts and treasure in Homeric society has both moral and material significance – value and honour are inseparable, and the same Greek word is used for both, and also for 'recompense' or 'reparation'. Gifts increase a man's possessions, and they also recognise or exalt his status. Agamemnon's offer to Achilleus, then, represents massive recompense, a huge increase in material possessions, and unambiguous recognition of Achilleus' claim to the highest honour. The offer fully meets the requirements. So did Chryses' offer of ransom at the very beginning (the ransom was 'unlimited' and 'splendid'), and so will Priam's ransom for Hektor's body at the very end (Achilleus himself calls out to the dead Patroklos, 'Do not be angry with me, Patroklos, if you learn, even where you are in Hades, that I have released godlike Hektor to his dear father, *as it was no unworthy ransom that he gave me*', 24. 592ff.).

Phoinix and Aias in their turn take up and amplify the moral and emotional elements of Odysseus' appeal, and Phoinix, as is proper for an old man, adds theological and historical arguments. Phoinix's is by far the longer speech (in fact the longest in the *Iliad*), and he approaches his object by circuitous paths – autobiography, allegory, and analogy. Phoinix's account of his own youth and his reception into Peleus' household, with the special relation that grew between him and the young Achilleus, serves to draw attention to the obligations between son and father, and so reinforces and expands Odysseus' reference to Peleus' advice, which Achilleus is forgetting: and Phoinix doubles the force of this appeal by exploring his own role as a sort of surrogate father to Achilleus. The emotive force of 'remember your father' will be yet more powerfully (and successfully) used by Priam when he meets Achilleus in Book 24 (24. 486ff.). The allegory of the 'Repents', daughters of Zeus, gives a theological context to the request that Achilleus should control his passion and accept Agamemnon's offer of reparation: and the elaborate historical paradigm of Meleagros, made closely parallel to Achilleus' own situation and its future development, warns of the honour that would be lost if the gifts are refused.

Aias is brief and brusque. How can Achilleus put 'one girl' above loyalty to comrades and the appeals of his closest friends? His plain man's irritation at a perverse sense of value anticipates that of Diomedes when the news is brought to the rest of the Achaians: and his insistence on Achilleus' lack of pity foreshadows the same accusation in Patroklos' fatally successful appeal to Achilleus in Book 16 (16. 33ff.). Pitilessness is the quality which characterises Achilleus from now until the final meeting with Priam.

The case is strong, and powerfully urged, but Achilleus refuses. His great speech of refusal, given in answer to Odysseus' appeal, rises to a magnificent impassioned rhetoric unequalled in the *Iliad*. It is sometimes said that in this speech Achilleus questions, or even rejects, the whole heroic code – or at least that part of it which drives a hero to expose his life to constant risk in the acquisition of honour and the pursuit of glory. This is not so. The main spurs to Achilleus' refusal are pride and a deep, unrelenting fury which swells to exclude judgment and all else – as Achilleus himself knows and frankly admits to Aias (9. 644ff.). That part of Achilleus' refusal which rests on rational argument is an intensification of his position in Book 1. It does not question or reject the code by which Achilleus has always lived, but rather complains that *Agamemnon* has stultified the pursuit of the heroic ideal, by making it impossible, even by the most heroic exertions, to win the honour which would make those exertions worthwhile. It is Agamemnon who has broken the rules. If there is no appropriate honour or glory, there is no point in inviting death. And Achilleus' case is sharper than any other's, because he knows *for certain* that he will die if he continues fighting (hence the introduction here of Achilleus' 'two fates' – a short life with glory, or a long life without – preparing for the choice that Achilleus makes in Book 18, after the death of Patroklos). The regular heroic equation sets risk of death against certainty of honour. For Achilleus, Agamemnon has devalued the equation so that certain death is set against no guarantee of honour. Why then should Achilleus give away his life?

In answer to Odysseus, Achilleus declares his intention of leaving for home in the morning. This absolute position is modified in response to Phoinix (he will decide in the morning whether to go or stay) and again in response to Aias – now Achilleus will fight, but only when Hektor has reached the Myrmidons' ships and huts. The next concession which Achilleus will make, in response to Patroklos' appeal at the start of Book 16, will mean Patroklos' death. Then Achilleus must return to battle, but what motivates him then is no 'professional' heroism but sharply personal fury, hatred, and urge for revenge – so that the quarrel, the gifts, and his own death mean nothing to him. There is an ironic reversal then of his argument in Book 1, 'It was not the spearmen of Troy who caused me to come here and fight – I have no quarrel with them' (1. 152ff.).

BOOK 10

The action of Book 10 takes place entirely at night (the night of the day that began in Book 8), and is in the nature of an interlude. Agamemnon, sleepless with worry after the failure of the embassy, wakes the other leading Achaians and calls a meeting out beyond the guard-posts, at which Nestor proposes that a spy should infiltrate the Trojan camp and gather what information he can. Diomedes volunteers, and chooses Odysseus to accompany him. Coincidentally, Hektor calls a meeting of the leading Trojans, and asks for a volunteer to spy on the ships and ascertain Achaian intentions. The Trojan spy is Dolon, an unheroic figure (this is established in advance by his ugliness, and by the fact that in a family of six he is the only son, with five sisters). Dolon is captured by Diomedes and Odysseus. He readily gives them information about the disposition of the Trojans and their allies, and particularly about the newly-arrived Thracians and their king Rhesos, who has beautiful white horses and a chariot and armour of gold. Dolon is then killed by Diomedes. Odysseus and Diomedes raid the Thracian position, killing Rhesos and twelve others, and then return triumphant to the Achaian lines, riding the white horses.

There is some doubt whether Book 10 was an original part of the *Iliad*, or composed by the poet of the rest of the *Iliad*. The composer of Book 10 seems at times not fully in command of his medium (there is occasional awkwardness and straining for effect): he shows some different interests – a relish for the macabre, a fondness for details of clothing and unusual armour: the conception and presentation of the narrative is not quite on all fours with the regular manner and tone of the *Iliad*. Whatever the truth about the origin of Book 10, the contents have interest and excitement enough, and effectively relax the tension between the high emotion of Book 9 and the intense fighting that starts in Book 11.

BOOK 11

The dawn that begins Book 11 introduces the most sustained and violent fighting in the *Iliad*, and a particular grimness invades the narrative. This long and crucial day stretches until the end of Book 18, and will see the Achaian wall breached, the ships fired, and Patroklos dead. This is the fulfilment of Zeus' promise to Thetis, a complete granting of Achilleus' wish, but with unwished consequences disastrous to Achilleus himself – the fairy-tale motif of the maliciously granted wish is turned to high tragedy.

The importance of this day's fighting is marked at the start of Book 11 by divine manifestations (Zeus' sending of Strife, thunder from Athene and Hera, a rain of blood), by the elaborate account of Agamemnon's arming and the description of his corselet, and by the similes which describe first the level fighting and then the time when the battle swings to the Achaians. Agamemnon now has his hour of glory, and drives the Trojans almost back into their city. Zeus tells Hektor to keep out of the fighting until Agamemnon is hit – then Zeus will grant him mastery until the end of the day. Three leading Achaian fighters are wounded and disabled in succession – Agamemnon, Diomedes, Odysseus. Of the great Achaians only Aias now remains on the field, and he threatens to reverse the tide of battle (Aias is constantly presented as a greater fighter than Hektor): but Zeus, in furtherance of his plan, causes Aias to retreat, and he slowly gives ground, like a donkey driven with difficulty out of a cornfield by little boys (11. 558ff.).

Achilleus, watching the general Achaian rout, sees Nestor bringing a wounded man (Machaon) out of the fighting, and sends Patroklos to find out who it is. There follows a long scene in Nestor's hut. Patroklos is anxious to get back to Achilleus with the news (observing how quick Achilleus is to anger), but Nestor holds him with the longest of his reminiscences, and turns to criticisms of Achilleus' attitude which recall the arguments of Book 9. He ends with the suggestion that Patroklos should persuade Achilleus to let him go into battle with the Myrmidons, wearing Achilleus' armour. On his way back to Achilleus, Patroklos meets the wounded Eurypylos: despite his main errand

Patroklos helps Eurypylos to his hut, attends to his wound, and, as we learn later (15. 390ff.), spends some time entertaining him with talk.

Achilleus' interest and Patroklos' errand set in train the sequence of events that leads directly to Patroklos' death, as is explicitly and succinctly noted by the poet – 'and this was to be the beginning of his doom' (11. 604). What is made clear also is that Patroklos' own character – the moral opposite of Achilleus' – is a major determinant of his fate. He is the kindest, one might even say the softest, of the Achaians, and treated with particular sympathy by the poet: the Greek epithet meaning 'kind' attaches to Patroklos alone in the *Iliad*. His kindness dooms him – the kindness shown in his willingness to hear out Nestor, in his response to Eurypylos' need for help, and, fatally, in the emotion which spurs his appeal to Achilleus at the beginning of Book 16.

BOOK 12

The Achaians, 'beaten down by the lash of Zeus' (12. 37), are penned behind their wall by Hektor. The simile (12. 41ff.) which likens Hektor at this point of his triumph to a boar or a lion also prefigures his death: 'his glorious heart feels no fear or fright, and it is his courage that kills him.' This recalls Andromache's words to Hektor in Book 6, 'your own brave spirit will destroy you' (6. 407), and foreshadows the simile used of Patroklos at the height of his glory, when his death is very close – 'So speaking he went for the hero Kebriones with the spring of a lion, who has been hit in the chest as he ravages the sheepfolds, and his own courage brings his death' (16. 751ff.). Such multiple reference is characteristic of the close-woven texture of the *Iliad*'s narrative. Characteristic also that these two books of concentrated and unremitting fighting are sown with a wealth of enlivening similes (compare the concentration of similes in Book 5).

The Trojans form into divisions for the assault on the wall. Sarpedon and Glaukos lead a powerful attack by the Lycians, and Sarpedon makes the first breach in the wall, pulling away a parapet. While the battle strains even over that part of the wall, Hektor smashes through the gate with a huge stone and leaps inside. The Trojans swarm through and over the wall, and the Achaians are sent running in panic among their ships.

BOOK 13

Now that Zeus has brought Hektor through to the ships, he turns his eyes away from Troy. Poseidon, one of the major divine supporters of the Achaian cause, takes this opportunity to intervene, and rallies the Achaians. The middle-aged Idomeneus, leader of the Cretans, plays a dominant part in the intense fighting which leads to general Achaian success. In the course of the battle Ares' son Askalaphos is killed: the death of a god's son, and the fighting over his body, prefigures the much more important death of Zeus' own son Sarpedon in Book 16. Several Trojan leaders are wounded or killed, a parallel to the wounding of the Achaian leaders in Book 11. At the end of this long book Hektor rallies the Trojans: but the Achaians stand firm.

BOOK 14

Nestor, coming out of his hut where he was entertaining the wounded Machaon, sees the wall fallen and the Achaians now running in confusion. The three wounded Achaian leaders meet him on their way up from the ships, and Nestor gives them news of the Achaians' present plight. The short scene of discussion which follows is skilfully constructed to present each of the three in the light of an essential characteristic – Agamemnon despondent and quick to propose flight, Odysseus forceful and clear-headed, Diomedes bluntly straightforward and bullish.

The pro-Achaian gods now plan to frustrate Zeus' purpose and bring aid to the Achaians. Poseidon puts new heart into Agamemnon and his troops, and Hera sets about distracting Zeus to give Poseidon more time to effect an Achaian victory. There follows the famous seduction of Zeus. Hera tricks herself out in all her finery, and with the aid of Aphrodite's magic band, borrowed on a cheerfully false pretext, and the help of the god Sleep (whom she bribes with the offer of his favourite among the Graces), Hera seduces her husband into lying with her on the peak of Ida. The story is brilliantly told, in a highly accomplished and sophisticated style which combines delicate fantasy and subtle humour (as, for example, in Zeus' delightful 'Leporello catalogue' of previous conquests in 14. 315ff.). Poseidon, given the word by Sleep, now spurs the Achaians to general success, in the course of which Aias disables Hektor with a stone.

BOOK 15

Zeus wakes, to see the Trojans driven in flight and Hektor lying stunned in the plain. His anger and threats against Hera, familiar from earlier books, turn to prophecy – of the deaths of Sarpedon and Patroklos, then the death of Hektor and the capture of Troy. This prepares for the increase in tragic intensity in the last third of the *Iliad* and, in a juxtaposition wholly characteristic of Homer's presentation of the gods, reestablishes the majestic, all-knowing, all-controlling Zeus after the humour and indignity of the seduction. The surpassing power of the gods is further illuminated in this book when Apollo smashes the Achaian wall with the ease and lack of concern of a little boy obliterating a sand-castle (15. 355ff.).

Zeus orders Poseidon to leave off, and Poseidon recalcitrantly obeys, speaking in terms which mirror the antagonism between Achilleus and Agamemnon in Book 1. Apollo, at Zeus' order, revives Hektor and spurs him back into battle: and the Trojans, aided by Apollo, sweep the Achaians back among their ships, across the ditch and the wall. The action now rises to a magnificent climax, as Hektor and Aias lead the intense fighting at the ships, and Hektor is seen at the height of his glory, almost transfigured by the power of Zeus under the shadow of his own imminent fate:

And he raged now like Ares with spear in hand, or as destroying fire rages on the mountains, in the thick wood of a deep forest. Foam gathered at his mouth, his eyes flashed under his grim brows, and the helmet shook fearfully round his temples as he fought – because his ally was Zeus himself in the sky above, who was giving honour and glory to this one man among the multitude of others, as he would live only a short time: already Pallas Athene was advancing the day of his fate, at the hands of the strong son of Peleus. (15. 605ff.)

With Zeus' aid Hektor breaks the Achaian resistance (this cardinal moment marked by two violent similes, 15. 624ff.), and the book ends with Hektor gripping one of the ships and calling for fire, opposed only by Aias.

BOOK 16

Patroklos, who had seen the crisis from the hut where he was comforting Eurypylos (15. 390ff.), now comes running to Achilleus and appeals to him with a cumulation of all the emotion that glowed in the previous formal appeals, begging him, as Nestor suggested, at least to allow Patroklos to lead the Myrmidons into battle, dressed in Achilleus' own armour. This is the hinge of the *Iliad*, turning events into a straight and tragic sequence which redirects Achilleus' anger and ensures the fall of Troy. Patroklos' appeal is specifically linked to his own death: 'So he spoke in entreaty, the poor fool – what he was begging would be a wretched death for himself and his own destruction' (16. 46f.). Achilleus agrees, but tells Patroklos to return after he has driven the Trojans away from the ships, and not to press on to Troy.

Meanwhile Aias is pushed back under Trojan pressure, and a ship is fired. Achilleus sees this, and urges Patroklos into action. The Myrmidons muster, and the importance of this sequence is marked, as so often, by a wealth of detail – the catalogue of the Myrmidons, a variety of similes, the long description of Patroklos' arming, Achilleus' careful libation and prayer, granted only partial fulfilment by Zeus.

Patroklos and the Myrmidons extinguish the fire and drive the Trojans in confusion and slaughter back across the plain. Sarpedon, leader of the Lycians and son of Zeus, faces Patroklos in single combat and is killed by him – the most important death in the *Iliad* so far, marked by furious fighting over his body and the moving account of his translation to Lycia by the twin brothers Sleep and Death, for full burial by his brothers and kinsmen (concern with burial or its denial now grows increasingly insistent as the *Iliad* moves to its climax). Patroklos presses on towards Troy, ignoring Achilleus' instruction, and called to his death by the gods (16. 693). (Blind rejection of advice brings disaster to all the great men of the *Iliad* – Agamemnon, Achilleus, Patroklos, and finally Hektor.) After success which threatens the very capture of Troy, Patroklos is ultimately met by Apollo, who knocks the armour from him and exposes him first to a stab from a minor Trojan, Euphorbos, and then to a fatal spear-thrust from Hektor. As he dies Patroklos prophesies the death of Hektor, a motif repeated when Hektor himself dies at the hands of Achilleus.

BOOK 17

Patroklos is dead, and there follows hard fighting over his body. The first and immediate encounter is between Menelaos, who runs to bestride the corpse, and Euphorbos. The logic of the narrative and the audience's expectation demand that Euphorbos should die – he was partly responsible for the tragic and momentous death of Patroklos, the most attractive figure in the *Iliad*, and we want him dead. Not so Homer, whose treatment of the death of this insignificant Trojan is steeped in sympathy and eloquent of the compassionate humanity which constantly informs the poet's attitude to war and suffering. Homer will not forget Euphorbos' youth and beauty. This was his first day of battle, his apprenticeship in war (16. 811). Homer gives him a sympathetic reason for attacking Menelaos (Menelaos had killed his brother, widowing his new wife and bringing intolerable grief to his parents), and lavishes on his death one of his most intricate and pathetic similes:

As Euphorbos was moving back Menelaos stabbed him at the base of the throat, and pressed on the spear with all his weight, trusting in the strength of his hand. The point went right through the soft neck: he fell with a crash, and his armour clattered about him. Blood soaked his hair, lovely as the Graces' hair, and his plaits tight-bound with gold and silver. As when a man nurtures a flourishing olive-shoot in a solitary place, where plenty of water wells up – a fine, healthy shoot it is, shaken by the breath of every wind that blows, and it blossoms thick with white flowers: but suddenly there comes a wind in a great storm, and uproots it from its trench and lays out its length on the earth. Such was the son of Panthoös, Euphorbos of the ash spear, as Menelaos son of Atreus killed him, and set to stripping his armour. (17. 47ff.)

The mention of the father, Panthoös, reminds of the grief that is caused to parents: and Euphorbos' death is dignified by the same formal obituary that deepened the significance of Patroklos' death (16. 827ff.). And more – the comparison of a cherished son to a carefully nurtured plant anticipates the moving lament that Thetis will make over the fate of her own son Achilleus:

'Oh, my misery! Oh, the pain of being mother to the best of men! I bore a son who was to be noble and strong, the greatest of heroes, and he shot up like a young sapling. I tended him like a plant in the crown of a garden, and sent him out with the beaked ships to Ilios, to fight the Trojans. But now I shall never welcome him back to Peleus' house – there will be no homecoming.' (18. 54ff.)

This brief episode illustrates where Homer's interest and sympathy characteristically lie – not in the end with Menelaos and his easy victory, but with Euphorbos, the poor young fool, in his death. And this tragic interest extends equally to all, Achaian or Trojan, admirable warrior or silly fool, 'greatest of heroes' or utterly minor invented figure. What is explicit on the large scale is implicit in the small. Homer's emphasis makes it clear that what is true and important of Patroklos is true and important of Euphorbos also: and what is true of Euphorbos is true of a host of others.

Menelaos is forced back from the body, and the Trojans strip the armour from Patroklos – Achilleus' armour, in which Hektor dresses himself, watched by Zeus with pity for his imminent doom. There is prolonged and furious fighting over the naked body of Patroklos, both sides aware of the great importance of winning it. Ultimately the

Achaians manage to lift the body and carry it back towards the ships, under strong pressure from the Trojan pursuit. In the course of the fighting Menelaos sends Antilochos to bring the news of Patroklos' death to Achilleus.

BOOK 18

Antilochos gives his terrible message. Achilleus' extreme of grief brings his mother to his side, and the second of the four scenes between Achilleus and Thetis is set in ironic parallel with the first (in Book 1): Achilleus' agony now is the direct result of that first appeal to his mother. His only interest now is the killing of Hektor, even though, as Thetis tells him, that will mean his own death. He is 'a useless burden on the earth' (18. 104), and he curses the anger that has caused the death of Patroklos and many others. Thetis reminds him that he cannot fight without armour, and promises to bring in the morning divine armour made by Hephaistos.

The Trojans now threaten to recover Patroklos' body, and Iris, sent by Hera, tells Achilleus to show himself at the ditch to frighten back the Trojans. He does so, with a flame set burning at his head by Athene, and shouts three times. The Trojans fall back, and Patroklos' body is rescued: Hera sends the sun down to end this long day's fighting.*

The Trojans meet in assembly, and Poulydamas urges them to go back to the city, and not risk another night in the plain, in view of Achilleus' evident return to the battle. Hektor's fatal dismissal of this advice, which he later regrets, evidences a double determination, human and divine, which is characteristic of the *Iliad*: there is a long-standing antagonism between Hektor and Poulydamas, and also Athene takes away the Trojans' wits when they vote in support of Hektor.

On the Achaian side there is night-long mourning for Patroklos, after the washing and anointing of the body.

Thetis comes to Hephaistos' house on Olympos, and asks him to

---

* Moving reference to this scene is made in a poem written in the Dardanelles in 1916 by Patrick Shaw-Stewart, a scholar of Eton College, who was killed in France on 30 December 1917:

> I will go back this morning
>   From Imbros over the sea;
> Stand in the trench, Achilles,
>   Flame-capped, and shout for me.

make new armour for her son – a change of scene and of tone, and a relaxation of tension before the final acts of the drama. The working of the shield is described in detail. The design of the decoration encompasses the whole world, a microcosm of human activity in war and peace – a pictorial representation of that wider world beyond the battle at Troy which is otherwise illuminated only in the similes and the vignettes which give brief and pathetic details of a warrior's life before the war.

BOOK 19

On the following morning Thetis brings the new armour to Achilleus. Achilleus calls an assembly (a parallel to the assembly he called in Book 1) and formally renounces his anger. Agamemnon replies, an uneasy speech, and admits that he was blinded: he offers all the gifts promised by the embassy in Book 9. Achilleus has no time now for gifts or formalities, or for the practicalities of war – he is urgent to enter the battle. But Odysseus characteristically insists on food before fighting, and on the full public formalisation, including the parade of the promised gifts, of the reconciliation between Achilleus and Agamemnon. Briseïs, returned now to Achilleus' hut as part of Agamemnon's compensation, makes a moving lament for Patroklos. Achilleus laments, remembering his father and his son, in terms which prefigure the emotion of his meeting with Priam in Book 24. The book ends with a description of Achilleus' arming for battle, and the prophecy of his horse Xanthos, briefly endowed with human speech by Hera. The prophecy, that Achilleus will be 'brought down in battle by a god and a man' (19. 417), adds one further stage of precision to the anticipation of Achilleus' death expressed by Thetis. The final detail is given by the dying Hektor: the man will be Paris, the god Phoibos Apollo, the place the Skaian gates (22. 359ff.).

BOOK 20

Zeus calls an assembly on Olympos, and tells the gods to take sides in the human struggle. They do so, in preparation for the conflict of gods in the following book. Hera, Athene, Poseidon, Hermes, and Hephaistos go to the Achaians: Ares, Apollo, Artemis, Leto, Xanthos (the river), and Aphrodite to the Trojans. Apollo spurs Aineias, reluctant, against Achilleus – a long retardation, with rambling nervous talk by Aineias, which ends with the rescue of Aineias by Poseidon. Among the victims of Achilleus' attack is Polydoros, the youngest and favourite son of Priam. Hektor attacks Achilleus in anger for the death of his young brother, and there follows a mysterious prefiguring of the final encounter – Hektor's cast is blown back by Athene, and Apollo snatches Hektor away in thick mist. Achilleus presses on, killing Trojans with a particular ferocity.

BOOK 21

Achilleus forces some of the Trojans into the river Xanthos, where he kills many and takes twelve young Trojans alive for slaughtering at Patroklos' funeral. His killing of Lykaon, son of Priam, and of Astero-paios, the leader of the Paionians, rouses the river to attack him. There follows a tour de force of description of the river's pursuit of Achilleus. The river threatens to overwhelm him, until Hephaistos, on Hera's instructions, forces Xanthos to submission with a conflagration which nearly dries his stream.

The gods now join in more general conflict, with the pro-Achaian gods getting the better of it. Athene disables Ares, and then Aphrodite: Hera boxes Artemis' ears with her own bow and arrows, sending her off to sit tearful and complaining in her father Zeus' lap: the more dignified gods decline to fight each other. The whole scene is light-hearted and humorous, and Zeus laughs for joy to see the gods fight (21. 389f.). It is a divine game, with no lasting pain and easily ended, a parody of the deadly serious and irremediable human conflict which it mirrors. There is the same chilling contrast with the death and destruction which follows on the mortal plane as there was between the human and divine quarrels which frame Book 1: and again contemplation of human insignificance is enough to turn away the gods' attention – 'Earthshaker', says Apollo to Poseidon, 'you would not say I was in my right mind if I do battle with you for the sake of wretched mortals, who are like leaves – for a time they flourish in a blaze of glory, and feed on the yield of the earth, and then again they fade lifeless. No, let us withdraw from battle immediately, and leave the mortals to fight on by themselves' (21. 462ff. Compare Hephaistos to Hera in 1. 573ff., and, for the comparison to leaves, Glaukos to Diomedes in 6. 145ff.).

Achilleus presses on towards Troy amid much slaughter, driving the Trojans in panic into their city. Apollo sets Agenor against him in a stand which prefigures in some detail the fatal stand made by Hektor soon afterwards. But Achilleus is cheated of his prey by Apollo, who takes Agenor's shape and leads Achilleus away from Troy in a fruitless chase, during which the rest of the Trojans pour into their city.

BOOK 22

As Achilleus is disabused by Apollo, and sets out running fast back to Troy, Hektor stays outside, in front of the Skaian gates. This fatal decision, like most of the major events in the *Iliad*, is doubly determined. Divine and human causation work in parallel: 'his cruel fate shackled Hektor to stay there outside' (22. 5), but it is also his own decision, prompted by shame at his costly refusal to take the Trojans back into the city for the previous night, and the thought that he has destroyed his people through his own folly (22. 99ff.).

Priam sees Achilleus speeding over the plain, glittering like a baneful star, and implores Hektor to come inside the city: beside him Hekabe, Hektor's mother, bares her breast in appeal to her son, but they cannot move him. The power of this heart-rending scene is increased by the contrast with the appeals to Achilleus in Book 9 – there his closest friends urge Achilleus to fight, here his own parents urge Hektor not to fight – and by the anticipation of Priam's appeal to Achilleus in Book 24: Priam cannot move his own son, but he can move the man who killed him.

As Achilleus comes on, Hektor's nerve breaks, and he runs. Achilleus pursues him three times round the walls of Troy, under the eyes of his parents and friends, past the landmarks of Troy and the reminders of peacetime, the two springs and beside them 'the fine broad washing-troughs made of stone, where the Trojans' wives and their lovely daughters used to wash their bright clothes, in earlier times, in peace, before the sons of the Achaians came' (22. 153ff.). Achilleus is now 'swift-footed' in full earnest. Two images drawn from events at funeral games prepare for the games in honour of Patroklos in Book 23, and make a grim point, intensified by the terse half-line 'and all the gods looked on' (22. 159ff.).

Zeus debates whether to save Hektor for the moment or let him be killed, as he had done with Sarpedon and Patroklos, a further link which places these three deaths in cumulative sequence. Zeus opens out his golden scales, as before in Book 8, and Hektor's pan sinks down into Hades. Apollo leaves Hektor, and Athene comes to Achilleus.

Athene tricks Hektor into fighting, by presenting herself as Deïphobos, Hektor's brother, come to give him aid. The duel begins, and Hektor realises that the gods have called him to his death, when 'Deïphobos' is no longer there to help him. He charges at Achilleus in a final quest for glory, and is killed by a spear-thrust through the throat. As he dies, he prophesies the circumstances of his killer's own death, as Patroklos had done when Hektor killed him.

Achilleus had refused to accept Hektor's plea that his body should be returned for burial, and he now ties it by the ankles behind his chariot and drags it back to the ships. 'As Hektor was dragged behind, a cloud of dust arose from him, his dark hair streamed out round him, and all that once handsome head was sunk in the dust: but now Zeus had given him to his enemies to defile him in his own native land' (22. 401ff.). This sullying of Hektor's head and hair answers in fully literal fact to the symbolic defilement of Achilleus' helmet when it is knocked from Patroklos' head in the prelude to his death (16. 793ff.).

The death and defilement of Hektor is witnessed by his parents, and the sound of their lamentation reaches Andromache where she sits at home engaged in her wifely duties and concerned that there should be hot water for Hektor's bath on his return from battle – 'poor child, she did not know that far away from any baths bright-eyed Athene had brought him down at the hands of Achilleus' (22. 445ff.). She rushes to the wall and faints at the sight of Hektor dragged lifeless behind Achilleus' horses. Her immediate lament, with which the book ends, dwells on the cruel change that awaits Astyanax, now that he is fatherless. Much in this deeply moving scene is set in a conscious relation to the scene between Hektor and Andromache in Book 6, and realises the tragedy there foreshadowed.

BOOK 23

Lamentation for Patroklos follows immediately on the Trojan lament for Hektor, and the treatment of the two bodies is set in the starkest contrast. Hektor is flung face-down in the dust beside Patroklos' bier, destined for the dogs: and Achilleus, still distraught with grief, supervises the most elaborate and honorific funeral for Patroklos.

The remaining two-thirds of this long book describe the Funeral Games which Achilleus then holds in honour of Patroklos. By far the most extensive treatment is given to the first event, the chariot race, which is described in a brilliant narrative style, full of incident and personality. This section forms a sort of analogue to the main action of the *Iliad*, in which the heroic virtues and vices are more innocently channelled, and characteristic ingredients of the large-scale narrative are seen again in miniature – there is furious action, humour, divine intervention, a bitter quarrel, anger and apology, magnanimity, and a reminiscence from Nestor. Seven other events are described in less detail, always with a careful statement of the prizes. Achilleus himself does not take part (he is the president, and his participation would unbalance the competition): but the games afford a last look at the other major Achaian heroes, whose presentation as they compete is much in character.

The games allow a relaxation of tension between the emotions of Books 22 and 24, and they show Achilleus in a new light – mature, dignified, generous of nature – in preparation for the Achilleus of the final book.

BOOK 24

Every day Achilleus, still grieving for Patroklos, drags Hektor's body three times round Patroklos' tomb. For eleven days the gods look on in anger and pity for Hektor, and then a divine assembly, roughened by a quarrelsome speech by Hera, causes Zeus to summon Thetis to Olympos with a proposal which will both save Hektor's body and do honour to Achilleus. The lapse of time, the gods' anger parallel in duration to that of Achilleus in Book 1, the troubled divine assembly thereafter, the presence of Thetis, first come to demand honour for Achilleus and in the end sent to achieve it, begin a series of explicit or implicit relations especially with Book 1, but also with the rest of the *Iliad*, which establish the final book as both climax and reversal.

Thetis is sent to tell Achilleus of the gods' anger, and request that he releases the body for ransom. In parallel Iris goes to Priam and tells him to bring ransom to Achilleus: 'he is not foolish or blind or godless, but will show a suppliant all kindness and spare him' (24. 186f.). Again, divine causation will work through human inclination.

Priam determines to go to the ships, despite Hekabe's strong opposition (this had been his own first impulse when he saw Hektor killed, and that passage, 22. 416ff., also prefigures the terms of his appeal to Achilleus). In a marvellously human scene he drives all the Trojan bystanders away, and rails at his other sons, those who had survived where Hektor was killed. As Priam says to Achilleus, Hektor was his 'one son'.

Priam is met on the plain as darkness falls and escorted to Achilleus' hut by the disguised Hermes, on Zeus' orders. This is the most extensive meeting between god and man in the *Iliad*, a mysterious scene, serving as an earnest and a visible expression of the rare divine pity which motivates this final act and works in parallel with human pity to bring a resolution.

Priam comes wordlessly into Achilleus' presence, and clasps his knees, and kisses his hands, 'those terrible, murderous hands, which had killed many of his sons' (24. 479), the full ritual of supplication. He succeeds by reminding Achilleus of his own father (in both senses of 'remind'), the appeal which had been made unsuccessfully by both Odysseus and Phoinix (the surrogate father) in Book 9, and Achilleus is moved to shared lamentation, and to pity. Achilleus' reply expresses the whole tragic vision of the *Iliad*. He sees the fellowship of suffering which links Peleus and Priam – both had reached the height of human greatness, but irretrievable misery had come to both in the loss of their 'only' son, since Achilleus can no more protect Peleus in his old age than Hektor now can Priam – and sets them in a universal context, as high paradigms of the human condition under divine governance. The gods have no sorrows: suffering and death are the fate of mortals: lamentation (for Patroklos, for Hektor, for any man) cannot change that.

Achilleus is still dangerous – for all his pity (and he had been 'pitiless' before), anger, controlled by self-knowledge, is close to the surface (24. 559f., 582ff.) – but his respect for Priam holds. He lifts Hektor's body on to the bier with his own hands, leaving clothing from the ransom to shroud it, insists on the full and symbolic hospitality of food and bed (as he had in Book 9), and agrees to hold the Achaians from hostilities for the time that Priam wants for Hektor's burial (a final interval that corresponds to the days of plague at the beginning of Book 1).

Hermes wakes Priam and escorts him out of the Achaian camp. As the new day breaks, and Priam brings Hektor's body to the gates of Troy, the whole population gathers in grief. There follow laments led by the three women – Andromache, Hekabe, and Helen – whose relation to Hektor, and dependence on him, had been explored in Book 6. Nine days are spent in preparation for a funeral which matches that of Patroklos. The long threat of desecration, abhorrent to gods and men, gives way to proper ritual: and the *Iliad* ends with a dwelling description of that which is denied in its opening lines, the honorific burial of a hero, duly lamented by family and people.

A NOTE ON NAMES

1. The representation of Greek names in English poses a familiar problem. There is no universally accepted 'system', and practice has varied over the centuries with prevailing fashion and personal predilection, from the wholly Latin or Latinising to ruthless transliteration. Few would now be happy with Jove, Minerva, Ulysses, or Ajax as means of referring to Greek gods and heroes whose names are Zeus, Athene, Odysseus, and Aias: and few can systematically stomach the printed barbarity of Thoukudides or Aiskhulos, or the unexpectedness of Platon. No practice is maintained with complete consistency, and that is just as well: those who rightly reject Ulysses and Ajax are unwilling to accept the 'purist' Priamos and Helene in place of the familiar Priam and Helen. In the end the question is an aesthetic one, depending on the balance struck between the proper desire to assert the Greekness of the Greek characters, and proper respect for the long tradition of English literature and literary reference.

The leading fighter on the Achaian side can be represented in English variously as *Achilles* (the familiar Latinising form), *Akhilleus* (the purist transliteration), and *Achilleus*, which I prefer as maintaining the Greek name without a disturbing appearance on the English printed page. With a few exceptions, where retention of the Greek form or the Greek spelling would be pedantic or involve an uncomfortable change in familiar pronunciation (so 'Priam', 'Crete', and 'Lycia' rather than 'Priamos', 'Krete', and 'Lykia'), I have kept the Greek names unlatinised – Patroklos, Hektor, and Hekabe, then, rather than Patroclus, Hector, and Hecuba.

2. Several of the leading characters in the poem are frequently referred to simply by their patronymic ('the son of X'). For example 'the son of Tydeus' (a single Greek word) is often used, without further definition, in reference to Diomedes. Except in a very few instances where clarity of reference might suffer, I have retained in translation this distinctive feature of the epic manner (which further testifies to the insistent importance of paternity in Homeric society).

The more frequent patronymics are these:

The son of Kronos	for	Zeus
The son of Atreus		Agamemnon *or*
		Menelaos (brothers)
The son of Peleus		Achilleus
The son of Tydeus		Diomedes
The son of Menoitios		Patroklos
The son of Telamon		the greater Aias (or 'Telamonian Aias')
The son of Oïleus		the lesser Aias
The son of Phyleus		Meges

Achilleus is also described as 'of Aiakos' stock' (his grandfather), and Priam as 'Dardanian Priam' or 'stock of Dardanos' (a remoter ancestor).

3. We naturally talk of Greeks and Trojans. Homer does not use the regular later Greek word for 'Greeks'. He refers to them by three names, used indifferently: Achaians, Danaans, and Argives.

4. A few people or places are known and referred to by two different names:

The city of Troy is also, and usually, known as Ilios
Paris is also known as Alexandros
Xanthos (one of the rivers of Troy) is also known as Skamandros (cf. p. 335)
Aphrodite is also known as Kypris

5. The name of Agamemnon's city in later Greek is Mykenai (latinised as Mycenae). Homer's regular form of the name is Mykene, and I have kept that form in the text.

6. The two Achaian heroes called Aias, when referred to as a pair, are called the Aiantes.

ACKNOWLEDGEMENTS

I am grateful to the Oxford University Press for permission to use in the Introduction to this book some parts of an article which I contributed to *Greece & Rome*, Second Series, Vol. XXIX No. 2 (October 1982).

I am conscious that I have borrowed from Prof. W. B. Stanford his felicitous translation of the alliterative half-line 4. 526 (= 21. 181).

A NOTE ON THE GREEK TEXT

For this translation I have used the text of D. B. Monro and T. W. Allen in the Oxford Classical Texts series (3rd edition, 1920). The text of the *Iliad* is more firmly established than that of most Greek authors, and there are relatively few occasions on which there is significant doubt about the true reading. In a number of places I have used a reading other than that printed in the Oxford Classical Text, or taken a different view of the status of a line or group of lines. I list here the more important of these divergencies, in each case giving first the reading adopted for this translation.

1. 5	οἰωνοῖσί τε δαῖτα, not οἰωνοῖσί τε πᾶσι
3. 119	ἄρνα, not ἄρνε
5. 638	ἀλλοῖον, not ἀλλ' οἷον
6. 285	κεν φίλον ἦτορ, not κε φρέν' ἀτέρπου
8. 349	ἠέ, not ἠδέ
9. 394	γαμέσσεται, not γε μάσσεται
9. 458–61	included
9. 602	ἐπὶ δώροις, not ἐπὶ δώρων
10. 463	ἐπιβωσόμεθα, not ἐπιδωσόμεθα
11. 439	βέλος κατὰ καίριον, not τέλος κατακαίριον
12. 340	πάσας γὰρ ἐπῴχετο, not πᾶσαι γὰρ ἐπῴχατο
16. 614–15	omitted
17. 176	ἠέ περ ἀνδρός, not αἰγιόχοιο
20. 135	omitted
24. 789	ἤγρετο, not ἔγρετο

THE ILIAD

BOOK I
THE ANGER OF ACHILLEUS

Sing, goddess, of the anger of Achilleus, son of Peleus, the accursed anger which brought uncounted anguish on the Achaians and hurled down to Hades many mighty souls of heroes, making their bodies the prey to dogs and the birds' feasting: and this was the working of Zeus' will. Sing from the time of the first quarrel which divided Atreus' son, the lord of men, and godlike Achilleus.

Which of the gods was it who set these two to their fighting? It was the son of Zeus and Leto. In anger at the king he raised a vile plague throughout the army, and the people were dying, because the son of Atreus had dishonoured Chryses, his priest. Chryses had come to the fast ships of the Achaians to gain release for his daughter, bringing with him unlimited ransom, and holding in his hands the sacred woollen bands of Apollo the far-shooter, wreathed on a golden staff. He began to entreat the whole body of the Achaians, but especially the two sons of Atreus, the marshals of the army. 'Sons of Atreus, and you other well-greaved Achaians, may the gods who live on Olympos grant you the sacking of Priam's city and a safe return to your homes. But release my dear child to me, and accept this ransom, in reverence for the son of Zeus, Apollo the far-shooter.'

Then all the other Achaians shouted their agreement, to respect the priest's claim and take the splendid ransom. But this was not the pleasure of Agamemnon's heart, the son of Atreus. He sent him shamefully on his way, with harsh words of command: 'Old man, let me never find you by our hollow ships, either dallying here now or coming back again in future – or you will have no protection from your god's staff and sacred bands. As for the girl, I shall not release her. Before that, old age will come upon her in our house, in Argos, far from her own country, where she will work at the loom and serve my bed. No, away with you: do not provoke me, if you want to return in safety.'

So he spoke, and the old man was afraid and did as he was ordered. He went in silence along the shore of the sounding sea. And then when he had gone a far way off, the old man prayed long to lord Apollo, the child of lovely-haired Leto: 'Hear me, lord of the silver bow, protector of Chryse and holy Killa, and mighty lord of Tenedos, Smintheus. If ever I have built a shrine that is pleasing to you, if ever I have burnt for you fat-wrapped thigh-bones of bulls and goats, grant this my prayer: may the Danaans pay for my tears with your arrows.'

So he spoke in prayer, and Phoibos Apollo heard him. Down he came from the peaks of Olympos with anger in his heart, the bow on his shoulders, and the enclosing quiver. The arrows clattered on the shoulders of Apollo in his anger, as the god himself rushed down: and his coming was like night. He settled then at a distance from the ships, and let fly an arrow: and there came a fearful twang from the silver bow. First he attacked the mules and the quick-running dogs: but then he sent his sharp arrows at the men themselves, and kept shooting them down. And constantly there burned, close-packed, the pyres of the dead.

For nine days the god's arrows plied throughout the army. On the tenth day Achilleus called the people to an assembly: the white-armed goddess Hera had put this in his mind, as she cared for the Danaans when she saw them dying. So when they were all gathered together in one place, swift-footed Achilleus stood up among them and spoke: 'Son of Atreus, I think we must now be forced back and return home again – supposing we can escape death – if now both war and plague together are to ravage the Achaians. No, let us ask some prophet or priest, or an interpreter of dreams (as dreams too come from Zeus), who might tell us why Phoibos Apollo has felt such anger against us, whether he faults our prayer or our sacrifice – if in any way he may be willing to accept the smoke of lambs and goats without blemish, and drive the plague away from us.'

So speaking Achilleus sat down. Then there stood up in the assembly Kalchas, Thestor's son, far the best of augurs, who knew what is, and what will be, and what was before. He had guided the Achaians' ships into Ilios through his seercraft, which Phoibos Apollo had granted him. In all good will he spoke and addressed the assembly: 'Achilleus, loved of Zeus, you ask me to tell of the anger of Apollo, the lord who shoots from afar, so tell I will. But you mark what I say and swear to me that you will readily come to my aid in word and action. I think that I shall anger a man who holds great power over all the Argives and command among the Achaians. When a king is angry at a lesser man, his is the greater power: even if he holds down his anger for the day, he still keeps resentment in his breast, until he can give effect to it at some later time. So you tell me if you will protect me.'

Then swift-footed Achilleus answered him: 'Take full courage and speak out what you know of the god's will. I swear by Apollo, loved of Zeus – the god whom you pray to, Kalchas, when you declare your prophecies to the Danaans – while I live and see the light upon earth, no man will lay violent hands on you by our hollow ships, no man among the whole number of the Danaans, even if you speak of Agamemnon, who now claims to be far the best of the Achaians.'

Then the excellent prophet took courage and spoke: 'Apollo does not fault our prayer or sacrifice, but his anger is for his priest, dishonoured by Agamemnon when he would not release his daughter and accept the ransom. That is why the far-shooter brought anguish on us, and will bring yet more. He will not drive this shameful plague from the Danaans until we give back the bright-eyed girl to her dear father without price or ransom, and take a holy hecatomb to Chryse. Then we might appease him and turn his mind.'

So speaking Kalchas sat down. Then there stood up in the assembly the hero son of Atreus, wide-ruling Agamemnon, in deep anger: fury filled his dark heart full, and his eyes were like blazing fire. First he spoke with a glare of malice at Kalchas: 'Prophet of evil, you have never told me anything to my liking. Always your heart's delight is to prophesy evil, and you have never spoken or brought to fulfilment any word of good. And now you declare in prophecy to the Danaans that this is the cause of the anguish the far-shooter is bringing them, that I refused to accept the splendid ransom for the girl Chryseïs – yes, because my wish is to keep her in my house: and indeed I prefer her to Klytaimestra the wife of my marriage, as she is in no way her inferior in body or stature, or good sense or the craft of her hands. But even so I am willing to give her back, if that is for the best – I wish my people to be saved, not die. But you must produce another prize for me without delay, so that I am not the only one of the Argives without a prize, as that would not be right – you can all see for yourselves that my own prize is leaving my hands.'

Then swift-footed godlike Achilleus answered him: 'Glorious son of Atreus, most acquisitive of all men, how are the great-hearted Achaians to give you a prize? We do not know of any stores of common treasure piled anywhere. What we took at the sacking of cities has all been divided, and it is not right that the army should gather it back again. No, you now let the girl go at the god's will: and we Achaians will recompense you three and four times over, if ever Zeus grants that we sack the well-walled city of Troy.'

Then lord Agamemnon answered him: 'Great man though you are, godlike Achilleus, do not think you can cheat me like this – you will not trick me or persuade me to it. Is it so that you can hold on to your own prize, while I just sit by and bear the loss of mine, is this why you tell me to give back the girl? No, if the great-hearted Achaians will give me a prize, suiting it to my heart's liking, to be of equal value – then so be it. But if they will not, then I myself shall go and take your prize, or Aias', or Odysseus', and carry it away with me: and he will be angry, whichever of you I visit. But this can be talk for the future. For the present, let us haul a black ship down into the holy sea, and gather a chosen crew, and place in it a hundred oxen for sacrifice, and put aboard the beautiful Chryseïs herself. And some man of counsel must be the leader, either Aias, or Idomeneus, or godlike Odysseus, or you, son of Peleus, most formidable of all men, so that by due sacrifice you can win the far-shooter's favour for us.'

Then swift-footed Achilleus scowled at him and said: 'Oh you, your thoughts are always set on gain, and shamelessness is your very clothing! How can any of the Achaians willingly follow your orders, to go on expeditions or fight an enemy with all their strength? It was not the spearmen of Troy who caused me to come here and fight – I have no quarrel with them. They have never rustled my cows or horses, or ravaged the crops in fertile Phthia, nurse of men: because between us there lie many shadowing mountains and the roar of the sea. No, it was you, you great shameless creature, you we came with, to give you satisfaction and win requital from the Trojans for Menelaos and for you, dog-face. You have no thought or regard for this. And now you even threaten to take away my prize yourself – I laboured hard for it, and it was awarded me by the sons of the Achaians. I never have a prize equal to yours, whenever the Achaians sack some well-founded Trojan town. My hands bear the brunt of the battle's fury. But when the division comes, your prize is by far the larger, and I come back to the ships with something small but precious, when I have worn myself out in the fighting. Now I shall leave for Phthia. It is a far better thing for me to return home with my beaked ships, and I have no mind to stay here heaping up riches and treasure for you and receiving no honour myself.'

Then Agamemnon, lord of men, answered him: 'Yes, run home, if that is what your heart urges. I do not beg you to stay for my sake. I have others with me who will show me honour, and chief among them Zeus the counsellor himself. Of all the kings whom Zeus sustains you are the most hateful to me – always your delight is in quarrelling and wars and battle. Strong man you may be, but that is the gift of a god. Go home then with your ships and your companions, and lord it over your Myrmidons. I care nothing for you, your anger does not touch me. But I make this threat to you. Just as Phoibos Apollo is taking Chryseïs away from me – I will send her home with my ship and my companions – so I shall take the beautiful Briseïs, your prize, going myself to fetch her from your hut, so that you can fully realise how much I am your superior, and others too can shrink from speaking on a level with me and openly claiming equality.'

So he spoke, and anger came over the son of Peleus. His heart in his shaggy breast was torn in thought, whether to draw his sharp sword from beside his thigh, break up the assembly, and kill Agamemnon, or to quell his anger and restrain his heart. While he was pondering this in his mind and his heart, and was pulling his great sword from the scabbard, Athene came down from heaven – the white-armed goddess Hera had sent her, as she loved both men alike in her heart and cared for them equally. Athene came up behind him and caught the son of Peleus by his yellow hair, visible to him alone – none of the others saw her. Achilleus was startled, and turned round, and immediately recognised Pallas Athene – there was a fearful gleam in her eyes. He spoke winged words to her: 'Why have you come this time, daughter of Zeus who holds the aegis? Is it to witness the insult done me by Agamemnon son of Atreus? Well, I tell you something which I think will certainly be done as I say: for this arrogance of his at some time soon he will lose his life.'

Then the bright-eyed goddess Athene said to him: 'I have come from heaven to stop your fury, if you will obey me. The white-armed goddess Hera sent me, as she loves both of you alike in her heart and cares for you equally. Come then, leave your quarrelling, and do not let your hand draw the sword. But use your tongue to bring shame on him, telling him how it will be. I tell you this, and it will certainly be as I say. There will be a day when three times these splendid gifts will be laid before you because of this insult. Restrain yourself, and do as we ask.'

Then swift-footed Achilleus answered her: 'A man should heed your words, goddess, however angry he is at heart. That will be better for him. Obey the gods, and they will hear you well.'

So he spoke, and stayed his massive hand on the silver hilt, and pushed the great sword back into the scabbard, and did not fail to obey Athene's words. She was on her way back to Olympos to join the other gods in the house of Zeus who holds the aegis.

Then the son of Peleus again attacked the son of Atreus with stinging words, his anger still unabated: 'Drunkard, with the eyes of a dog and the heart of a deer, you have never had the courage to join your people in arming for battle, or to go with the leading men of the Achaians into ambush – that seems sheer death to you. Oh, far better to go the length and breadth of the Achaian camp stealing the prizes of anyone who speaks against you – a king who feeds fat on his people, with mere ciphers for subjects: otherwise, son of Atreus, this would now be your last outrage. But I tell you this, and will swear a great oath to it. I swear by this staff, which will never again put out leaves and branches, from the moment it parted from its stump in the mountains, and it will sprout no more, since the bronze stripped it of its leaves and bark all round. Now the sons of the Achaians carry it in their hands when they give judgments, those who guard the ways of justice under Zeus: an oath by this staff has power to bind. I swear now that there will come a time when the loss of Achilleus will be felt by the whole number of the sons of the Achaians. Then for all your anguish you will have no power to protect them, when many fall dying at the hands of murderous Hektor. And you will tear your heart within you in remorse, that you showed no honour to the best of the Achaians.'

So the son of Peleus spoke, and he threw the staff to the ground, studded with its golden nails, and sat down himself. And the son of Atreus kept up his fury on the other side. Then there rose among them Nestor the sweet-spoken, the clear-voiced speaker of Pylos: from his tongue the words flowed sweeter than honey. He had already seen the passing of two generations of humankind, the men who in earlier days had been born and reared with him in holy Pylos, and now he was ruling over the third. In all good will he spoke and addressed the assembly: 'Oh, shame! Great sorrow is coming on the land of Achaia. There would surely be joy for Priam and his children, and all the other Trojans would feel great gladness at heart, if they learnt of all this quarrelling between you two, who are the best of the Danaans in counsel and the best in fighting. No, you must listen to me, since both of you are younger men than I. In my time I have kept company with greater men even than you, and they never failed to respect me. The like of such men I have not seen since, nor will I ever see – Peirithoös and Dryas, shepherd of his people, and Kaineus and Exadios and godlike Polyphemos, and Theseus son of Aigeus, the image of the immortals. They were the mightiest of all men bred upon earth. Mighty they were, and mighty their opponents, the Centaurs, beasts of the mountains – and they put them to terrible destruction. And I was of their company, coming from Pylos, a long journey from a distant land, at their summons: and I fought among them in my own right. Not one of the mortals now upon earth could do battle with those men. And yet they listened to my advice and followed my words. So you too should listen to me, since it is best to listen. You, great man though you are, do not take the girl from him, but let her be, as the sons of the Achaians gave her to him in the beginning as his prize. And you, son of Peleus, do not seek open quarrel with the king, since there is no equality with the honour granted to a sceptred king, whom Zeus has glorified. You may be a man of strength, with a goddess for your mother, but he is the more powerful, because his rule is wider. Son of Atreus, you must stop your fury. I beg you to put aside your anger for Achilleus, who for all the Achaians is their great defence against the horror of war.'

Then lord Agamemnon answered him: 'Yes, all that you say, old man, is right and true. But this man wants to be above all others: he wants to control all, to rule all, to dictate to all, and there are some of us I doubt will obey him. The ever-living gods may have created him a warrior, but is that any cause for abuse to spring to his lips?'

Godlike Achilleus made abrupt answer: 'Coward and nobody would be my names, if I defer to you in everything you care to say. Others can take these commands of yours, but do not give your orders to me, because I doubt I shall obey you now. I tell you another thing, and you mark it well in your mind. I will not come to hand-fighting over the girl with you or any other – you Achaians gave her, and you have taken her away. But as for the other possessions I hold by my fast black ship, you will not take and carry away any one of them without my will. Come, try, if you wish, to make it clear to all: in an instant your dark blood will drip from my spear.'

Such were the wrangling words of their quarrel. The two men stood, and broke up the assembly by the Achaians' ships. The son of Peleus went to his huts and his balanced ships with the son of Menoitios and his other companions. And the son of Atreus hauled a fast ship down to the sea, and chose twenty oarsmen for it, and put a hundred oxen in it for sacrifice to the god, and brought the beautiful Chryseïs and set her aboard: and resourceful Odysseus went on ship to lead them.

They then boarded and set sail over the paths of the water. Meanwhile the son of Atreus gave orders to the army for a purification. They washed themselves clean and threw the scourings into the sea, then they sacrificed to Apollo unblemished hecatombs of bulls and goats along the shore of the harvestless sea: the smell of sacrifice reached the sky, curling upwards in the smoke.

So the men busied themselves throughout the camp. But Agamemnon would not leave his threat, once made, in his quarrel with Achilleus. He called to Talthybios and Eurybates, his heralds and ready servants: 'Go to the hut of Achilleus son of Peleus. Take the beautiful Briseïs by the hand and bring her. If he will not give her to you, I shall come with a larger force and take her myself, and that will be the worse for him.'

So speaking he sent them on their way, with stern instructions. They went reluctantly along the shore of the harvestless sea, and came to the huts and the ships of the Myrmidons. They found him by his hut and his black ship, sitting idle: and Achilleus had no joy in seeing them. They stood there silent, without word or question, in fear and respect for the king. But he understood their purpose in his mind, and spoke to them: 'Welcome, heralds, messengers of Zeus and of men. Come closer. It is not you I blame, but Agamemnon, who has sent you here for the girl Briseïs. Come, lord Patroklos, bring the girl out and give her to them for the taking. And these two themselves can be my witnesses before the blessed gods and mortal men, and before that heartless king, if ever in time to come there arises a need for me, to protect the others from shameful destruction. His mind's madness is set on disaster, and he will not take thought for the future as well as the past, to preserve his Achaians as they fight by the ships.'

So he spoke, and Patroklos did as his dear friend told him. He brought the beautiful Briseïs out of the hut, and gave her to the heralds to take. They went back again to the ships of the Achaians, and the woman went with them, reluctant. Then Achilleus broke in tears, and quickly drew far away from his companions, and sat down on the shore of the grey sea, looking out over the boundless ocean. He stretched out his hands, and prayed long to his dear mother: 'Mother, since it was you that bore me, if only to a life doomed to shortness, surely honour should have been granted to me by Olympian Zeus, the high-thunderer. But now he has shown me not even the slightest honour. The son of Atreus, wide-ruling Agamemnon, has dishonoured me: he has taken my prize with his own hands, and keeps it for himself.'

So he spoke with the tears falling, and his honoured mother heard him, where she sat by the side of her old father in the depths of the sea. Quickly she rose up from the grey sea like a mist, and sat down in front of him as he wept, and stroked him with her hand, and spoke to him, saying: 'Child, why are you crying? What pain has touched your heart? Tell me, do not hide it inside you, so that both of us can know.'

With a heavy groan swift-footed Achilleus said to her: 'You know. What need for me to tell you all when you know it? We had gone to Thebe, Eëtion's sacred city. We sacked it, and brought all the spoils here. The sons of the Achaians made proper division of all the rest among themselves, and chose for the son of Atreus as his gift of honour the beautiful Chryseïs. But then Chryses, the priest of Apollo the far-shooter, came to the fast ships of the bronze-clad Achaians to gain release for his daughter, bringing with him unlimited ransom, and holding in his hands the sacred woollen bands of Apollo the far-shooter, wreathed on a golden staff. He began to entreat the whole body of the Achaians, but especially the two sons of Atreus, the marshals of the army. Then all the other Achaians shouted their agreement, to respect the priest's claim and take the splendid ransom. But this was not the pleasure of Agamemnon's heart, the son of Atreus. He sent him shamefully on his way, with harsh words of command. The old man went back in anger: and Apollo heard his prayer, since he was very dear to him, and sent his deadly arrows against the Argives. The people were dying, death upon death, as the god's arrows plied everywhere throughout the breadth of the Achaian camp. Our seer in full knowledge declared to us the will of the far-shooter, and I was the first to urge the appeasement of the god. But then anger seized the son of Atreus: he leapt up and declared the threat which has now been carried out. That girl the bright-eyed Achaians are now taking in a fast ship to Chryse, and carrying gifts for the lord Apollo. But the heralds have just now come to my hut and taken away with them the daughter of Briseus, my gift from the sons of the Achaians. So now, if it is in your power, protect your own son. Go to Olympos and beseech Zeus by any service you have ever done his godhead in word or action. I often heard you in my father's house telling with pride how you alone among the immortals rescued the son of Kronos, lord of the dark clouds, from a shaming plight, when other Olympian gods sought to bind him fast — Hera and Poseidon and Pallas Athene. But you came and released him from his bonds, goddess, quickly calling up to wide Olympos the hundred-hander, called Briareos by the gods, but Aigaion by all humans. He is yet stronger than his father, and he took his seat beside the son of Kronos glorying in his splendour. The blessed gods shrank in fear from him, and there was no more binding. Remind him of this now, and sit beside him and take his knees, asking that it may be his will to bring aid to the Trojans, and pen the Achaians back by the shore and the sterns of their ships amid much slaughter, so that all may have enjoyment of their king, and even the son of Atreus, wide-ruling Agamemnon, may come to recognise his folly, in paying no honour to the best of the Achaians.'

Then Thetis answered him with her tears falling: 'Oh my child, what did I rear you for, after the pain of your birth? If only you could sit by your ships without tears or sorrow — because your fate is of short span, not at all long. But now you are both short-lived and miserable as well beyond all others: so it was a cruel fate under which I bore you in our house. But I shall go myself to snow-capped Olympos and make this appeal to Zeus who delights in thunder, in the hope that he will grant it. But you now must sit close by your speedy ships and continue your rage against the Achaians, and withdraw completely from the fighting. Zeus went yesterday to Ocean, to feast with the blameless Ethiopians, and all the gods went with him. But on the twelfth day he will return again to Olympos, and then be sure that I shall go to Zeus' bronze-floored house: I shall take his knees in entreaty, and I think I shall persuade him.'

So speaking she went away, and left her son there where he was, with anger in his heart because of the girdled woman, taken from him by force against his will. Meanwhile Odysseus was approaching Chryse, bringing the holy hecatomb. When they had come inside the deep harbour, they took in the sails and stowed them in the black ship, then let down the mast by the forestays and lowered it smartly to the mast-crutch, and pulled the ship in to the anchorage with the oars. Out went the anchor-stones, and they made fast the stern-cables. They jumped out themselves where the surf breaks, and brought out the hecatomb for Apollo the far-shooter: and out came Chryseïs from the seafaring vessel. The resourceful Odysseus took her to the altar and gave her into her dear father's arms, and said to him: 'Chryses, Agamemnon, lord of men, has sent me here to bring you your daughter, and to sacrifice a holy hecatomb to Phoibos on behalf of the Danaans, so that we can appease the lord god who has now brought sorrows and much lamentation on the Argives.'

So speaking he gave the girl into her father's hands, and he received his dear child with joy. Then they quickly set the holy hecatomb for the god in proper order round the well-built altar, and then washed their hands and took up the barley-grains for sprinkling. Chryses lifted up his arms among them and prayed in a great voice: 'Hear me, lord of the silver bow, protector of Chryse and holy Killa, and mighty lord of Tenedos. As you heard my former prayer, and brought honour to me and great harm to the Achaian people, so now grant this my further desire – now at last drive the shameful plague away from the Danaans.'

So he spoke in prayer, and Phoibos Apollo heard him. When they had offered prayers and sprinkled the barley-grains, first they pulled back the victims' heads and slaughtered them and flayed them: and they cut out the thigh-bones and covered them with fat, folding it twice over, and placed pieces of raw meat on top. The old man burnt them on cut firewood, and poured libations of gleaming wine, while the young men stood by him with five-tanged forks in their hands. Then when the thighs were burnt up and they had tasted the inwards, they chopped the rest into pieces and threaded them on spits, roasted them carefully, and then drew all the meat off. When they had finished their work and prepared the meal, they set to eating, and no man's desire went without an equal share in the feast. When they had put away their desire for eating and drinking, the young men filled the mixing-bowls to the brim with wine, poured a libation into each man's cup, and then served them all. So all day long the young men of the Achaians appeased the god with music, singing a lovely hymn and dancing for the god who works from afar – and he listened with delight in his heart.

When the sun set and darkness came on, they lay down to sleep beside the ship's stern-cables. Then when early-born Dawn appeared with her rosy fingers, they put out to sea to return to the broad Achaian camp, and Apollo the far-worker sent a favouring breeze to speed them. They set up the mast and spread the white sails, and the wind swelled the belly of the sail, and the wave rising at the keel's stem hissed loud as the ship moved on: and she ran ever onwards, cutting her path through the swell. When they reached the broad camp of the

Achaians, they hauled the black ship on land, high on the sandy beach, and set props beneath her. The crew then scattered to their own huts and ships.

But the royal son of Peleus, swift-footed Achilleus, still sat idle by his speedy ships and kept up his anger. He would not ever go to the assembly where men win glory, nor into the fighting, but stayed where he was, wasting his heart out day after day, and yearning for the clamour of battle.

But when the twelfth dawn came round from that first day, the ever-living gods returned to Olympos all in a body, with Zeus at their head. And Thetis did not forget her son's demand, but she rose through the swell of the sea at early morning, and went up to the vast sky and Olympos. She found the wide-seeing son of Kronos sitting away from the others, on the highest peak of ridged Olympos. She crouched in front of him, and took his knees with her left hand, and reached with her right hand to hold him under the chin. Then she spoke in entreaty to lord Zeus son of Kronos: 'Father Zeus, if ever I have done you service among the immortals in word or in action, grant this my desire. Show honour to my son, who is short-lived beyond all other men. Now Agamemnon, lord of men, has dishonoured him: he has taken his prize with his own hands, and keeps it for himself. But you now show him honour, Zeus, counsellor, Olympian lord. Grant victory to the Trojans for such time until the Achaians recompense my son and raise him in honour among them.'

So she spoke, and Zeus the cloud-gatherer made her no answer, but sat long in silence. But Thetis kept her grasp on his knees and clung tight to him, and asked him a second time: 'Promise me now without fail and nod your assent: or else refuse me – you have no cause for fear – so that I can be sure how far I am the lowest in honour among all the gods.'

Zeus the cloud-gatherer answered her in vexation: 'This is a grievous business – you will set me at odds with Hera, when she stings me to anger with her taunts. Even without this she is always carping at me among the immortal gods, and saying that I help the Trojans in battle. Well, you must go back now, so that Hera does not see anything – I shall take care of these things, and see that they are brought about. Look, I shall nod my head in assent, so you can be sure. This is the strongest pledge I can give among the immortals. No word of mine can be revoked, or prove false, or fail of fulfilment, when I nod my head in assent to it.'

So the son of Kronos spoke, and he nodded his dark brows. The lord god's immortal hair streamed forward from his deathless head, and he shook the heights of Olympos.

With this agreement made, the two parted. Thetis then leapt down from bright Olympos into the deep sea, and Zeus went to his own house. All the gods rose together from their seats in the presence of the father: not one of them dared to keep his place at Zeus' approach, but all rose to greet him. So he then sat down on his throne. But when Hera looked at him, she could tell that plans had been laid with him by silver-footed Thetis, the daughter of the old man of the sea. She immediately attacked Zeus the son of Kronos with scornful words: 'Crafty one, which of the gods has been laying plans with you this time? It is always your way to keep apart from me and decide your purposes in secret. You have never yet been prepared to tell me frankly of any design you have in your mind.'

Then the father of men and gods answered her: 'Hera, do not expect to know of all my thoughts – they will be hard for you, even though you are my wife. When it is right for you to hear my thought, no-one, god or man, will know of it before you do. But when I wish to lay my plans apart from the other gods, please do not question me and enquire into every detail.'

Then the ox-eyed queen Hera answered him: 'Dread son of Kronos, what is this you are saying? I have not questioned you or enquired too closely in the past, but you are quite free to make whatever plans you wish. This time, though, I have a terrible fear in my mind that you have been won over by silver-footed Thetis, the daughter of the old man of the sea – early in the morning she came and sat by you and took your knees. I suspect that you have given her your solemn word to bring honour to Achilleus, and death to many by the Achaian ships.'

Zeus the cloud-gatherer answered her: 'My dear wife, you are always suspecting, and no action of mine can escape you. But even so there is nothing you can do, except to put yourself yet further from my heart – and that will be the worse for you. If the matter is as you say, then that must be how I wish it. No, sit still and be quiet, and do as I tell you, or all the gods in Olympos will be no help to you, when I come close and lay my invincible hands on you.'

So he spoke, and the ox-eyed queen Hera was afraid, and sat in silence, bending her heart to obey. There was uproar among the heavenly gods in Zeus' house. But Hephaistos the famous craftsman began to speak to them, anxious to do service to his dear mother, white-armed Hera: 'This will be a grievous business, and beyond endurance, if you two are to quarrel in this way over mortal men, and set the gods to wrangling: and we shall have no pleasure in the excellent feast, since unworthy things will be foremost. I urge my mother – though she knows it herself – to make her peace with our dear father Zeus, so that the father does not scold her again and spoil our feasting. If the Olympian lord of the lightning is minded to dash us from our seats – well, he is far stronger than all of us. No, you should approach him with soft words, and then the Olympian will be kindly to us again.'

So he spoke, and jumped up and put a two-handled cup in his dear mother's hands, and said to her: 'Have patience, mother, and bear with it despite your distress. Otherwise, dear as you are to me, I may see you beaten about before my eyes, and then I shall not be able to help you for all the pain I will feel – it is hard to stand against the Olympian. Once before when I was eager to defend you he caught me by the foot and threw me from the threshold of the gods: all day long I dropped, and with the setting of the sun I fell to earth in Lemnos, and there was little breath left in me. There the Sintians took care of me after my fall.'

So he spoke, and the white-armed goddess Hera smiled, and smiling took the cup from her son. Then beginning from the left he poured for all the other gods, drawing sweet nectar from the bowl. And uncontrollable laughter arose among the blessed gods, as they watched Hephaistos bustling to and fro in the palace.

So they feasted all day long till the setting of the sun, and no-one's desire went without an equal share in the feast, nor did they lack the beautiful music of the lyre in Apollo's hands, and the lovely singing of the Muses, voice answering voice.

Then when the brightness of the sun had set, they each went home to sleep, in the houses made for them in the cunning of his craft by the famous lame god Hephaistos. And Zeus the Olympian lord of the lightning went to his own bed, where he always lay down when sweet sleep came over him. He climbed to his bed and slept there, and beside him slept Hera of the golden throne.

BOOK 2
THE CATALOGUE OF SHIPS

The other gods, and the warrior men, slept the night long. But sleep did not keep its sweet hold on Zeus, who was pondering in his mind how he might bring honour to Achilleus, and death to many by the Achaian ships. This seemed the best plan to his thinking, to send evil Dream to Agamemnon son of Atreus. And so he spoke winged words to him: 'Away with you, evil Dream, to the fast ships of the Achaians. Go into the hut of Agamemnon son of Atreus, and speak to him exactly as I tell you. Tell him to arm the long-haired Achaians for battle with all speed, because now he can take the Trojans' broad-wayed city. The immortals who live on Olympos are no longer divided in purpose – Hera's entreaties have turned them all, and sorrows are in store for the Trojans.'

So he spoke, and Dream went on his way, after hearing his instructions. Quickly he came to the fast ships of the Achaians, and went to Agamemnon son of Atreus. He found him sleeping in his hut, wrapped in the divine sweetness of sleep. He stood above his head in the likeness of Nestor son of Neleus, whom Agamemnon honoured most of all the elders. In this shape, then, the divine Dream spoke to him: 'You are sleeping, son of wise Atreus the horse-tamer. Sleep should not last night-long for a man of command, who has an army in his keeping and so much to concern him. Now listen quickly to me. I bring a message from Zeus who, though far away, cares greatly for you and pities you. He tells you to arm the long-haired Achaians for battle with all speed, because now you can take the Trojans' broad-wayed city. The immortals who live on Olympos are no longer divided in purpose – Hera's entreaties have turned them all, and sorrows are in store for the Trojans from Zeus. Keep this in your mind, and do not let forgetfulness come over you, when honey-sweet sleep releases its hold.'

So speaking Dream went back, and left him there with thoughts in his mind which would not see fulfilment. He thought that he would take Priam's city on that very day – poor fool, he knew nothing of Zeus' design, how he would pile yet further anguish and groaning on Trojans and Danaans alike in the fury of battle. He woke then from his sleep, and the divine voice was floating all round him. He sat upright, and put on a fine soft tunic, newly-made, and over it he threw a great cloak: he bound his fine sandals under his shining feet, and slung from his shoulders his sword with its silver rivets: and he took up the sceptre of his fathers, imperishable for all time, and with this in his hands he went down to the ships of the bronze-clad Achaians.

The goddess Dawn had risen to the heights of Olympos, proclaiming the light of day to Zeus and the other immortals. And Agamemnon gave orders to his clear-voiced heralds to summon the long-haired Achaians to assembly. The heralds made their summons, and the people quickly gathered.

First Agamemnon held a council of the great-hearted elders beside the ship of Nestor, the Pylos-born king. He called the elders together and laid before them a plan of his devising: 'Listen, friends. A divine dream came to me in the immortal night, as a vision in my sleep – in appearance and size and build it was most closely like godlike Nestor. It stood above my head and spoke to me: "You are sleeping, son of wise Atreus the horse-tamer. Sleep should not last night-long for a man of command, who has an army in his keeping and so much to concern him. Now listen quickly to me. I bring a message from Zeus who, though far away, cares greatly for you and pities you. He tells you to arm the long-haired Achaians for battle with all speed, because now you can take the Trojans' broad-wayed city. The immortals who live on Olympos are no longer divided in purpose – Hera's entreaties have turned them all, and sorrows are in store for the Trojans from Zeus. Keep this in your mind." So speaking the dream winged away, and sweet sleep released me from its hold. Come then, let us see if we can arm the Achaians for battle. But first, as is the proper way, I shall test them with an address, and tell them to make for home with their many-benched ships: and you must try to restrain them with your orders, each from his own position.'

So speaking he sat down, and Nestor rose to speak, the king of sandy Pylos. In all good will he addressed the council and said: 'Friends, leaders and lords of the Argives, if any other of the Achaians had spoken of this dream, we would rather call it false and reject it. But now it has been seen by the man who has claim to be the best of the Achaians. Come then, let us see if we can arm the sons of the Achaians for battle.'

So speaking he led the way back from the council, and the other sceptred kings rose from their seats and followed the shepherd of the people: and the army streamed out to meet them. As when a mass of bees comes swarming out from a hollow in the rock in a never-ending stream: squadrons take wing this way and that, and they fly in tight clusters to settle on the springtime flowers. So the many tribes of the Achaians marched in troops from their ships and their huts along the deep shore's front to the place of assembly: and Rumour, Zeus' messenger, went blazing among them, urging them on. So they gathered together, and the assembly was in uproar. The earth groaned under them as the troops tried to take their seats, and there was hubbub. Nine heralds shouted in the effort to control them, to make them stop their clamour and listen to the god-ordained kings. At length the army was settled, and they sat disciplined in their places and stopped their din. Then lord Agamemnon rose, holding his sceptre, the work of Hephaistos' labour. Hephaistos gave it to lord Zeus the son of Kronos: and Zeus gave it to Hermes the guide, the slayer of Argos: and lord Hermes gave it to Pelops the charioteer, then Pelops in turn gave it to Atreus, shepherd of the people. Atreus as he was dying left it to Thyestes, rich in flocks, then in turn Thyestes left it to Agamemnon to carry, to be king over many islands and all of Argos. Leaning on this sceptre Agamemnon spoke to the Argives: 'My friends, Danaan heroes, Ares' men-at-arms. Zeus the son of Kronos has snared me wholly in grievous delusion. Cruel god – in the beginning he promised me, with solemn assent, that I would sack well-walled Ilios before my return: but now he has planned a vile deception, and tells me to go back to Argos in dishonour, after I have lost many of my people. So it seems must be the pleasure of Zeus the almighty, who has already shattered the crowns of many cities and will break yet more, such is his matchless power. This is a shameful thing for future men to hear of, that an Achaian army of such power and size should wage a war like this without success or issue, fighting an enemy fewer in number, and no result yet seen. If we were both to agree, Achaians and Trojans, to make a binding truce and then be counted, the Trojans to number every man whose home is in the city, and we Achaians dividing into groups of ten: if each of our tens were then to choose a single Trojan to serve their wine, many tens would go without a wine-steward. That, I tell you, is how far the sons of the Achaians outnumber the Trojans who live within the city. But they have allies, spearmen from many other cities, who greatly hamper me and thwart my will to sack the well-founded citadel of Ilios. Nine years now have passed from mighty Zeus' store, and our ships' timbers have rotted and their rigging decayed. And our wives and young children are sitting in our homes, waiting for us: while the task which brought us here stands quite without completion. No, come, let us all do as I say – let us away with our ships to our own dear native land. We shall never now take the broad streets of Troy.'

So he spoke, and his words lifted the hearts of all in the mass of the army, all those who were not privy to his purpose: and the assembly was stirred like the great waves of the sea, in the deep water by Ikaria, when the east wind and the south wind rush down from father Zeus' stormclouds and raise them high. As when the west wind stirs a deep cornfield with its coming, and the standing crop bows its ears in the fury of the blast, so the whole assembly was stirred to movement. The men swarmed cheering to the ships, and under their feet the dust rose high in a cloud. They urged each other to lay hands to the ships and drag them down to the holy sea, and they set to clearing the slipways. Their shouts reached heaven as they surged for home: and they began to pull the props from under the ships.

Then the Argives would have made a homecoming beyond what was fated, if Hera had not spoken to Athene: 'Shame on it, Atrytone, daughter of Zeus who holds the aegis! This way the Argives will run back home over the sea's broad back to their own dear country, and leave behind Argive Helen to the triumph of Priam and the Trojans: yet for her sake many of the Achaians have lost their lives in Troy, away from their dear native land. So go now and move among the bronze-clad Achaian army. Use gentle words to turn the men back one by one, and do not let them haul their balanced ships down to the water.'

So she spoke, and the bright-eyed goddess Athene did not fail to obey. She went darting down from the peaks of Olympos, and quickly came to the fast ships of the Achaians. Then she found Odysseus, Zeus' equal in his mind's resource. He was standing still, and would not put his hands to his well-benched black ship – anguish was touching his heart and spirit. Bright-eyed Athene stood by him and said: 'Royal son of Laertes, resourceful Odysseus, are you all indeed going to throw yourselves like this into your benched ships and run back home to your own dear country, and leave behind Argive Helen to the triumph of Priam and the Trojans? Yet for her sake many of the Achaians have lost their lives in Troy, away from their dear native land. So go now and move among the bronze-clad Achaian army. Use gentle words to turn the men back one by one, and do not let them haul their balanced ships down to the water.'

So she spoke, and Odysseus heard the goddess' voice, and set off at the run, throwing off his cloak, which was picked up by the herald Eurybates from Ithaka, his attendant. Odysseus ran straight up to Agamemnon son of Atreus, and took from him the sceptre of his fathers, imperishable for all time: then with this in his hands he went down to the ships of the bronze-clad Achaians. Whenever he met with a king or a man of importance, he would come up to him and turn him back with gentle words: 'Friend, it would not be right for me to threaten you like an inferior. Rather you take your seat again and make the rest of the army return to their places. You do not yet fully understand the son of Atreus' purpose. Now he is testing them, but soon he will punish the sons of the Achaians. Did we not all hear what he said in the council? I fear he may be enraged by this and do some harm to the sons of the Achaians. Kings ordained by god have an anger that runs high: their honour comes from Zeus, and Zeus the counsellor loves them.'

But whenever he saw a commoner and found him shouting, he would strike him with the sceptre and berate him, saying: 'Friend, sit quiet and listen to what others tell you, your superiors – you are a coward and a weakling, of no account either in war or in counsel. We cannot all be kings here, every one of the Achaians. To have each man his own master is ruin: there must be one master, one king, the man endowed by the son of devious-minded Kronos with the sceptre and the ways of law, to make judgments for his people.'

Such was his mastering way with the army. And they streamed back again to the place of assembly from their ships and their huts, with a roar like that of the sounding sea, when the breakers crash on a wide open shore, and the deep sea thunders.

Now the others sat down, and stayed disciplined in their places. But one man still railed on, the loose-tongued Thersites. His head was full of vulgar abuse, reckless insubordinate attacks on the kings, with anything said that he thought might raise a laugh among the Argives. He was the ugliest man that went to Ilios. He was bandy-legged and lame in one foot: his humped shoulders were bent inwards over his chest: above, his head rose to a point, sprouting thin wisps of wool. He was hated most of all by Achilleus and Odysseus, the two whom he constantly reviled. But this time it was godlike Agamemnon who received his shrill screams of abuse. The Achaians felt furious anger and resentment at him, but he kept on shouting his taunts at Agamemnon, his voice raised high: 'Son of Atreus, what is your complaint this time?

What are you missing? Your huts are filled with bronze, and there are women enough in your quarters – choice girls, offered to you before all others by us Achaians whenever we capture a town. Or is it yet more gold you are wanting, that will be brought out of Ilios by one of the horse-taming Trojans as ransom for his son – a son bound and brought in by me or some other Achaian? Or some young woman, so you can twine in love with her, and keep her secluded all for yourself? You are the commander: it is quite wrong for you to lead the sons of the Achaians on the road to disaster. My poor weak friends, you sorry disgraces, mere women of Achaia now, no longer men – yes, let us go back home with our ships, and leave this man here in Troy to brood on his prizes, so that he can see whether the rest of us are of some help to him or not. Now he has even dishonoured Achilleus, a much better man than he: he has taken his prize with his own hands and keeps it for himself. But Achilleus has no fury in his heart, he lets things pass – otherwise, son of Atreus, this would now be your last outrage.'

So Thersites spoke, taunting Agamemnon, the shepherd of the people. But godlike Odysseus quickly came up to him, and scowling at him gave the man a harsh rebuke: 'Thersites, you loud-mouth, fluent speaker though you are, stop this, enough of your lone attacks on the kings. I tell you there is no worse man than you among all the numbers that came to Ilios with the sons of Atreus. So we will not have you prating to us with talk of kings, and hurling abuse at them, while watching for your chance to get home. We cannot yet be sure how this business will end, whether we sons of the Achaians will return home in triumph or in failure. So you now sit here abusing Agamemnon son of Atreus, shepherd of the people, because the Danaan heroes give him many gifts – your talk is nothing but insult. Well, I tell you this, and it will certainly be done as I say. If I find you again in this same foolishness, then may Odysseus' head no longer sit on his shoulders, may I no longer be called father to Telemachos, if I do not take you and strip off your clothing, cloak and tunic as well, all that covers your shame, and send you blubbering back to the fast ships, flogging you out of the assembly with blows to shame you.'

So he spoke, and then used the sceptre to beat him on the back and shoulders. Thersites writhed, and a heavy tear fell from him, and a bloody weal sprang up on his back under the gold-studded sceptre. He sat down frightened and in pain, and with a helpless look wiped away the tears. For all their disaffection the men laughed happily at him, and one would glance at his neighbour and say: 'Oh yes, Odysseus has done thousands of fine things before now, proposing good plans and leading in battle. But this now is far the best thing he has done among the Argives, putting a stop to this horror's rantings in assembly. I doubt that his proud heart will ever again impel him to taunt the kings with insults.'

So spoke the soldiery. And then Odysseus, sacker of cities, rose to speak with the sceptre in his hand. Beside him bright-eyed Athene, in the form of a herald, called for silence from the people, so that both nearest and furthest of the sons of the Achaians could hear his words and consider his advice. In all good will he spoke and addressed the assembly: 'Son of Atreus, as things are, my lord, the Achaians are intent on bringing you into utter disgrace before all mortal men, and they will not make good the promise they undertook when still on their journey here from horse-rearing Argos, that they would return only after you had sacked well-walled Ilios. Like young children or widowed women they wail to each other about their return to their homes. But surely it is painful too to go home frustrated. If a man is even one month away from his wife with his many-benched ship, he will chafe when the winter storms and the troubled sea pen him in port – and for us this is the ninth year's circle of our waiting here. So I do not blame the Achaians for chafing beside their beaked ships. But for all that it is a shaming thing to wait long and return with empty hands. Bear with it, my friends, and wait for a time longer, until we can learn whether Kalchas' prophecy is true or not. We remember it well in our minds, and you are all witnesses to it, those whom the fates of death have not since carried away. Not so long ago, when the Achaian ships were gathering at Aulis, carrying doom to Priam and the Trojans, and we were sacrificing unblemished hecatombs to the immortals at the sacred altars circled round a spring, under a beautiful plane-tree, where the water ran sparkling – there then appeared a great sign: a snake with blood-red back, a fearful thing, sent up to the light by the Olympian himself, slid from under an altar and darted for the plane-tree. In the tree there were a sparrow's chicks, little babies, out on the topmost branch cowering under the leaves, eight of them, and the mother who bore the brood made nine. Then the snake ate the chicks as they screamed pitifully, and their mother fluttered round it crying for her dear children: but the snake coiled out and caught her by the wing as she shrieked above it. Then when it had eaten her children and the sparrow herself, the god who had brought the snake to light made it a miracle, plain for all to see – it was turned into stone by the son of devious-minded Kronos, and we stood there in amazement at what had happened. So when the fearful monsters had invaded the gods' hecatombs, Kalchas then immediately began to speak to us in prophecy: "Why fall silent, you long-haired Achaians? This is a great sign revealed to us by Zeus the counsellor – a sign late-pointing, late-fulfilled, whose fame will never perish. Just as this snake ate the sparrow's children and the sparrow herself, eight of them, and the mother who bore the brood made nine, so we shall battle there for that many years, and in the tenth year we shall take the broad streets of the city." Such were his words to us: and all is now coming to fulfilment. So come, you well-greaved Achaians, all of you stay here where we are, until we have taken the great city of Priam.'

So he spoke, and the Argives roared loud, and round them the ships echoed mightily to the Achaians' cheers, as they shouted their approval of godlike Odysseus' words. Then the Gerenian horseman Nestor spoke among them: 'Shame on you! You behave in assembly like children, little children who have no concern for the doings of war. Where will our agreements be gone, and the oaths we swore? Let the fire take our deliberations and the strategies that men devised, our solemn pledges poured in wine, and the giving of right hands, in which we had trusted! We do nothing but fight with words, and can find no solution, for all the length of time that we have been here. Son of Atreus, you must still hold as before unshakeably to your purpose, and take command of the Argives in the fury of warfare. And let these others go hang, these one or two at variance with the Achaians whose desire – though they can never achieve it – is to go back to Argos before we discover if the promise given by Zeus who holds the aegis is false or the truth. Because I tell you that the almighty son of Kronos gave his assent on that day when the Argives were setting off in their speedy ships, bringing death and destruction to the Trojans – he sent lightning on the right, showing us signs of good omen. So let no-one be in haste to return to his home, until he has slept beside a Trojan's wife and avenged Helen's struggles and her groaning. If any man has an enormous desire to go back home, let him just put his hands to his well-benched black ship to meet his death and doom in the sight of all others. No, my lord, take careful thought yourself and listen to another's words. What I tell you is advice not to be scorned. Divide your men by tribes and by clans, Agamemnon, so that clan can support clan and tribe help tribe. If you do this and the Achaians follow your orders, you will then be able to discover the cowards among your leaders and your troops, and the brave men, because they will be fighting in their own divisions. And then if the city does not fall to you, you will know whether it is through god's will or men's cowardice and incompetence in war.'

Lord Agamemnon answered him: 'Once again, old man, you are master of the sons of the Achaians in assembly. Oh father Zeus and Athene and Apollo – if only I had ten such advisers among the Achaians! Then lord Priam's city would soon topple, captured and sacked at our hands. But the son of Kronos, Zeus who holds the aegis, has dealt me troubles, throwing me into useless quarrels and contention – so I and Achilleus fought with wrangling words over a girl, and I was the first to grow angry. If ever we become of one mind and purpose, then there will be no more postponement of the Trojans' fate, not even for a short while. Now you should go to take your food, so we can then join again in battle. And let every man of you prepare well for the fighting – put a good edge on your spears, and a good hang to your shields, give a good feed to your swift-footed horses, and cast a good eye over your chariots, so that we can run the trial of hateful Ares all day long. There will be no resting, not even for a short while, except when the coming of night separates the fighters' fury. There will be sweating on a man's chest under the strap of his covering shield, and his hand will tire on the spear: there will be sweating on a man's horse as it strains at the polished chariot. And any man I see trying to keep back from the battle by the beaked ships – he cannot be sure then of escaping the dogs and the birds.'

So he spoke, and the Argives roared loud, like the waves on a sheer headland, when the south wind whips them with its coming, and they roar against a jutting cliff: storm-waves never leave it, driven by every wind there is, blowing on this side or on that. The assembly rose, and they scattered milling to their ships: then they made fire in their huts, and took their meal. And each man sacrificed to one of the ever-living gods, praying to escape death and the moil of war. Agamemnon, lord of men, sacrificed a fat ox, five years old, to the almighty son of Kronos, calling to join him the elders and leading men of the Achaians – Nestor first of all, and lord Idomeneus, then the two Aiantes and the son of Tydeus, and then sixth Odysseus, Zeus' equal in his mind's resource. And Menelaos, master of the war-cry, came without need for summons, as he knew in his heart how his brother was suffering. They then stood round the ox and took up the barley-grains for sprinkling, and lord Agamemnon spoke in prayer among them: 'Zeus, greatest and most glorious, lord of the dark clouds, dweller in heaven, grant that the sun should not sink and the darkness come on before I have thrown Priam's palace headlong to the ground, blackened in the smoke, and burnt its gateways with ravaging fire, and ripped Hektor's tunic on his chest to tatters with the bronze: and may many of his companions fall face down in the dust about him and sink their teeth in the earth.'

So he spoke, but the son of Kronos would not yet grant his prayer — he took the sacrifice, but heaped higher their joyless hardship. When they had offered prayers and sprinkled the barley-grains, first they pulled back the victim's head and slaughtered it and flayed it: and they cut out the thigh-bones and covered them with fat, folding it twice over, and placed pieces of raw meat on top. These they burnt on cut sticks of dead wood, and they spitted the inwards and held them over the fire. Then when the thighs were burnt up and they had tasted the inwards, they chopped the rest and threaded the pieces on spits, roasted them carefully, then drew all the meat off. When they had finished their work and prepared the meal, they set to eating, and no man's desire went without an equal share in the feast. When they had put away their desire for eating and drinking, the Gerenian horseman Nestor was the first to speak: 'Most glorious son of Atreus, Agamemnon, lord of men, let us spend no more time here talking, or delay for any longer the task which god puts in our hands. Come, let the heralds of the bronze-clad Achaians gather the army at the ships by proclamation, and let us go in a body as we are throughout the breadth of the Achaian camp, to wake war's anger all the faster.'

So he spoke and Agamemnon, lord of men, did not fail to do as he said. He immediately gave orders to his clear-voiced heralds to summon the long-haired Achaians to war. The heralds made their summons, and the people quickly began to gather. And the god-ordained kings with Agamemnon hurried to and fro marshalling the army, and among them went bright-eyed Athene, holding the precious aegis which is ageless and immortal: a hundred tassels of pure gold hang fluttering from it, tight-woven each of them, and each the worth of a hundred oxen. With this in her hands she rushed darting through the Achaian army, spurring them on, and in each man's heart she raised the strength for warfare and battle without ceasing. Then war became a sweeter thought to them than returning in their hollow ships to their own dear native land.

As annihilating fire blazes through the deep forest on a mountain's peaks, and the glare can be seen from far off, so as they marched the gleam from the awesome bronze struck glinting through the air and reached the heavens.

Like the great flocks of flying birds – geese, or cranes, or long-necked swans – in an Asian water-meadow, by the streams of Kaÿstrios, which wheel this way and that in their wings' glory, and the meadow echoes to their cries as they settle in tumult: so the many companies of men poured out from their ships and their huts on to the plain of Skamandros, and beneath them the earth rang fearfully, under the feet of the men and the horses. They stood-to in the flowering meadow by Skamandros, in their tens of thousands, as many as the leaves and flowers that come in springtime.

Like the great crowds of swarming flies which hover about a shepherd's steading in the spring season, when the milk floods the pails: such were the numbers of the long-haired Achaians massed in the plain against the Trojans, and yearning to break them.

As herdsmen easily separate their ranging flocks of goats, when they have mixed together at pasture, so the commanders ordered their men into separate troops for the advance to battle, and among them went lord Agamemnon, looking in eyes and head like Zeus who delights in thunder, like Ares at his waist, and his chest like Poseidon's. Just as in a herd the bull is far the foremost of all the cattle, and among the crowding cows he stands preeminent: so Zeus made the son of Atreus on that day, outstanding in the mass and foremost among the heroes.

Tell me now, you Muses who have your homes on Olympos – you are gods, and attend all things and know all things, but we hear only the report and have no knowledge – tell me who were the leaders of the Danaans and their rulers. As for the mass of men, I could not tell of them or name them, not even if I had ten tongues and ten mouths, and in me a voice unbreakable and a heart of bronze, unless the Olympian Muses, daughters of Zeus who holds the aegis, were to tell over the names of all the many who came to Ilios. Yet I will give the leaders of the ships, and the ships in all their number.

The Boiotians were led by Peneleos and Leïtos and Arkesilaos and Prothoënor and Klonios. These were the men who lived in Hyria and rocky Aulis, Schoinos and Skolos and the mountain spurs of Eteonos, Thespeia and Graia and Mykalessos with the broad spaces for the dance; those who lived about Harma and Eilesion and Erythrai; those who held Eleon and Hyle and Peteon, Okalea and the well-founded citadel of Medeon, Kopai and Eutresis and Thisbe where the doves abound; those who held Koroneia and grassy Haliartos; those who held Plataia and those who lived in Glisas; those who held the well-founded citadel of Lower Thebes, and sacred Onchestos, the lovely precinct of Poseidon; those who held Arne with its many vines, and Mideia and holy Nisa and Anthedon set far on the border. Of these men there were fifty ships that sailed, and in each ship there went a hundred and twenty of Boiotia's youth.

Those who lived in Aspledon and Minyan Orchomenos were led by Askalaphos and Ialmenos, sons of Ares, borne by Astyoche in the house of Aktor, Azeus' son, to the mighty Ares: a virgin girl and chaste, she went up to her room and there he lay with her in secret. These commanded an array of thirty hollow ships.

The Phocians were led by Schedios and Epistrophos, sons of Iphitos the great-hearted son of Naubolos: those who held Kyparissos and rocky Pytho and holy Krisa and Daulis and Panopeus; those who lived about Anemoreia and Hyampolis, and those living beside the divine river Kephisos, and those who held Lilaia at the springs of Kephisos. With these two there followed forty black ships. They were the marshals of the Phocian ranks, setting them at their arming station beside the Boiotians, on the left of the army.

The leader of the Locrians was quick Aias, Oïleus' son – the smaller Aias, not the great size of Aias son of Telamon, but much smaller. He was a short man, with armour of cloth, but in skill with the spear he excelled among all the Hellenes and the Achaians. The Locrians were those who lived in Kynos and Opoëis and Kalliaros, Bessa and Skarphe and lovely Augeiai, Tarphe and Thronion and around the waters of Boagrios. With him there followed forty black ships of the Locrians who live across the water from sacred Euboia.

The men who held Euboia, the Abantes who breathe out fury – Chalkis and Eretria and Histiaia with its many vines, and Kerinthos by the sea and the steep fortress of Dion; and those who held Karystos and had their homes in Styra – these were led by Elephenor, branch of Ares, Chalkodon's son, commander of the great-hearted Abantes. He was followed by the fast-running Abantes, who grow their hair long at the back, spearmen longing to rip the armour on their enemies' chests with the stabs of their ash-shafted spears. With him there followed forty black ships.

Those who held the well-founded citadel of Athens, the land of great-hearted Erechtheus – Athene, daughter of Zeus, reared him, when the grain-giving ploughland had given him birth, and she settled him in

Athens, in her own rich temple: there the young men of Athens propitiate him with sacrifice of bulls and rams in each year's circle – these were led by Menestheus son of Peteos. No man yet born on earth was his equal in the marshalling of chariots and fighting men: only Nestor could rival him, as he was of an older generation. With him there followed fifty black ships.

Aias brought twelve ships from Salamis, and placed them where the Athenian lines were stationed.

The men who held Argos and walled Tiryns, Hermione and Asine which lie on a deep bay, Troizen and Eïones and Epidauros with its vineyards, and those sons of the Achaians who held Aigina and Mases: these were led by Diomedes, master of the war-cry, and Sthenelos, dear son of the famous Kapaneus. With them as a third leader went Euryalos, a man like the gods, son of lord Mekisteus the son of Talaos, but the commander over all was Diomedes, master of the war-cry. With them there followed eighty black ships.

Those who held the well-founded citadel of Mykene and wealthy Corinth and well-founded Kleonai, and lived in Orneai and lovely Araithyrea and Sikyon, where Adrestos had first been king; and those who held Hyperesia and the heights of Gonoessa and Pellene, and lived in Aigion and all along the coastline and round broad Helike – a hundred ships of these men were led by lord Agamemnon son of Atreus. With him there followed far the largest army and the bravest fighters. And among them he himself armed in gleaming bronze, in the pride of his glory, and outstanding among all the heroes, because he was the greatest of men and brought by far the largest army.

Those who held the bowl of Lakedaimon with its many ravines, Pharis and Sparta and Messe where the doves abound, and lived in Bryseiai and lovely Augeiai, and those who held Amyklai and the coastal town of Helos, and those who held Laäs and lived round Oitylos: these were led by his brother Menelaos, master of the war-cry, in sixty ships. They were arming in a separate station, and among them went Menelaos himself, in the confidence of his passion, urging them to battle. His heart was set most of all on avenging Helen's struggles and her groaning.

Those who lived in Pylos and lovely Arene, and Thryon where the Alpheios is forded, and well-founded Aipy, and peopled Kyparisseëis and Amphigeneia, and Pteleon and Helos and Dorion, where the Muses met Thamyris the Thracian and stopped his singing, when he had come from Oichalia, from Eurytos the Oichalian king – in his boasting he had claimed that he would win even if the Muses themselves were to sing against him, the daughters of Zeus who holds the aegis: they grew angry with him and maimed his sight, then took from him the divine gift of song and drove away his memory for the lyre. These men were led by the Gerenian horseman Nestor, and he commanded an array of ninety hollow ships.

Those who held Arcadia below the sheer peak of Kyllene, by Aipytos' tomb, where the men are skilled in close fighting, men who lived in Pheneos and Orchomenos, rich in sheep, and Rhipe and Stratië and windy Enispe, and held Tegea and lovely Mantinea, and lived in Stymphelos and Parrhasia: these were led by Ankaios' son, lord Agapenor, in sixty ships, and in each ship there went many men of Arcadia, skilled fighters. Agamemnon himself, the son of Atreus and lord of men, had given them the well-benched ships to cross over the sparkling sea, as they had no concern with seafaring.

Those who lived in Bouprasion and the noble land of Elis, all that is bounded by Hyrmine and Myrsinos, set far on the border, and the rock of Olenos and Alesion, these had four leaders, and ten fast ships followed each with many Epeian men aboard. Two companies were led by Amphimachos and Thalpios, one the son of Kteatos, the other of Eurytos, both grandsons of Aktor. The leader of the third squadron was the mighty Diores, son of Amarynkeus, and of the fourth godlike Polyxeinos, son of lord Agasthenes the son of Augeias.

Those from Doulichion and the sacred islands of Echinai which lie facing Elis across the sea, these were led by Meges, a man like Ares, Phyleus' son, born to the horseman Phyleus, loved of Zeus, who had quarrelled with his father and moved away to Doulichion. With him there followed forty black ships.

And Odysseus led the great-hearted men of Kephallenia, those who held Ithaka and mount Neriton with its quivering leaves, and lived in Krokyleia and rugged Aigilips, and those who held Zakynthos and the inhabitants of Samos, and those who held the mainland and peopled the lands opposite. These were led by Odysseus, Zeus' equal in his mind's resource. With him there followed twelve ships with their bows' cheeks painted red.

The Aitolians were led by Thoas son of Andraimon, those who lived in Pleuron and Olenos and Pylene and Chalkis by the sea and rocky Kalydon. Great-hearted Oineus' sons were no longer alive, nor Oineus himself, and fair-haired Meleagros had died: so all power to rule the Aitolians had then been laid on Thoas, and with him there followed forty black ships.

Leader of the Cretans was Idomeneus, famous with the spear – those who held Knosos and the walls of Gortyn, Lyktos and Miletos and white-shining Lykastos and Phaistos and Rhytion, well-founded cities, and the others who lived in the hundred cities of Crete. These men were led by the famous spearman Idomeneus, and Meriones, a warrior like the war-god himself, the man-killer. With them there followed eighty black ships.

From Rhodes Tlepolemos the son of Herakles, huge and brave, brought nine ships of proud Rhodians, those who lived in Rhodes in three divisions, in Lindos and Ialysos and white-shining Kameiros. These were led by the famous spearman Tlepolemos, borne by Astyocheia to the mighty Herakles – he had brought her from Ephyre, from the river Selleëis, after sacking many a royal warrior's town. Now when Tlepolemos had grown up in their well-built house, soon he killed his father's loved uncle, Likymnios, branch of Ares, a man by then grown old. Immediately he built ships, and gathered a large company to join him, and set off in exile over the sea, as the other sons and grandsons of the mighty Herakles had threatened him. In his wandering he came to Rhodes, in suffering and hardship. They settled the land by tribes in three divisions, and they were loved by Zeus, the king over gods and men, and the son of Kronos poured down over them a miracle of wealth.

Then Nireus brought three balanced ships from Syme, Nireus the son of Aglaïa and lord Charopos, Nireus who was the handsomest man that came to Ilios of all the Danaans, after the peerless son of Peleus: but he was a man of little power, and the people who followed him were few.

Those who held Nisyros and Krapathos and Kasos and Kos, Eurypylos' city, and the Kalydnai islands, these were led by Pheidippos and Antiphos, two sons of lord Thessalos, son of Herakles. These commanded an array of thirty hollow ships.

Now all those who lived in Pelasgian Argos, those who peopled Alos and Alope and Trachis, and held Phthia and Hellas where the women are handsome, and were called Myrmidons and Hellenes and Achaians, their fifty ships were commanded by Achilleus. But they had no mind for the grim clash of war, as there was no-one to lead them to the battle-front. Swift-footed godlike Achilleus was keeping by his ships, in anger over the girl, the beautiful Briseïs, whom he had chosen as his spoil from Lyrnessos after he had laboured hard for its taking, and sacked Lyrnessos and the walls of Thebe, and felled the spearmen

Mynes and Epistrophos, sons of lord Euenos, the son of Selepios. She was the sorrow he lay grieving for, but he was soon to rise up again.

Those who held Phylake and Pyrasos full of flowers, the precinct of Demeter, and Iton the mother of flocks, and Antron by the sea and the deep meadows of Pteleos, these were led by the warrior Protesilaos, while he lived: but by then the black earth held him under. He had left a wife in Phylake, her cheeks torn with grieving, and a house half-finished. A Dardanian man killed him as he jumped from his ship, by far the first to land of the Achaians. But even these men were not left leaderless, though they longed for their lost leader, but they were marshalled by Podarkes, branch of Ares, son of Iphiklos rich in flocks, the son of Phylakos. Podarkes was whole brother of the great-hearted Protesilaos, his younger brother – but the warrior hero Protesilaos was both the older and the better man: his people did not lack a leader, but they longed for the brave man they had lost. With him there followed forty black ships.

Those who lived in Pherai by lake Boibeïs, in Boibe and Glaphyrai and well-founded Iolkos, these were led by Admetos' dear son Eumelos, in eleven ships: he was borne to Admetos by Alkestis, queen among women, the most beautiful of Pelias' daughters.

Those who lived in Methone and Thaumakia, and held Meliboia and rugged Olizon, these were led by Philoktetes, in seven ships: in each ship fifty rowers had embarked, all skilled fighters with the bow. But Philoktetes was lying in an agony of pain on an island, in sacred Lemnos, where the sons of the Achaians had left him suffering from the vile wound of the vicious water-snake's bite. So he lay there in torment: but the Argives in their camp by the ships were soon to remember lord Philoktetes. But even these men were not left leaderless, though they longed for their missing leader: but they were marshalled by Medon, bastard son of Oïleus, whom Rhene bore to Oïleus the sacker of cities.

Those who held Trikke and the rocky terraces of Ithome, and those who held Oichalia, the city of Eurytos the Oichalian king, these were led by the two sons of Asklepios, the skilled healers Podaleirios and Machaon. They commanded an array of thirty hollow ships.

Those who held Ormenion, and the spring of Hypereia, and those who held Asterion and the white hills of Titanos, these were led by Eurypylos the splendid son of Euaimon. With him there followed forty black ships.

Those who held Argissa and lived in Gyrtone, in Orthe and Elone and the white city of Oloösson, these were led by the staunch fighter Polypoites, son of Peirithoös, whose father was immortal Zeus. He was conceived to Peirithoös by the renowned Hippodameia, on the day when Peirithoös took vengeance on the hairy Centaurs and drove them out of Pelion towards the land of the Aithikes. Polypoites was not alone, but partnered by Leonteus, branch of Ares, son of proud-hearted Koronos, Kaineus' son. With them there followed forty black ships.

Gouneus led twenty-two ships from Kyphos. He was followed by the Enienes and the Peraibians, staunch fighters, who had made their homes around stormy Dodona, and those who worked the fields round the delightful river Titaressos, which pours its lovely stream into the Peneios, and does not mingle with the silvery swirls of Peneios, but floats on the top of its current like olive oil: because this is a branch of the water of Styx, the oath of fearful power.

The people of Magnesia were led by Prothoös, Teuthredon's son, those who lived round Peneios and mount Pelion with its quivering leaves: these were led by Prothoös the quick runner, and with him there followed forty black ships.

These then were the leaders and rulers of the Danaans. Tell me now, Muse, which was the finest of them, of the men and the horses, of those who came with the sons of Atreus.

Of the horses by far the best were those of Admetos the son of Pheres, driven now by his son Eumelos: they were fast as birds, a perfect match in coat and age, and plumb-level along the length of their backs. Apollo of the silver bow had bred them in Pereia, mares both of them, and they carried the terror of Ares himself. Of men by far the best was Aias, Telamon's son, as long as Achilleus kept up his anger – because he was far the strongest, and the horses too which carried the peerless son of Peleus. But Achilleus was keeping by his beaked seafaring ships in his fury at Agamemnon son of Atreus, shepherd of the people. And his men were amusing themselves along the shore where the sea breaks with games of discus and spear-throwing and archery: and their horses stood idle, each by its own chariot, cropping the clover and the parsley which grows in marsh-land: their masters' chariots lay tightly covered in the huts, and the men, missing their warrior leader, wandered to and fro throughout the camp, and did no fighting.

But all the rest moved on, and it was as if the whole land was being eaten by fire. The earth groaned under them, as it does under the anger of Zeus who delights in thunder, when he lashes the ground over Typhoëus, in Arima, which they say is the place where Typhoëus lies. So the earth groaned loud under their feet as they marched: and they came on at speed over the plain.

Bringing the news to the Trojans came swift Iris on feet quick as the wind, coming from Zeus who holds the aegis with the message of danger. They were holding an assembly at the doors of Priam's palace, all gathered together, young and old alike. Swift-footed Iris came close and spoke to them, in voice like Priam's son Polites, who was set as the Trojans' look-out, confident in the speed of his running, high on the top of the tomb of old Aisyëtes, looking for the moment when the Achaians would move out from their ships. Taking his form then swift-footed Iris spoke to them: 'Old man, you still delight in endless talking, as before in the time of peace: but war now is on us, relentless. Many is the time I have been in men's battles, but I have never yet seen an army like this, in this number. They are just like leaves or grains of sand, innumerable, coming at our city over the plain to do battle. Hektor, this is your task above all – you must do as I say. There are many allies with us in Priam's great city, but they are men from far and wide and each speaks a different tongue. Have each leader give his orders to the men he commands, and have him marshal his own countrymen and lead them out to battle.'

So she spoke: Hektor did not fail to hear the goddess speaking, and immediately broke up the assembly. They rushed to their arms. All the gates were opened and the army streamed out, foot-soldiers and horse-men, and the din rose loud.

In front of the city there is a steep mound, standing alone in the plain with open space around it on all sides: men's name for it is Batieia, but the immortals call it the barrow of dancing Myrine. It was here that the Trojans and their allies then formed into their divisions.

The Trojans were led by great Hektor of the glinting helmet, Priam's son. With him there went under arms far the largest army and the bravest fighters, men eager to use their spears.

Next the Dardanians were led by Anchises' noble son Aineias, whom the divine Aphrodite bore to Anchises, when goddess had lain with mortal on the spurs of Ida. Aineias was not alone in command, but with him were two sons of Antenor, Archelochos and Akamas, both skilled in all the ways of battle.

Those who lived in Zeleia down at the very furthest foot of Ida, rich men of Trojan stock, drinking the dark water of Aisepos, these were led by Lykaon's splendid son Pandaros, whose bow was the gift of Apollo himself.

Those who held Adresteia and the district of Apaisos, and held Pityeia and the steep mountain of Tereia, these were led by Adrestos and Amphios with his armour of cloth, two sons of Merops from Perkote, who had knowledge of seercraft beyond all others, and kept trying to stop his sons from going to war which takes men's lives. But they would not listen to him, as the fates of black death were leading them on.

Those who lived round Perkote and Praktios, and held Sestos and Abydos and noble Arisbe, these were led by Hyrtakos' son Asios, chief of his people, Asios son of Hyrtakos, whose great bay horses had carried him from Arisbe, from the river Selleëis.

Hippothoös led the companies of Pelasgian spearmen, those who lived on the fertile soil of Larisa: these were led by Hippothoös and Pylaios, branch of Ares, two sons of Pelasgian Lethos, son of Teutamos.

Akamas and the hero Peiroös led the Thracians, all those bounded by the strong stream of Hellespont.

Euphemos was the leader of the Kikones, fighters with the spear, the son of the god-ordained king Troizenos, son of Keas.

Pyraichmes led the Paionians with their curved bows, coming from far-off Amydon, from the broad river Axios, Axios whose water is the loveliest that streams over earth.

The Paphlagonians were led by the strong heart of Pylaimenes, from the country of the Enetoi, where the wild mules breed – those who held Kytoros and lived about Sesamos, and had their fine homes round the river Parthenios, and Kromna and Aigialos and high Erythinoi.

The Halizones were led by Odios and Epistrophos, coming from far-off Alybe, the birthplace of silver.

The Mysians were led by Chromis and Ennomos the augur – yet his augury could not protect him from the black fate of death, but he was brought down at the hands of the fast runner Achilleus, of Aiakos' stock, in the river where he slaughtered others of the Trojans too.

Phorkys and godlike Askanios led the Phrygians, from far-off Askania, eager for the clash of battle.

The Maionians were led by Mesthles and Antiphos, sons of Talaimenes, and their mother was the nymph of the Gygaian lake. They were the leaders of the Maionians born under mount Tmolos.

Nastes led the Carians whose speech is foreign, those who held

Miletos and mount Phthires thick-covered in leaves, and the streams of Maiandros and the sheer peaks of Mykale. These were led by Amphimachos and Nastes, Nastes and Amphimachos, Nomion's splendid children. Nastes went into battle wearing gold like a girl, poor fool, and it did not save him from a miserable death, but he was brought down at the hands of the fast runner Achilleus, of Aiakos' stock, in the river: and the warrior Achilleus took the gold from him.

Sarpedon and the excellent Glaukos led the Lycians, coming from far-off Lycia, from the swirling water of Xanthos.

BOOK 3
PARIS, HELEN, APHRODITE

When the divisions on both sides had been marshalled under their leaders, the Trojans came on with cries and shouting, like birds – as when the cries of cranes fill the sky, when they make their escape from the huge downpours of winter, and with loud cries they fly on towards Ocean's stream, bringing death and destruction to the Pygmies: and at early morning they launch their grim battle. But the Achaians came on in silence, breathing boldness, their hearts intent on supporting each other.

As when the south wind gathers a mist round a mountain's peaks – no joy to the shepherds, but better than night for the thief, and a man can see only as far as a stone's throw – so a thick swirl of dust arose under their feet as they marched: and they came on at speed over the plain.

When the two armies had advanced to close range, godlike Alexandros kept moving out in front of the Trojan ranks, wearing a leopard-skin over his shoulders, and a curved bow and sword. Shaking a pair of bronze-capped spears he constantly challenged all the best men of the Argives to fight him one to one in grim combat.

When the warrior Menelaos saw him stepping out in front of the massed troops with long strides, he felt the joy of a lion that has come across a great carcass, an antlered stag or a wild goat he has found in his hunger: he eats it greedily, even though the running hounds and the strong young huntsmen try to drive him away. So Menelaos felt joy when his eyes saw godlike Alexandros. He thought he could take his vengeance on the culprit, and he immediately jumped to the ground from his chariot with all his armour.

But when godlike Alexandros saw Menelaos appear among the front fighters, his heart quailed and he shrank back into the mass of his companions to avoid destruction. As when a man sees a snake in a mountain glen, and starts backwards, and trembling takes over his limbs: he goes back again on his tracks, with fear set pale in his cheeks. So godlike Alexandros slipped back into the body of the proud Trojans in his fear of Atreus' son.

Hektor saw this and attacked him with insulting words: 'Paris you pest, good for nothing but looks, you woman-crazed seducer! If only you had never been born, or died unmarried. Yes, I wish it were so – and that would be far better than to have you the disgrace that you are and a creature of loathing to others. Oh, the long-haired Achaians must be cackling at this, saying that we put up a prince as champion only for his good looks, when his heart is empty of strength or courage. Is this the man you were when you gathered your trusted companions and sailed out over the sea in your seafaring ships, mingled with foreign peoples, and brought back on board a beautiful wife from a distant land, a woman married into a race of fighting men – a great plague to your father and your city and all your people, to the joy of our enemies and your own shame? Will you not then stand up to the warrior Menelaos? That would teach you the measure of the man whose ripe young wife you have taken. There would be no help then in your lyre-playing and the gifts of Aphrodite, your long hair and your looks, when you have your union with the dust. But the Trojans are cowardly folk – otherwise by now they would have given you a coat of stones for all the harm that you have done.'

Then godlike Alexandros said to him: 'Hektor, your taunt is not unfair, and there is justice in it – your heart is always untiring as an axe, which cuts its way through wood in a man's hands and doubles his power, as he carves out a ship's timber in the skill of his craft: in your breast there is a heart just as dauntless – but do not charge against me golden Aphrodite's lovely gifts: there is no discarding the glorious gifts that come of the gods' own giving, though a man would not take them of his choice. But if you want me now to fight and do battle, have the others sit down, the rest of the Trojans and all the Achaians, and pit me and the warrior Menelaos together in the middle, to fight it out over Helen and all her goods. Whichever of us wins and proves the stronger may take full possession of her goods and carry her home as wife. The rest of you then make a solemn truce of friendship: you live on in fertile Troy, and let them return to the horse-pasture of Argos and Achaia where the women are handsome.'

So he spoke, and Hektor then was delighted at what he heard. He stepped into the open, and kept back the Trojan lines, holding his spear at the middle: and they all settled on the ground. The long-haired Achaians kept up a barrage against him, making him the target of their arrows and stones. But then Agamemnon, lord of men, shouted loud to them: 'Hold your fire, Argives – no more shooting, sons of the Achaians! Hektor of the glinting helmet is set to speak to us.'

So he spoke, and they stopped their fighting and fell to eager silence. Hektor then spoke out to both sides: 'Listen to me, Trojans and well-greaved Achaians, while I tell you the proposal of Alexandros, the man who gave rise to our quarrel. He says that the rest of the Trojans and all the Achaians should lay their fine arms on the nourishing earth, while he and the warrior Menelaos fight it out alone between us over Helen and all her goods. Whichever of them wins and proves the stronger may take full possession of all her goods and carry her home as wife: and the rest of us should make a solemn truce of friendship.'

So he spoke, and they all stayed silent. But then Menelaos, master of the war-cry, spoke out to them: 'Listen now to what I say. It is my heart above all which is touched by pain, and I wish that the Argives and the Trojans should now be parted in friendship, since you have suffered much hardship because of my quarrel and Alexandros who began it. Whichever of us two has death and his fate laid up for him, let him die – and you others then part without delay. Bring two lambs, a white male and a black female, for the Sun and Earth, and we will bring a third for Zeus. And fetch the great Priam, to solemnise the oaths himself – his sons are violent men and not to be trusted – so that no violation should ruin the oaths we swear by Zeus. Younger men's minds are always lighter than air, but when an old man joins them, he considers both past and future, to make the outcome the very best for both sides.'

So he spoke, and both Achaians and Trojans were overjoyed, thinking this was the end of the misery of war. They held their chariots back in their ranks, and the men dismounted and took off their armour, laying it on the earth close to their neighbours, and there was little free ground uncovered. Hektor sent two heralds hurrying to the city to bring the lambs and summon Priam: and lord Agamemnon sent Talthybios on his way to the hollow ships, telling him to bring a lamb, and he did not fail godlike Agamemnon.

Now Iris came bringing the news to white-armed Helen, in the form of her sister-in-law, the wife of Antenor's son, married to lord Helikaon son of Antenor – she was Laodike, the most beautiful of Priam's daughters. Iris found Helen in her room, working at a great web of purple cloth for a double cloak, and in it she was weaving many scenes of the conflict between the horse-taming Trojans and the bronze-clad Achaians, which they were enduring for her sake at the hands of Ares. Swift-footed Iris came close and spoke to her: 'Come this way, dear girl, to see something wonderful done by the horse-taming Trojans and the bronze-clad Achaians. Before now they were bringing the misery of war against each other in the plain, eager for battle's destruction. But now there is an end to the fighting, and they are sitting quietly, leaning on their shields, and their long spears stuck in the ground beside them. And Alexandros and the warrior Menelaos will fight together with their long spears over you: and you will be called the dear wife of the man who wins.'

So speaking the goddess put in Helen's heart a sweet yearning for her past husband and her city and her parents. Quickly she covered herself with a white veil of fine cloth, and set out from the house with soft tears falling – not alone, but two maids went with her, Aithre, the daughter of Pittheus, and ox-eyed Klymene. And they quickly came to where the Skaian gates stood.

Now the elders of the people were sitting by the Skaian gates with Priam: Panthoös and Thymoites and Lampos and Klytios and Hiketaon, branch of Ares; and Oukalegon and Antenor, wise men both. Old age had put an end to their warfare, but they were excellent men of words: and they sat there on the tower, the leading men of the Trojans, like cicadas, which settle on a tree in the woods and pour out their lily-soft song. When they saw Helen coming towards the tower, they spoke softly to each other with winged words: 'No shame that the Trojans and the well-greaved Achaians should suffer agonies for long years over a woman like this – she is fearfully like the immortal goddesses to look at. But even so, for all her beauty, let her go back in the ships, and not be left here a curse to us and our children.'

That is what they said, but Priam called out to Helen: 'Come here, dear child, and sit in front of me, so you can see your former husband and your relatives and friends. It is not you I blame – I blame the gods, who brought on me the misery of war with the Achaians. Sit here, so you can tell me the name of that huge man there – who is he, this tall and manly Achaian? There are others of greater stature, but I have never yet set eyes on a man so fine-looking or so dignified: he has the look of a king.'

Helen, queen among women, answered him with these words: 'Dear father-in-law, you are a man I honour and revere. Oh, if only vile death had been my choice when I came here with your son, leaving behind the house of my marriage, and my family and my darling child and the sweet company of friends! But this did not happen, and so I am wasted with weeping. But as for the question you ask me, I shall tell you. This man is the son of Atreus, wide-ruling Agamemnon, both a good king and a strong fighter with the spear: and he was once my brother-in-law, whore that I am – if those times were ever real.'

So she spoke, and the old man said in admiration of him: 'Blessed son of Atreus, child of fate and fortune's favourite, many indeed are the young men of the Achaians under your command. Once before now I travelled to Phrygia where the vines grow, and there I saw a host of Phrygian men with their quick horses, the armies of Otreus and godlike Mygdon, which were then camped along the banks of Sangarios. I too was numbered among them as their ally on the day when the Amazons came, women the equal of men. But even they were not as numerous as these bright-eyed Achaians.'

Then next the old man saw Odysseus, and asked her again: 'Come, tell me, dear child, who this man is too. In height he is shorter than Agamemnon son of Atreus, but broader to the eye in shoulders and chest. His armour lies piled on the nourishing earth, and the man is patrolling the ranks of his troops like a wether – yes, he looks to me like some thick-fleeced ram, ranging through a great flock of whitewoolled sheep.'

Then Helen, offspring of Zeus, answered him: 'This is the son of Laertes, resourceful Odysseus, who was bred in the land of Ithaka, rugged country though it is, and is master of all kinds of trickery and clever plans.'

Then the wise Antenor said to her: 'My lady, what you have said is true indeed. Once before now godlike Odysseus came here with the warrior Menelaos on a mission about you. I was their host, and entertained them in my house, and came to know the build of both and the thoughts of their minds. Well, when they joined the assembled Trojans, Menelaos' broad shoulders were higher when they were standing, but when both were seated Odysseus had the more impressive dignity. Now when they came to weave their thoughts in speech before all the company, Menelaos would speak with the words running fast, at little length, but very clearly – there was nothing long-winded or rambling about him: and he was indeed the younger man. But whenever resourceful Odysseus leapt up to speak, he would stand there, staring down with his eyes fixed on the ground, and making no gestures with the staff, forwards or backwards, but gripping it stiff, like a man unskilled in its use – you would take him for a churl and a mere booby.

But when he released that great voice from his chest and the words which flocked down like snowflakes in winter, no other mortal man could then rival Odysseus. And then we forgot our surprise at the sight of Odysseus' manner.'

Next the old man saw Aias and asked a third time: 'Now who is this other tall and manly Achaian, standing out among the Argives for his height and broad shoulders?'

Long-dressed Helen, queen among women, answered him: 'That is the huge Aias, a great defence for the Achaians. And over there is Idomeneus, standing among his Cretans like a god, and the Cretan leaders gathered round him. Many times the warrior Menelaos entertained him in our house, when he would come from Crete. And now I can see all the other bright-eyed Achaians whom I could recognise and name for you. But there are two marshals of the people I cannot see, Kastor the horse-breaker and the boxer Polydeukes, my own brothers, born with me to the same mother. Either they did not join with the others from lovely Lakedaimon, or they did come here in the seafaring ships, but now do not want to enter the fighting, for fear of the shame and the curses that are heaped upon me.'

So she spoke, but the life-giving earth already held them under, there in Lakedaimon, in their dear native land.

Now the heralds were carrying through the town the offerings to seal the truce before the gods, two lambs and kindly wine, fruit of the soil, in a sack of goatskin: and the herald Idaios carried a gleaming mixing-bowl and cups of gold. He came and stood by the old man Priam, and urged him to action: 'Up, son of Laomedon! The leading men of the horse-taming Trojans and the bronze-clad Achaians are calling you down to the plain, to make a solemn truce between you. Alexandros and the warrior Menelaos will fight together over the woman. And she and her possessions will go with the victor, while the rest of us make a solemn truce of friendship, and we live on in fertile Troy and they return to the horse-pasture of Argos and Achaia where the women are handsome.'

So he spoke, and the old man shuddered, and ordered his companions to harness his chariot: and they obeyed with speed. Priam mounted and held back on the reins while Antenor stepped into the fine chariot beside him: and they drove the fast-running team through the Skaian gates out to the plain.

When they reached the two armies, they stepped down from the chariot on to the nourishing earth, and strode to the middle ground between the Trojans and Achaians. Then Agamemnon, lord of men, rose at once to meet them, and with him resourceful Odysseus. The solemn heralds led up the offerings to seal the truce before the gods, and mixed wine in the bowl, then poured water over the kings' hands. The son of Atreus drew the knife which always hung beside his sword's great scabbard and cut hairs from the heads of the lambs: and then the heralds handed these round to the leading men of the Trojans and Achaians. The son of Atreus lifted up his arms among them and prayed in a great voice: 'Father Zeus, ruling from Ida's height, greatest and most glorious; and Sun, who sees all things and hears all things; and rivers and earth; and you gods below who punish the dead, when any has falsely sworn: you be our witnesses, and watch over the keeping of these oaths. If Alexandros kills Menelaos, let him then keep Helen and all her possessions, and we return home in our seafaring ships. But if fair-haired Menelaos kills Alexandros, the Trojans then are to give back Helen and all her possessions, and pay in compensation to the Argives a fitting price, which will be told of even among generations yet to be born. But if Priam and the sons of Priam refuse to pay me the price when Alexandros has fallen, then I shall stay here and fight on to win satisfaction, until I bring the war to its goal.'

So he spoke, and cut the lambs' throats with the pitiless bronze and laid them on the ground gasping, as the life left them, their strength robbed by the bronze. Then they drew wine from the bowl into the cups, and poured it out on the ground, making their prayers to the ever-living gods. And this is what any one of the Achaians and Trojans would say: 'Zeus, greatest and most glorious, and you other immortal gods: whichever side first offends against these oaths, may their brains spill on the ground as this wine is spilled, their own and their children's, and may their wives be other men's conquest.'

This is what they said, but the son of Kronos would not yet grant their prayers. Then Priam, of Dardanos' line, spoke to them: 'Listen to me, Trojans and well-greaved Achaians. I shall go back to windy Ilios, because I will not yet bear to look with my own eyes on my dear son fighting against the warrior Menelaos. Zeus must know, and the other immortal gods, which of them has the end of death appointed for him.'

So he spoke, and placed the lambs in the chariot, and mounted himself, a godlike man, and held back on the reins: and beside him Antenor mounted the fine chariot. These two then set back for Ilios. Hektor, Priam's son, and godlike Odysseus first measured out the ground, then took two lots and shook them in a bronze helmet, to see which of the two should be the first to throw his bronze spear. And the armies made their prayers, holding up their hands to the gods, and this is what any one of the Achaians and Trojans would say: 'Father Zeus, ruling from Ida's height, greatest and most glorious: whichever of the two it was that brought these troubles on our peoples, grant that he be killed and sink down to the house of Hades, and we make between us a solemn truce of friendship.'

This is what they said, and great Hektor of the glinting helmet shook the lots, with his eyes turned away – and immediately Paris' lot leapt out. The rest of them then sat down in their ranks, each where his high-stepping horses stood and his intricate armour lay piled. And godlike Alexandros, husband of lovely-haired Helen, put on his fine armour. First he placed greaves on his legs, a fine pair, fitted with silver ankle-pieces. Next he put a corselet round his chest: it was his brother Lykaon's, and it fitted him. Over his shoulders he slung a bronze sword, the hilt nailed with silver, and then a great massive shield. On his mighty head he placed a well-made helmet with a plume of horse-hair, and the crest nodded fearfully from its top. And he took up a strong spear, well fitted to the grip of his hand. In the same way the warrior Menelaos put on his armour.

So when these two had armed themselves on either side of the gathered forces, they strode into the middle ground between Trojans and Achaians, glaring terror at each other: and the horse-taming Trojans and the well-greaved Achaians looked on in wonder. And they stood at close range, within the measured space, shaking their spears at each other in fury. First Alexandros let fly his long-shadowed spear, and hit the even circle of the son of Atreus' shield. The bronze of the spear did not break through, but its point was turned in the stout shield. Then Atreus' son Menelaos rose to his cast, making a prayer to father Zeus: 'Zeus, lord, grant me vengeance on the man who did me first wrong, godlike Alexandros, and bring him low under my hands, so that even among generations yet to be born a man may shrink from doing wrong to a host who gives him hospitality.'

So he spoke, and steadying his long-shadowed spear he let it fly, and hit the even circle of the son of Priam's shield. Through the bright shield the strong spear went, and on through the worked corselet, forcing its way: pushing straight on it tore through the tunic at his side – but he swerved away and escaped black doom. The son of Atreus drew his silver-nailed sword, swung it high for the blow, and brought it crashing down on the helmet's ridge – there it shattered and slipped in shivers from his hand. The son of Atreus looked up into the wide heaven and cried out: 'Father Zeus, there is no deadlier god than you! I thought I had vengeance on Alexandros for his crime. But now my sword has broken in my hands, and my spear flew fruitless from my grip, and I could not hit him.'

So he spoke, then sprang forward and seized Alexandros by the thick horse-hair of the helmet, spun him round, and started to drag him back towards the well-greaved Achaians: at his soft neck the stitched strap was throttling him, the helmet-strap tight under his chin. And now he would have dragged him back and won limitless glory, if Zeus' daughter Aphrodite had not quickly seen. She broke the strap, made from the hide of a slaughtered ox, and Menelaos' massive hand pulled away the helmet empty. The hero then whirled it round and flung it into the well-greaved Achaians, and his trusty companions retrieved it. He then sprang back ready to kill Alexandros with his bronze spear. But Aphrodite snatched him away with the ease of a god, wrapped him in thick mist, and set him down in his sweetly-scented bedroom. Then the goddess went herself to call Helen. She found her on the high tower, with many Trojan women round her. She took hold of Helen's sweet-smelling dress and twitched it with her hand, and spoke to her in the form of an old woman of many years, a wool-worker, who when Helen lived in Lakedaimon used to work beautiful wool for her, and was much loved by her. Taking this woman's likeness divine Aphrodite spoke to Helen: 'Come this way: Alexandros is calling you back to the house. He is there in the bedroom, on the carved bed, shining in his own beauty and his clothing. You would not think he had come from fighting a man – you would say he was going to the dance, or had just left dancing and was taking his rest.'

So she spoke, and stirred the heart in Helen's breast. And then when she recognised the goddess' beautiful neck, and her lovely breasts and the eyes that flashed brightness, she was astounded, and spoke out to her: 'Strange goddess, why so eager to work this seduction on me? Will you carry me on to some settled city yet further away – somewhere in Phrygia, perhaps, or lovely Maionia – if there too there is some mortal man you love? Is it because now Menelaos has beaten godlike Alexandros, and wants to take me, hateful creature that I am, back to his home – is that why you have come here now with your trickery? Go and sit by him yourself – abandon the paths of the gods, never again turn your feet back to Olympos: no, stay with him, for ever whimpering round him and watching over him, until he makes you his wife – or else his slave. But I will not go to him – that would bring shame on me – to serve that man's bed. All the women of Troy will blame me afterwards: and I have misery enough in my heart.'

Then, angered, divine Aphrodite said to her: 'Do not provoke me, wilful girl, in case I grow angry and abandon you, and show a hate for you as extreme as the love I have shown you till now. I might bring about a fatal hatred of you in both sides, shared by Trojans and Danaans alike, and you then die a miserable death.'

So she spoke, and Helen, child of Zeus, was afraid. She covered her face with shining white cloth and went silently, and none of the Trojan ladies saw her: and the goddess walked ahead.

When they reached Alexandros' fine house, the maids then turned quickly to their work, and Helen, queen among women, went to the high-roofed bedroom. And Aphrodite, smiling goddess, herself took up a chair for Helen, and brought it and placed it in front of Alexandros. There Helen, daughter of Zeus who holds the aegis, took her seat, turning her eyes aside, and spoke slightingly to her husband: 'You came back from the fighting, then. I wish you had died there, brought down by a man of strength, who was once my husband. Oh, before now you used to boast that you were superior to the warrior Menelaos in strength and power of hand and spear. Well, go now, challenge the warrior Menelaos to fight you again face to face. No, I would advise you to stop now, and not pit yourself against fair-haired Menelaos in warfare or combat without thinking – you might well be brought down by his spear.'

Paris then answered her: 'Wife, do not deride my courage with these hard taunts. This time Menelaos has beaten me with Athene's aid, but another time I shall beat him: there are gods on our side too. No, come, let us enjoy the bed of love. Never before has desire so enveloped my heart, not even on that first time when I stole you away from lovely Lakedaimon and sailed off with you in my seafaring ships, and lay with you in love's union in the island of Kranaë – even that was less than the love and sweet desire for you that comes over me now.'

So he spoke, and led the way to their bed: and his wife followed.

They then lay down together on the fretted bed. But the son of Atreus went ranging up and down the mass of troops like a wild beast, looking for a sight of godlike Alexandros. But none of the Trojans or their famous allies could then point out Alexandros to the warrior

Menelaos: certainly they were not trying to conceal him out of friendship, if any were to have seen him – he was hated by all of them like black death. Then Agamemnon, lord of men, spoke out to them: 'Listen to me, Trojans and Dardanians and allies. Victory plainly rests with the warrior Menelaos. You then give back Argive Helen and her possessions with her, and pay in compensation a fitting price, which will be told of even among generations yet to be born.'

So the son of Atreus spoke, and the other Achaians applauded.

BOOK 4
THE BREAKING OF THE TRUCE

Now the gods were sitting by Zeus' side, gathered in assembly in the golden courtyard, and queen Hebe went among them pouring the nectar: they pledged each other in golden cups, looking out over the city of Troy. Soon the son of Kronos set himself to provoke Hera with a taunting speech, and there was devious purpose in his words: 'Menelaos has two helpers among the goddesses, Hera of Argos and Alalkomenaian Athene – but here they both are, sitting aloof, mere onlookers enjoying the spectacle. Whereas the other has Aphrodite, smiling goddess, constantly by his side to keep destruction from him: just now she rescued him when he thought his death had come. Well, victory certainly rests with the warrior Menelaos. But we must consider how this business is to end, whether to start grim war again and the horror of battle, or set friendship between the two sides. Now if somehow this second way could be the wish and pleasure of us all, then lord Priam's city may still be peopled, and Menelaos take back Argive Helen to his home.'

So he spoke, and Athene and Hera muttered at his words – they were sitting close by each other, and plotting hardship for the Trojans. Athene stayed silent and said nothing, furious at her father Zeus, and gripped by savage anger. But Hera's breast could not contain her rage, and she spoke out: 'Dread son of Kronos, what is this you are saying? How can you intend to make empty and fruitless all my labours, and the sweat that I sweated in my exertions, and the weariness of my horses as I gathered together an army of doom to Priam and his children? Do it, then: but we other gods will not all applaud you.'

Zeus the cloud-gatherer answered her in vexation: 'My dear wife, what can be the great crimes of Priam and Priam's children against you, to make you so hot in your desire to destroy the well-founded city of Ilios? If you could go in yourself through the gates and the great battlements of Troy and eat the raw flesh of Priam and Priam's children and the other Trojans, perhaps then you could assuage your anger. Do as you please: I would not want such an issue as this to become a great quarrel between the two of us for the future. But I tell you something else, and you mark it well in your mind. Whenever I in my turn am eager to destroy a city peopled by men who are dear to you, do not try to thwart my anger, but let me have my way – because I have agreed to grant you this of my own will, though not my heart's will. Of all the cities of earthly men that lie beneath the sun and the starry heaven, the most cherished in my heart was sacred Ilios, and Priam and the people of Priam of the fine ash spear. My altar there was never without a share of the feasting, libation of wine and the smoke of sacrifice, which is our rightful honour.'

Then the ox-eyed queen Hera answered him: 'There are three cities dearest of all to me, Argos and Sparta and wide-wayed Mykene. Sack these, whenever your heart feels strong hatred for them. I shall not stand to defend them, or grudge their destruction. Because even if I should resent it and try to refuse you their sack, I can achieve nothing by resentment, as you are far the stronger. But my labour too must not be denied its fruit. I too am a god, and of the same descent as you: I am the senior of the daughters born to devious-minded Kronos, for double reason, both by birth and because I am called your wife, and you are lord over all the immortals. Let us then defer to each other in this, I to you and you to me: and the other immortal gods will follow. You now quickly instruct Athene to go down to the place of grim battle between Trojans and Achaians, and try to make the Trojans first to break the oaths and do harm to the triumphant Achaians.'

So she spoke, and the father of men and gods did not fail to do her will. At once he spoke winged words to Athene: 'Go quickly to the place where the Trojan and Achaian armies are, and try to make the Trojans first to break the oaths and do harm to the triumphant Achaians.'

With these words he urged on Athene what she herself already desired, and she went darting down from the peaks of Olympos. Like a star that the son of devious-minded Kronos sends down as a sign to sailors or to an army's broad encampment, a bright star with sparks of light streaming thick from it: that was how Pallas Athene came shooting down to earth and plummeted between the armies. The horse-taming Trojans and the well-greaved Achaians looked on in wonder: and one would glance at his neighbour and say, 'There will surely be grim war again and the horror of battle – or else Zeus who holds the issue of men's fighting is setting friendship between the two sides.'

This is what they said among Achaians and Trojans alike. But

Athene passed into the mass of Trojans in man's form, that of Lao-dokos, Antenor's son, a strong spearman: she was in search of godlike Pandaros, to see if she could find him. And she did find the son of Lykaon, an excellent man and strong. He was standing still, and around him the strong ranks of the shield-bearing army that had come with him from the stream of Aisepos. She came close and spoke winged words to him: 'Do something now that I tell you, warlike son of Lykaon. You could bring yourself to shoot a quick-flying arrow at Menelaos, and then you would gain gratitude and glory among all the Trojans, and most of all with prince Alexandros. From him before all others you would win splendid gifts, if he sees Menelaos, Atreus' warrior son, brought down by your arrow and set on the pyre of sorrow. Come then, shoot at glorious Menelaos: and vow to Apollo the Lycian-born, the archer, to make him a splendid sacrifice of first-born lambs on your return home to the town of holy Zeleia.'

So Athene spoke, and persuaded his foolish mind. At once he took out his polished bow, made of horn from a leaping wild goat that he himself had once shot under the chest as it sprang down from a rock: he had lain in wait in a hide, and hit the goat in the chest, so it crashed on its back on the rock below. The horns growing from its head were sixteen palms long. These a bowyer skilled in hornwork had prepared and fitted into a bow, then smoothed the whole to a fine polish and capped it with a tip of gold. Pandaros bent back this bow, strung it, and laid it carefully on the ground: his brave companions held their shields in front of him, so that the warrior sons of the Achaians should not rush him before he could hit Menelaos, Atreus' warrior son. He then took the lid from his quiver, and chose out an arrow – unused, well-feathered, the carrier of black pain. Then he quickly fitted the bitter arrow to the string, and vowed to Apollo the Lycian-born, the archer, to make him a splendid sacrifice of first-born lambs on his return home to the town of holy Zeleia. Then he took hold of the notched arrow-butt and the ox-gut string together and pulled them back. He brought the string right back to his nipple, and the iron head to the bowstave. Then when he had drawn the great bow into a circle, the bow twanged, the string sang loud, and the arrow leapt forward, sharp-pointed, eager to fly on into the mass of men.

And you, Menelaos, the gods, the blessed immortals, did not forget you – and first among them Zeus' daughter, goddess of spoil, who stood in front of you and kept the piercing arrow from its mark. She brushed it just a little from the flesh it sought – like when a mother brushes a fly from her child, as he lies sweetly sleeping – and herself aimed its flight instead to where the belt's golden buckles joined and the corselet opposed a double layer. The bitter arrow hit home in the belt's fastening. Through the elaborate belt it drove on, and on through the worked corselet, forcing its way, and through the skirt-piece, which he wore to guard his body and protect against spears, and this was his strongest defence – but even that was pierced right through. And the arrow scratched the very surface of the man's flesh: and immediately dark blood trickled from the wound.

As when a woman stains ivory with crimson dye, in Maionia or Caria, making a cheek-piece for horses. It lies there in her room, and many horsemen yearn to have it for the wearing: but it waits there to be treasure for a king, both horse's finery and rider's glory. Such, Menelaos, was the staining with blood of your sturdy thighs, and your legs, and your fine ankles below.

Then Agamemnon, lord of men, shuddered in horror as he saw the black blood trickling down from the wound. And the warrior Menelaos himself shuddered also: but when he saw that the arrow's head-binding and the barbs were still outside, his spirit gathered back again in his breast. With heavy groans lord Agamemnon spoke to them, holding Menelaos by the hand, and his companions joined with their lamentation: 'It was your death, then, the truce that I swore to, when I set you as the Achaians' champion to fight alone against the Trojans. So now the Trojans have shot you, and trampled on the faith of their oaths. But there can be no failure of an oath, of the blood of lambs and the unmixed libations and the giving of right hands, in which we had trusted. If the Olympian does not indeed exact immediate penalty, his exactment comes late but full, and they pay with a great price, with their own heads and their wives and children. One thing I know well in my heart and in my mind. The day will come when sacred Ilios shall be destroyed, and Priam, and the people of Priam of the fine ash spear, and Zeus the son of Kronos who sits on high and dwells in heaven shall himself shake the darkness of his aegis against them all, in anger for this betrayal. These things shall not fail of fulfilment. But I shall suffer terrible pain for you, Menelaos, if you die and fill the measure of your fated life. And I would return to thirsty Argos in deepest shame – because the Achaians will turn their minds at once to their native land. And we would leave behind Argive Helen to the triumph of Priam and the Trojans: and your bones will rot in the soil of Troy, where you lie in the failure of our task. And this is what some arrogant Trojan will say, leaping in exultation on the tomb of glorious Menelaos: "Oh, let us hope that Agamemnon's anger always ends like this time! He brought an army of Achaians here to no result, and now he has gone back home to his dear native land with empty ships, and left behind the brave Menelaos." That is what they will say – and then may the wide earth gape for me.'

Then fair-haired Menelaos cheered him, saying: 'No cause for worry, and do not alarm the Achaian army. The sharp arrow is not lodged in a fatal spot – before it could, my shining belt protected me, and beneath that my binder and skirt-piece, which the smiths made for me in bronze.'

Lord Agamemnon answered him: 'May it be as you say, Menelaos, dear brother. But a healer will treat your wound, and put medicines on it to stop the black pain.'

So he spoke, and then said to Talthybios, his sacred herald: 'Talthybios, quickly, call Machaon here, the hero son of Asklepios the peerless healer, to look at Menelaos, Atreus' warrior son: someone has shot and hit him, some skilled archer among the Trojans or Lycians – to his glory and our sorrow.'

So he spoke, and the herald did not fail to do as he had heard. He set on his way through the bronze-clad Achaian army, looking closely for the hero Machaon. He saw him standing still, and around him the strong ranks of the shield-bearing army that had come with him from Trikke where the horses pasture. Talthybios came close and spoke winged words to him: 'Up, son of Asklepios! Lord Agamemnon sends for you, to look at Menelaos, Atreus' warrior son: someone has shot and hit him, some skilled archer among the Trojans or Lycians – to his glory and our sorrow.'

So he spoke, and stirred the heart in Machaon's breast. And they took their way through the mass of men across the broad Achaian camp. When they came to the place where fair-haired Menelaos lay wounded, and round him all the leading men had gathered in a circle, then the godlike man came through to the centre and at once pulled the arrow out from the belt's fastening, and the sharp barbs broke off as he pulled it. He then unfastened the shining belt and beneath that the binder and skirt-piece, which the smiths had made for him in bronze. When he saw the wound where the bitter arrow had struck home, he sucked the blood from it and in the skill of his craft applied soothing medicines, which once Cheiron had given to his father in friendship.

While they were tending Menelaos, master of the war-cry, the ranks of the Trojan warriors came on. They put on their armour again, and their spirits filled for battle.

Then you would not have seen godlike Agamemnon sleeping, or cowering in fear, or reluctant to fight, but driving on in full eagerness for the battle where men win glory. He abandoned his horses and his chariot trimmed with bronze, and the horses were held aside, snorting, by his servant Eurymedon, son of Ptolemaios, Peiraios' son: Agamemnon gave him repeated orders to hold them close, for the time when weariness overcame his legs with the inspection of many troops. And so he went on foot to review the ranks of his men. Whenever he saw eagerness for battle in a group of fast-horsed Danaans, he would come up to them and speak words of encouragement: 'Argives, keep up your fighting spirit! Liars and cheats will get no help from father Zeus – they were the first to break the oaths and do us harm, and vultures will feed on their soft flesh while we carry away their dear wives and little children in our ships, when we have taken their city.'

Those though that he saw hanging back from hateful battle he would sternly berate with anger in his words: 'You bletherskate Argives, you disgraces, have you no shame? What are you doing standing here bemused like fawns, who tire themselves out running over a wide expanse and then just stand there, without any courage left in their hearts? You just stand bemused like that, and do no fighting. Are you waiting for the Trojans to come in close, where our fine-sterned ships are drawn up on the grey sea's shore, to see if the son of Kronos will hold out his hand to protect you?'

So Agamemnon went on his kingly review of the ranks of his men. And on his way through the throng of men he came to the Cretans. They were arming for battle under the warrior Idomeneus. Idomeneus was up among the front lines, boar-like in his fighting spirit, and had Meriones urging on the ranks at the rear. Agamemnon, lord of men, was delighted when he saw them, and at once spoke warmly to Idomeneus: 'Idomeneus, of all the fast-horsed Danaans I hold you in highest regard both in war and any other action, and in the feast, when the gleaming wine of kings is mixed in the bowl by the leading men of the Argives. The other long-haired Achaians drink only as their ration allows, but your cup always stands full beside you, as does mine, to drink at your desire. Onwards then to battle, and show yourself the man you have always claimed to be!'

Then Idomeneus, leader of the Cretans, answered him: 'Son of

Atreus, for my part I shall be fully loyal in your support, as I promised and pledged at the beginning. Rather go and urge on the other long-haired Achaians, so we can join battle without delay, as the Trojans have broken their oaths. So death and lamentation are in store for them, as they were the first to break the oaths and do us harm.'

So he spoke, and the son of Atreus passed on with delight in his heart. And on his way through the throng of men he came to the two Aiantes. They were arming themselves, and with them there went a cloud of foot-soldiers. As when from some high point a goatherd sees a cloud coming over the sea at the west wind's blast: to his eyes in the distance it shows black as pitch as it crosses the sea, and it brings a great storm with it: and he shivers at the sight and drives his flock into a cave's shelter. Such were the dense-packed battalions of fine young men, god-blessed, moving with the Aiantes to the ravage of war – black, and shivering with shields and spears. Lord Agamemnon was again delighted when he saw them, and spoke to them with winged words: 'Aiantes, leaders of the bronze-clad Argives, to you two I give no orders – it would not be right to urge you on, as you yourselves are pressing your people to fight with all their strength. Oh, father Zeus and Athene and Apollo, if only all my men had such spirit in their breasts! Then lord Priam's city would soon topple, captured and sacked at our hands.'

So speaking he left them there and went to see others. Then he came on Nestor, the clear-voiced speaker of Pylos, ordering his company and urging them to battle, under the huge Pelagon and Alastor and Chromios, and lord Haimon and Bias, shepherd of the people. He set his horsemen in front with their horses and chariots, and the foot-soldiers behind, brave men in large numbers, a wall to front the fighting: the cowards he penned in their middle, so that even the reluctant would be forced into war. First he gave his instructions to the horsemen. He told them to hold in their horses and not charge wildly in among the mass: 'And do not let pride in your skill and bravery tempt any of you to engage the Trojans alone, ahead of the others. And no retreating either – this will weaken your force. Any man who can reach an enemy chariot from his own position should thrust with his spear, as this is far the best way. This is how fighters before you sacked cities and their battlements, holding to this plan and this determination in their hearts.'

So the old man urged them on, in his long experience of war's skill. And lord Agamemnon was delighted when he saw him, and spoke to him with winged words: 'Old man, if only the strength of your knees could match the spirit you keep in your breast, and the power was still in you. But old age, the leveller, is sapping you: if only some other man could take your age, and you be one of the younger men!'

Then Nestor, the Gerenian horseman, answered: 'Son of Atreus, I too would dearly wish to be the man I was when I killed the godlike Ereuthalion. But the gods do not give men all things at the same time. If I was a young man then, now in turn old age is at my heels. But even so I shall be up with my horsemen, and direct them with advice and instruction – such is the old man's privilege. The hurling of spears I shall leave to younger men, those born after my years and sure of their strength.'

So he spoke, and the son of Atreus passed on with delight in his heart. He came on the son of Peteos, Menestheus the horse-driver: he was standing still, and round him the Athenians, rousers of the battle-cry. Close by was standing resourceful Odysseus, and with him, round about, there stood the ranks of the Kephallenians, no feeble force. Their people had not yet heard the cry to battle. It was only just now that the battalions of horse-taming Trojans and Achaians had been roused into movement: and they stood waiting for when some other Achaian division should move forward and attack the Trojans, and the fighting begin. When he saw them Agamemnon, lord of men, abused them, and spoke to them with winged words: 'Son of Peteos the god-ordained king: and you, the expert in low trickery, you with your thoughts always set on gain, why are you cringing here on the side and waiting for others? You two should be up taking your stand in the front lines and sharing the scorch of battle. You are the first to hear my call to the feast, whenever we Achaians are preparing a meal for the elders. Then you are pleased to eat the roast meats and drink your desire in cups of honey-sweet wine. But now you would happily look on even if ten Achaian divisions were fighting with the pitiless bronze before you.'

Resourceful Odysseus scowled at him and said: 'Son of Atreus, what is this you have let slip the guard of your teeth? How can you claim that I shirk the fighting, whenever we Achaians wake war's anger against the horse-taming Trojans? You will see, if you wish, if you have the mind for it, you will see Telemachos' dear father right among the foremost fighters of the horse-taming Trojans. What you say now is wind and nothing.'

Lord Agamemnon answered with a smile, when he saw his anger, and took back what he had said: 'Royal son of Laertes, resourceful Odysseus, I have no great quarrel with you, and I give you no orders. I know how loyal your heart's intentions are in your breast: your thoughts are my thoughts. Come, we will make it good later, if any hard words have been spoken now – may the gods turn all this to air.'

So speaking he left them there and went to see others. And he came on Tydeus' son, high-hearted Diomedes, standing behind his horses in the strongly-made chariot: and by him stood Sthenelos, the son of Kapaneus. When he saw Diomedes, lord Agamemnon abused him, and spoke to him with winged words: 'Shame on you, son of Tydeus, that warrior and tamer of horses, why are you skulking here, just staring at the avenues of battle? It was not Tydeus' way to skulk like this, but rather to engage the enemy far ahead of his own company – so said those who had seen him at his work: I myself never met him or saw him, but they say he was the best of them all. Once he came to Mykene, with peaceful intent, on a visit of friendship with godlike Polyneikes, levying troops. They were then campaigning against the sacred battlements of Thebes, and they earnestly begged us to provide fine troops to help them. Our men were ready to give them, and agreed to what was asked: but then Zeus turned their minds, showing signs of ill omen. Now when they had left and were some distance on their road, and had reached the Asopos, where the rushes grow thick and the banks are smooth grass, then the Achaians sent Tydeus on to take a message to Thebes. He went there, and found a large company of Kadmeians feasting in the palace of the mighty Eteokles. Then, stranger though he was, the horseman Tydeus felt no fear, alone among a crowd of Kadmeians, but he challenged them to the games, and won every event with ease – such was the help given him by Athene. The Kadmeians, horsemen skilled with the whip, were angered, and on his road back they set a massed ambush for him, bringing fifty young men: and there were two leaders, Maion, Haimon's son, a man like the immortals, and the son of Autophonos, the staunch fighter Polyphontes. Tydeus brought these men too to a shameful fate. He killed them all, allowing just one to return home – he sent back Maion, in obedience to signs from the gods. This was the man that Tydeus the Aitolian was – but he fathered a son his inferior in battle, though better at talk.'

So he spoke, and strong Diomedes made no answer, silenced by respect for the king and his rebuke. But the son of glorious Kapaneus did reply: 'Son of Atreus, do not give us lies when you know the clear truth. We can claim to be much better men than our fathers. We did capture the seat of seven-gated Thebes, though we brought a smaller army against a stronger wall. We trusted in signs from the gods and Zeus' aid: but the others were destroyed through their own arrant folly. So please do not set our fathers in equal honour with us.'

Then strong Diomedes scowled at him and said: 'Friend, stay still and be quiet, and do as I tell you. I do not resent Agamemnon, shepherd of the people, for urging the well-greaved Achaians into battle: because his will be the glory that follows if the Achaians slaughter the Trojans and capture sacred Ilios, but his again the depth of grief if the Achaians are slaughtered. Come then, let us too recall our fighting spirit.'

So speaking he jumped to the ground from his chariot with all his armour, and the bronze rang fearfully on the chest of the king as he leapt into movement. Even a strong-hearted man would have felt the grip of fear.

As when the sea's swell hurls on a booming shore, wave after wave at the west wind's stirring: first it rears in the open water, then breaks in loud roaring on the land's edge, and round the head-rocks it rises arching into crests, and flings spits of salt foam. So then, rank after rank, the Danaan battalions moved in ceaseless advance to war. Each of the leaders gave commands to his men: and the rest of the army moved in silence, and you would not think that so many men with voices in their chests were marching behind them, as they went silently, in fear of their commanders: and round each of them as they marched was the gleam of the beaten armour they wore. But the Trojans, like ewes standing innumerable in a rich man's farmyard, ready to give their white milk, and bleating incessantly as they hear their lambs' voices – so hubbub rose from the Trojans throughout the breadth of the army: since there was no common speech or single language shared by all, but a mixture of tongues, and men called from many different lands. Gods drove the two sides on, Ares the Trojans and bright-eyed Athene the Achaians, and Terror and Panic and Strife the insatiable, sister and workmate of Ares the man-killer. She is of little stature at first, but then in time she rears up high till her head is fixed in the heaven while she walks the earth below. So then she went among the massed armies and set hatred equally between them, heaping high men's misery.

When they had advanced together to meet on common ground, then there was the clash of shields, of spears and the fury of men cased in bronze: bossed shields met each other, and the din rose loud. Then there were mingled the groaning and the crowing of men killed and killing, and the ground ran with blood. As when two winter-swollen streams coursing down from the mountains hurl together the mass of their waters where the valleys meet, joining in the gash of a ravine from the great well-heads above, and a shepherd hears their thunder from far in the mountains: such was the noise and the violence of the armies' meeting.

Antilochos was the first to kill a Trojan warrior, a brave fighter of the front line, Echepolos son of Thalysias. First with his cast he hit him on the ridge of his horse-plumed helmet, and the bronze point of the spear lodged in his forehead, driving in through the bone: darkness covered over his eyes, and he crashed, like a tower, in the battle's fury. When he fell lord Elephenor took hold of his feet, Chalkodon's son, commander of the great-hearted Abantes, and began to drag him out from the weapons' range, eager to strip his armour as soon as he could. But his effort was doomed to shortness: great-hearted Agenor saw him pulling away the body, and where his side was exposed under the shield as he stooped, stabbed him there with his bronze-headed spear-shaft, and collapsed his strength. So the life left him, and there was painful work for Trojans and Achaians in the fighting over his body. They leapt at each other like wolves, and man tumbled man in the fray.

Then Telamonian Aias struck the son of Anthemion, Simoeisios, a strong young man not married. His mother had given birth to him by the banks of the Simoeis, coming down from Ida where she had gone with her parents to watch over their flocks: and so they called him Simoeisios. But he could not repay his dear parents for the care of his rearing, but his life was cut short, brought down by the spear at the hands of great-hearted Aias. As he came through the front line Aias struck him in the chest, by the right nipple, and the bronze spear pushed straight on through his shoulder. He fell to the ground in the dust like a poplar, which grows in the grassy flat of a great water-meadow, smooth-trunked, with branches springing at its very top: then a wainwright fells it with the gleaming iron, to bend its wood into a felloe for a chariot of finest make, and it lies there seasoning along the bank of the river. Such was Anthemion's son Simoeisios, killed by royal Aias. Then Priam's son Antiphos, glinting in his corselet, cast his sharp spear at Aias through the mass of men. He missed his man, but hit Leukos, one of Odysseus' brave companions, in the groin, as he was dragging the body to one side. He crashed down on top of it, and the corpse fell from his hand. Odysseus' heart was enraged at his killing. He strode through the front ranks helmeted in gleaming bronze, and going in close he took his stand, looked sharply all around him, and cast with his shining spear: the Trojans gave ground, faced by a man's spear-cast. And his shot was not wasted, but hit Demokoön, a bastard son of Priam, who had joined him from Abydos, where his racing mares were kept. Odysseus, casting in anger for his companion, hit him with his spear in the temple: the bronze point passed out through the temple on the other side, and darkness covered over his eyes. He fell with a crash, and his armour clattered about him. Then the front-fighters and glorious Hektor fell back: and the Argives gave a great shout, and dragged away the dead bodies, and pressed far forward. Apollo, looking down from Pergamos, was angry, and called shouting to the Trojans: 'On, you horse-taming Trojans, do not give the battle to the Argives! Their bodies are not stone or iron, to keep the bronze from tearing their flesh when you hit them. And Achilleus, son of lovely-haired Thetis, is not fighting with them either, but back by the ships, brooding on the anger that pains his heart.'

So the fearful god spoke from the city. And Athene Tritogeneia, most glorious daughter of Zeus, ranged through the Achaian army and spurred them on, wherever she saw a man slacking.

Then his fate shackled Diores, son of Amarynkeus. He was hit by a jagged rock on the right shin, near the ankle: it was thrown by the leader of the Thracians, Peiros son of Imbrasos, who had come from Ainos. The brute stone crushed utterly the two tendons and the bone: and he collapsed on his back in the dust, holding out both arms to his dear companions, the life breathing from him. Then the thrower of the stone, Peiros, ran up and stabbed him with his spear by the navel: and all his guts gushed on the ground, and darkness covered over his eyes.

As Peiros ran back, Thoas the Aitolian caught him with his spear in the chest above the nipple, and the bronze fixed in his lung. Thoas came up close to him, and pulled the massive spear out of his chest, then drew his sharp sword and struck him in the middle of the belly, and took away his life. But he did not strip the armour, because Peiros' companions, Thracians with their hair in a top-knot, surrounded him with long spears in their hands, and for all his size and strength and pride pushed him away from them, and he was shaken back in retreat. So those two lay stretched in the dust side by side, leading men both of them, one of the Thracians, the other of the bronze-clad Epeians. And many others were killed over them.

Then no-one who had part in it would now make light of the action – any man who still wheeled at the battle's centre unscathed by throw or stab of the sharp bronze, even with Pallas Athene leading him by the hand and keeping him safe from the flying weapons. Because on that day many of the Trojans and Achaians lay stretched side by side, face down in the dust.

BOOK 5
DIOMEDES TRIUMPHANT

Then Pallas Athene imparted strength and courage to Diomedes son of Tydeus, so that he should stand out among all the Argives and win heroic glory. She set untiring fire blazing from his helmet and shield, like the late summer star, which rises from its bath in the Ocean to shine brightest of all. Such was the fire she made burn from his head and shoulders, and she spurred him into the eye of battle, where the fighters swarmed thickest.

There was a man among the Trojans called Dares, a man of wealth and worth, the priest of Hephaistos: he had two sons, Phegeus and Idaios, both skilled in all the ways of battle. These two separated from the line, and rushed out to oppose Diomedes, their attack made from a chariot, his from the ground on foot. When they had advanced to close range, Phegeus let fly his long-shadowed spear first, and the point of the spear passed over Diomedes' left shoulder and did not hit him. Then after him Tydeus' son rose to his cast, and the weapon did not fly wasted from his hand, but hit him in the chest between the nipples, and dropped him from the chariot. Idaios jumped out and left the fine chariot, and had not the courage to stand in protection over his brother's dead body. And he too would not have escaped black doom, but Hephaistos rescued him and took him away safe in a covering of darkness, so that he should not leave the old father wholly desolated. The son of great-hearted Tydeus drove away the horses, and gave them to his companions to lead back to the hollow ships. When the great-hearted Trojans saw that one of Dares' sons had run away and the other was killed beside his chariot, all their hearts stirred in anger. But bright-eyed Athene took raging Ares by the hand and spoke to him: 'Ares, Ares, curse of men, murderer, breaker of cities, shall we not now leave the Trojans and Achaians to fight it out and see which side will be given the triumph by father Zeus – while we two withdraw and keep clear of Zeus' anger?'

So speaking she led raging Ares out of the battle. She sat him down then on the high river-bank of Skamandros: and the Danaans turned the Trojans, and each of the commanders killed his man. First was Agamemnon, lord of men, who hurled the huge Odios, leader of the Halizones, out of his chariot: he was the first to die, as he turned in flight and Agamemnon fixed his spear in his back between the shoulder-blades, and drove it on out through the chest. He fell with a crash, and his armour clattered about him.

Idomeneus killed Phaistos, son of the Maionian Boros, who had come from the fertile ground of Tarne. Idomeneus the famous spearman stabbed him with his long spear in the right shoulder, as he tried to mount behind his team: he crashed from the chariot, and the hateful darkness took him. Idomeneus' followers then set to stripping his armour.

Strophios' son Skamandrios, skilled in the hunt, was caught by Menelaos son of Atreus with his sharp spear – he was a fine huntsman: Artemis herself had taught him to shoot down all the wild things that the forest breeds in the mountains. But Artemis the archer-goddess did not protect him then, nor his archer's skill in which he had excelled before: but the son of Atreus, the great spearman Menelaos, stabbed him with his spear as he fled before him, in the back between the shoulder-blades, and drove it on out through the chest. He crashed down on his face, and his armour clattered about him.

Meriones killed Phereklos, son of Tekton, Harmon's son, who had the skill in his hands to make all things of craft, since Pallas Athene had special love for him. It was he who had built for Alexandros those balanced ships, the start of their doom, which brought disaster on all the Trojans and on him himself, as he knew nothing of the gods' decreed will. As Meriones caught up with him, running him down, he struck him in the right buttock: and the spearpoint went right on through under the bone into his bladder. He screamed, and dropped on his knees, and death enfolded him.

And Meges killed Pedaios, Antenor's son – a bastard son, but godlike Theano reared him with all the care she gave her own dear children, to please her husband. Phyleus' son, the famous spearman, came close behind him and struck him with his sharp spear in the nape at the back of his head: the bronze pushed straight on through his teeth and cut away his tongue. He crashed in the dust, the cold bronze clenched in his teeth.

Eurypylos, Euaimon's son, killed godlike Hypsenor, son of proud-hearted Dolopion, who was the priest of Skamandros and honoured like a god by the people. As he fled before him, Eurypylos, the splendid son of Euaimon, running him down lunged forward with his sword and slashed at his shoulder, and sheared away his whole massive arm. The arm dropped bloody on the ground: and over his eyes came the surge of death, and strong fate took him.

So they laboured in the fighting's fury. But as for the son of Tydeus, you would not know which side he fought on, whether he was of the Trojan camp or the Achaian. He swept over the plain like a river full in winter spate, which bursts the dykes in the speed of its current. The close-built dykes cannot hold it, nor is it checked by the banks of the thriving vineyards as it comes in a sudden flood, when the rain from Zeus falls heavy: and many sturdy farmers see it flatten the fruit of their labour. So the close-packed battalions of the Trojans were driven flying by the son of Tydeus, and for all their numbers they could not resist him.

Now when Lykaon's splendid son, Pandaros, saw him sweeping over the plain and driving the battalions before him, he quickly drew his curved bow against the son of Tydeus and shot him as he came charging on, hitting in the right shoulder, on the corselet's front-piece: the bitter arrow flew on through, keeping its way straight on, and the corselet was spattered with blood. At this Lykaon's splendid son gave a great shout: 'On, Trojans, you great hearts, horsemen skilled with the whip! The best of the Achaians is hit, and I do not think he will hold out long against the arrow's power, if it was truly lord Apollo, son of Zeus, who inspired my coming here from Lycia.'

So he spoke in triumph. But the sharp arrow had not brought Diomedes down, but he turned back and stood by his horses and chariot, and spoke to Sthenelos, Kapaneus' son: 'Come, friend, son of Kapaneus, get down from the chariot so you can pull the bitter arrow out of my shoulder for me.'

So he spoke, and Sthenelos jumped to the ground from the chariot, and standing at his side pulled the sharp arrow out right through the shoulder: and blood spurted through the twill of his tunic. Then Diomedes, master of the war-cry, prayed aloud: 'Hear me, daughter of Zeus who holds the aegis, Atrytone. If ever before in love for my father you stood by him in the ravage of battle, now show me too your love, Athene. Grant that I may kill this man, that he comes within my spear's throw, the man who shot me before I saw him and is now triumphing over me, saying I have not long now to look on the sun's brightness.'

So he spoke in prayer. And Pallas Athene heard him, and made his limbs light, his legs and his arms above. She came close and spoke winged words to him: 'Go now, Diomedes, and fight in all confidence against the Trojans. I have put your father's strength in your heart, a fearless spirit such as the horseman Tydeus always had, the great shield-fighter. And again I have taken from your eyes the mist that covered them before, so that you can clearly tell both god and man. So now, if a god comes down here in trial of battle, you must not make open fight with the immortal gods, with any of them except Aphrodite, daughter of Zeus – if she enters the fighting, you may stab her with the sharp bronze.'

So speaking bright-eyed Athene left him, and the son of Tydeus went back again to join the front-fighters. His heart had been raging before to do battle with the Trojans, but now three times that fury took hold of him, like a lion, whom a shepherd tending his thick-fleeced sheep in the wilds has wounded as he jumps the wall of the fold – a graze that does not bring him down, but rouses the strength in him, and then the shepherd can resist no more, but the lion penetrates the pens and the sheep run in panic, defenceless. They are left tumbled on each other in heaps, and he in the rush of his fury jumps back out of the wide enclosure. Such was strong Diomedes' fury as he joined with the Trojans.

Then he killed Astynoös and Hypeiron, shepherd of the people, hitting the first above the nipple with his bronze-tipped spear, and the other he struck with his great sword on the collar-bone by the shoulder, and hacked the shoulder away from neck and back. He let them lie, and went after Abas and Polyïdos, sons of Eurydamas, an old interpreter of dreams: the old man had not expounded their dreams for them as they went to the war, but strong Diomedes killed them both. He went then in pursuit of Xanthos and Thoön, sons of Phainops, both children late-born and loved: but he was worn by cruel age, and could father no other son to leave over his possessions. So then Diomedes killed them, and took the dear life from them both, leaving lamentation and cruel sorrow to their father, when he did not welcome them back alive on their return from the battle: and distant relatives divided the inheritance.

Then he took two sons of Priam of Dardanos' line, Echemmon and Chromios, together in one chariot. As a lion springs among cattle and breaks the neck of a heifer or a cow, as they graze in a coppice, so Tydeus' son sent these two hurling from their chariot, brutally, without a choice, and then stripped the armour from them: the horses he gave to his companions to drive back to the ships.

Aineias saw him breaking the ranks of men, and set off through the fighting and the flurry of spears in search of Pandaros, to see if he could find him. And he did find the son of Lykaon, an excellent man and strong, and stopped beside him and spoke straight to him: 'Pandaros, where is your bow and your feathered arrows, and your archer's fame? No man here can rival it, and there is none in Lycia either who has claim to be better than you. Come then, raise your hands in prayer to Zeus, and let fly an arrow at this man, whoever it is who is holding the field and has done much damage to the Trojans, collapsing the strength of many brave men – unless it is some god working his fury on the Trojans, in anger at sacrifice missed, and a god's anger lies hard on us.'

Then Lykaon's splendid son said to him: 'Aineias, counsellor of the bronze-clad Trojans, to me the man seems in every way like the warrior son of Tydeus, judging by his shield and the mask of his helmet and the look of his horses – though I do not know for sure that it is not a god. But if he is the man I think, Tydeus' warrior son, then this rampage of his cannot be without a god's help, but one of the immortals is standing by him, with mist wrapped round his shoulders, and turned aside the sharp arrow that was finding its mark in him – I have already let fly an arrow at him, and struck him in the right shoulder, straight through the corselet's front-piece. And I thought that I would send him on his way to Hades, but for all that I did not bring him down – so this must be some god in anger. But I have no horses here or chariot that I could mount. And yet stored somewhere in Lykaon's house there are eleven chariots, lovely ones, all new made and fresh from the joiner's hands: cloths cover them over, and by each one there stands a pair of horses munching their white barley and wheat. The old spearman Lykaon advised me constantly in his strong-built house as I set out on my way here: he told me to take horses and chariots and lead the Trojans mounted in the fighting's fury. But I did not take his advice – it would have been far better if I had – in consideration for my horses, so I should not see them short of fodder in a place where the people were all cooped up, and they accustomed to plentiful eating. So I left them, and came on foot to Ilios, relying on my bow, which it seems was to do me no good. I have already shot at two leading fighters, the son of Tydeus and the son of Atreus, and I set the blood running from both with a plain hit, but only roused them to greater fury. So it was under a cross fate that I took my curved bow from its peg on that day when I led my Trojans to lovely Ilios, as a service of friendship to godlike Hektor. If I return and set eyes again on my homeland and my wife and my great high-roofed house, then let some stranger cut the head straight from my body if I do not snap this bow in pieces with my own hands and throw it on the blazing fire – it is mere useless baggage.'

Then Aineias, leader of the Trojans, said to him: 'No more of this talk! There can be no difference made until you and I go against this man with chariot and team and face him in the trial of armed fighting. Come then, mount my chariot, so you can see the mettle of these horses of Tros' stock, and their skill in speeding up and down through the plain in pursuit or retreat: this pair will bring us safe to the city if Zeus again gives the triumph to Diomedes son of Tydeus. Come, you now take the whip and the shining reins, and I will dismount from the chariot to fight him – or you stand up to him while I manage the horses.'

Lykaon's splendid son answered him: 'Aineias, you yourself take the reins and your own horses. They will pull the curved chariot better under the driver they know, if we have to run this time before Tydeus' son. Otherwise they may panic and dither, and refuse to carry us out of the battle, missing the sound of your voice – and then the son of great-hearted Tydeus could rush on and kill us and drive away the strong-footed horses. No, you yourself drive the chariot and your own horses, and I shall face his attack with my sharp spear.'

So speaking they mounted the worked chariot, and in full fury held the speeding horses against the son of Tydeus. Sthenelos saw them, Kapaneus' splendid son, and quickly spoke winged words to the son of Tydeus: 'Diomedes, son of Tydeus, pleasure of my heart, I see two powerful men coming at you in fury for the fight, men of huge strength. One is the skilled bowman Pandaros, who owns himself son of Lykaon – and the other Aineias, whose pride is to be the son born to excellent Anchises, and his mother was Aphrodite. So come, let us mount and give way: I beg you not to rage on in this way through the front-fighters, or you may destroy your own life.'

Then strong Diomedes scowled at him and said: 'Do not talk to me of flight, as you will never persuade me. It is not in my blood to fight a shirker's battle or to cower away – my courage is still strong in its place. Pride makes me shrink from mounting the horses – no, I shall go to meet them just as I am: Pallas Athene will not let me run in fear. Their speeding horses will not carry back both of these two away from us, even though one of them may escape. I tell you something else, and you mark it well in your mind. If Athene whose plans are many gives me the triumph to kill both, you hold our own quick horses here, tying their reins to the chariot rail, and remember to run out to catch Aineias' horses, and drive them away from the Trojans back to the well-greaved Achaians: because I tell you they are of that stock from which wide-seeing Zeus once gave horses to Tros as compensation for his son Ganymedes, as they were the best of all the horses that exist under the sun and the spread of day. Anchises, lord of men, stole from this stock, by secretly putting mares under them without Laomedon's knowledge: and from these he had six young born on his estate. He kept four himself and reared them in his own stable: and these two he gave to Aineias, horses that drive men to flight. If we could capture these, we would win a fine glory for ourselves.'

Such were their words to each other: and as they talked the other two closed quickly on them, driving their speeding horses. Lykaon's splendid son spoke first to Diomedes: 'Son of proud Tydeus, strong-hearted man of battle, my shot did not bring you down then, the bitter arrow sped from my bow. Now this time I shall try for a hit with my spear.' So he spoke, and steadying his long-shadowed spear he let it fly, and hit home in the son of Tydeus' shield: the bronze point flew on right through it and reached the corselet. At this the splendid son of Lykaon gave a great shout: 'You are hit, straight through the hollow of your side! I do not think you will hold out much longer – you have given me my great triumph.'

Undismayed strong Diomedes replied: 'You have missed – you did not hit me. But for you two I do not think there will be an end of it until one of you falls and gives his glut of blood to Ares, the fighter with the bull's-hide shield.'

So speaking he let fly: and Athene guided the weapon to hit on the nose by his eye, and it pierced through his white teeth. The tireless bronze sheared away the tongue at its root, and the point came out by the base of his chin. He crashed from the chariot, and his bright glinting armour clattered about him, and his swift-footed horses shied apart. Life and strength collapsed where he lay.

Aineias jumped down with his shield and long spear, afraid that the Achaians would drag away the body. He took his stand over Pandaros like a lion sure of his power, and held out over him his spear and the even circle of his shield, intent on killing any man who came against him, and shouting fearfully. But the son of Tydeus took up a boulder in his hand, a huge great thing, that two men could not carry between them, of the folk that live now – but he swung it easily on his own. With this he hit Aineias on the hip-joint, where the thigh-bone turns in the hip, and men call it the cup. He smashed Aineias' cup, and broke both tendons as well, and the rough stone forced back the skin. The hero dropped to his knees and stayed there, leaning with his heavy hand on the earth: and black night covered over his eyes.

And now Aineias, lord of men, would have perished there, if Zeus' daughter Aphrodite had not quickly seen it, his mother, who had conceived him to Anchises, when he was herding cattle. She threw her white arms round her dear son, and held the fold of her shining robe in covering over him, to shield him from the spears, so that no fast-horsed Danaan should cast a bronze spear in his chest and take the life from him.

She then began to carry her dear son out of the fighting. And Kapaneus' son did not forget the instructions given him by Diomedes, master of the war-cry, but held back his own strong-footed horses away from the roar of battle, tying their reins to the chariot rail, and ran out and drove Aineias' lovely-maned horses away from the Trojans back to the well-greaved Achaians, and gave them to Deïpylos to drive to the hollow ships – his dear friend, whom he valued most of all men of his own age, because their minds thought alike. Then the hero Sthenelos mounted his own chariot and took up the shining reins, and eagerly set the strong-footed horses at once to follow the son of Tydeus. He was pressing after Aphrodite Kypris with the pitiless bronze, knowing that she was a god without strength, and not one of the goddesses who have mastery in men's battles, not Athene or Enyo, the sacker of cities. But when he came up with her in his pursuit through the masses of men, then the son of great-hearted Tydeus sprang at her and lunging with his sharp spear stabbed at the wrist of her soft hand: and the spear pierced straight through the skin, through the immortal robe which the Graces themselves had made for her, above the base of the palm: and immortal god's blood dripped from her, ichor, which runs in the blessed gods' veins – they do not eat food, they do not drink gleaming wine, and so they are without blood and are called immortals. She shrieked loud, and let her son fall from her: and Phoibos Apollo took him in his arms and kept him safe in a dark cloud, so that no fast-horsed Danaan should cast a bronze spear in his chest and take the life from him. Then Diomedes, master of the war-cry, called out loud to her: 'Away, daughter of Zeus, keep clear of battle and fighting! Is it not enough for you to seduce the wits of weak women? If you start frequenting the battle-field, then I think you will come to shudder at war, even hearing of it somewhere else.'

So he spoke, and she turned back distraught, in terrible affliction. And Iris with feet quick as the wind took her and led her out of the massed fighting, in an agony of pain, her lovely skin darkening with blood. Then on the left of the battle she found raging Ares, sitting still, his spear and fast chariot resting on a cloud. She fell on her knees and with long entreaty begged her dear brother for his horses with their headpieces of gold: 'Dear brother, rescue me, give me your horses, so that I can reach Olympos where the immortals have their home. I am in agony with a wound which a mortal man dealt me, the son of Tydeus, who would now fight even with father Zeus.'

So she spoke, and Ares gave her the horses with their headpieces of gold. She mounted the chariot in anguish at heart, and Iris mounted beside her and took up the reins in her hands: she whipped the pair on, and they flew eagerly on their way. Then they quickly reached the gods' home, steep Olympos. There swift Iris with feet quick as the wind reined in the horses, unyoked them from the chariot, and tossed immortal fodder down for them. Then divine Aphrodite threw herself into the lap of Dione, her mother: and she took her daughter in her arms, and stroked her with her hand, and spoke to her, saying, 'Which of the heavenly gods was it, dear child, who did this naughty thing to you, as if you were openly doing something wicked?'

Then Aphrodite, smiling goddess, answered her: 'It was Tydeus' son, proud-hearted Diomedes, who stabbed me, because I was carrying my dear son out of the fighting – Aineias, who is far the dearest of all men to me. The grim battle is no longer between Trojans and Achaians, but the Danaans are now fighting even the immortals.'

Then Dione, queen among goddesses, answered her: 'Have patience, dear child, and bear with it for all your distress. Many of us who have our homes on Olympos have suffered at men's hands, in the cruel pain that we bring on each other. Ares suffered, when Otos and powerful Ephialtes, children of Aloëus, bound him in a strong prison. He was imprisoned in a bronze jar for thirteen months – and there Ares the war-glutton would even have perished, if their step-mother, beautiful Eëriboia, had not told Hermes of it: he stole Ares out of the jar when his strength was then failing and the cruel prison was wearing him down. And Hera suffered, when the powerful son of Amphitryon hit her in the right breast with a three-barbed arrow – then she too was seized with pain that could not be soothed. And monstrous Hades had to suffer with the others – he endured a speeding arrow, when this same man, son of Zeus who holds the aegis, shot him in Pylos among the dead men and put him to agony. And he went up to Zeus' house and high Olympos sore at heart, the pains piercing him through: the arrow had been driven into his massive shoulder and was galling his spirit. But Paiëon spread pain-killing medicines on it and healed him, since he was not of mortal make. Criminal wretch that he was, Herakles, to care nothing for his wickedness in using his bow to trouble the gods, the holders of Olympos! In your case it was the bright-eyed goddess Athene who sent this man against you. Poor fool! The son of Tydeus has no thought in his mind that life is not long for the man who fights the immortals – for him no homecoming from war's grim struggle to have his children climb his lap with cries of "Daddy!". So now the son of Tydeus, for all his power, should beware that no greater opponent than you meets him in battle – or else good Aigialeia, Adrestos' daughter, strong wife of Diomedes the horse-tamer, may rouse her fond houshold from their sleep with her long lamentations, crying for the loss of the husband of her marriage, the best of the Achaians.'

So she spoke, and with both her hands she wiped away the ichor from her daughter's hand: the hand was healed, and the heavy pains soothed away. Now Athene and Hera were watching, and they began to tease Zeus the son of Kronos with mocking words. The bright-eyed goddess Athene began: 'Father Zeus, will you be at all angry at what I say? Kypris must have been coaxing some Achaian girl to go with the Trojans, who are now such favourites of hers, and when caressing one of these Achaian women with their lovely dresses she must have scratched her delicate hand on a gold dress-pin.'

So she spoke, and the father of men and gods smiled, and calling golden Aphrodite to him he said: 'War's work, my child, is not your province. No, you busy yourself with marriage and the work of love, while all this will be for quick Ares and Athene to see to.'

Such were their words to each other. But Diomedes, master of the war-cry, sprang forward to attack Aineias, recognising that Apollo himself held his hands' protection over him: but he had no fear even of the great god, and kept pressing on to kill Aineias and strip the glory of his armour. Three times he sprang forward in the urge to kill him, and three times Apollo slammed back his shining shield. But when for the fourth time he flung himself on like a god, then Apollo the far-worker called to him with a fearful shout: 'Think, son of Tydeus, and shrink back! Never think yourself gods' equal – since there can be no likeness ever between the make of immortal gods and of men who walk on the ground.'

So he spoke, and the son of Tydeus gave back a little way, avoiding the anger of Apollo the far-shooter. And Apollo set Aineias down away from the fighting, on sacred Pergamos, where his temple was built: and there in the great inner chamber Leto and Artemis the archer-goddess healed him and restored his glory. But Apollo, god of the silver bow, created an image, the very likeness of Aineias and armed as he was, and round this image the Trojans and godlike Achaians hacked at each other, at the ox-hides held over their chests, great round shields or fluttering targes. Then Phoibos Apollo spoke to raging Ares: 'Ares, Ares, curse of men, murderer, breaker of cities: will you not go after this man and take him out of the fighting – the son of Tydeus, who would now fight even with father Zeus? First he closed with Kypris and stabbed her hand in the wrist, then he even flung himself at me, attacking like a god.'

So speaking Apollo settled on the height of Pergamos, and murderous Ares went out among the Trojan ranks and spurred them on, taking the form of quick Akamas, leader of the Thracians. He called to the royal sons of Priam: 'You sons of Priam, god-ordained king, how much longer will you let your people be killed by the Achaians? Until they are fighting round the strong-built city gates? A man is fallen whom we held in equal honour with godlike Hektor – Aineias, son of great-hearted Anchises. Come then, let us rescue our brave companion from the seethe of battle.'

So speaking he spurred the strength and heart in each of them. Then Sarpedon too spoke in strong complaint to godlike Hektor: 'Hektor, where has that strength gone that you had before? You used to say – did you not? – that you could hold this city alone, without help from your people or allies, just you and your brothers and brothers-in-law. I cannot now catch sight or glimpse of any of them – no, they are cowering back like dogs round a lion. But we are fighting, we allies in your city. I am one of them, an ally come from a great distance. Lycia is far away, by the swirling river Xanthos, and there I have left behind my dear wife and my infant son, and much property, the envy of every poor man. And yet for all that I spur on my Lycians and am eager myself to face my man in battle – but I have nothing here that the Achaians might loot or carry off. But you just stand there idle, and do not even give orders to the rest of your people to hold their ground and fight in defence of their wives. Take care you are not caught like fish in the meshes of a net that captures all, and become your enemies' spoil and prize – they will soon be sacking your well-founded city. All this should be your concern every day and night – you should be begging the leaders of your far-famed allies to hold fast and persevere, and give them no cause for bitter complaint.'

So Sarpedon spoke, and his words stung Hektor's heart. He immediately jumped to the ground from his chariot with all his armour, and shaking a pair of sharp spears in his grip he ranged all through the army, spurring them to fight, and rousing their spirit for grim battle. They rallied and turned to stand against the Achaians: and the Argives stood their ground in full strength with no retreat. As the wind carries the chaff across the sacred threshing-floors, when men are winnowing and golden-haired Demeter separates the grain and the chaff in the winds' stream, and the piles of settling chaff grow white: so then the Achaians turned white with the dust that rained on them, kicked up to the brazen sky by the hooves of the horses across their ranks, as the battle clashed again, and the drivers wheeled and wheeled about their teams. The fighters pushed their hands' fury straight on: and raging Ares, ubiquitous, set a covering of darkness over the battle as aid to the Trojans. He was carrying out the instructions of Phoibos Apollo, god of the golden sword, who told him to rouse the Trojans' courage, when he saw Pallas Athene leaving the field – she had been the Danaans' helper. Apollo himself sent Aineias out from the centre of his rich temple, and instilled strength in the heart of the shepherd of the people. Aineias came and joined his companions. They were overjoyed to see him come back to them alive and safe and in soundness of strength, but they asked him no questions – no time for that given by the rest of war's work, stirred up for them by the god of the silver bow and Ares the curse of men and Strife the insatiable.

On the other side the two Aiantes and Odysseus and Diomedes were spurring the Danaans into battle. But without need for encouragement the men faced the Trojans' attacks and sallies undaunted, standing firm like the clouds which in a windless calm the son of Kronos sets motionless at the peaks of high mountains, when the north wind's fury sleeps and the other raging winds, who when they blow scatter the shadowing clouds with their howling blasts. So it was that the Danaans stood their ground firm against the Trojans and would not turn in flight. The son of Atreus ranged through the mass of his army with constant exhortation: 'Be men, my friends, and put courage in your hearts! In the battle's fury think proudly of your honour in each other's eyes. When men have pride, more are saved than killed: but when they turn to flight, there can be no glory there or courage to resist.'

So he spoke, and quickly cast with his spear, and hit a leading fighter, a companion of great-hearted Aineias, Deïkoön son of Pergasos, a man honoured by the Trojans as highly as Priam's sons, since he was always busy in the front-rank fighting. Lord Agamemnon's spear hit home in his shield: and the shield could not stop the spear, but the bronze went right on through, and drove through the belt into the base of his belly. He fell with a crash, and his armour clattered about him.

Then in turn Aineias killed two leading men of the Danaans, the sons of Diokles, Krethon and Orsilochos. Their father lived in well-founded Phere, a man rich in substance, descended from the river Alpheios, which flows broad through the land of the Pylians. Alpheios fathered Ortilochos, to be king over many men, and Ortilochos was the father of great-hearted Diokles: and to Diokles there were born twin sons, Krethon and Orsilochos, both skilled in all the ways of battle. When they had grown to manhood they went with the Argives in their black ships to Ilios the city rich in horses, to win compensation for the sons of Atreus, Agamemnon and Menelaos: and there the end of death covered them over. They were like two lions reared by their mother on the mountain peaks, in the thick wood of a deep forest: they plunder men's steadings, seizing on their cattle and sturdy sheep, until they too are killed, cut down by the sharp bronze in the men's hands. Such were these two when they were brought low at the hands of Aineias, and fell to the ground like tall pine-trees.

When they fell the warrior Menelaos felt pity for them, and strode through the front ranks helmeted in gleaming bronze, shaking his spear: and Ares spurred the courage in him, intending that he should be brought down at the hands of Aineias. But Antilochos saw him, great-hearted Nestor's son, and strode through the front ranks in great fear for the shepherd of the people, in case he came to some harm and so brought all their labour to frustration. Now Menelaos and Aineias were facing each other, hands and sharp spears held ready in their eagerness to fight, when Antilochos came up and stood close by the shepherd of the people: and Aineias would not stand his ground, agile fighter though he was, when he saw two men facing him side by side. So when the two of them had dragged the bodies back to the Achaian lines, they gave the poor twins into the hands of their companions, and turned back themselves to fight on in the front ranks.

Then they caught Pylaimenes, a man like Ares, leader of the great-hearted Paphlagonians, fighters with the shield. The son of Atreus, the great spearman Menelaos, stabbed him with his spear where he stood on the ground, hitting on the collar-bone. And Antilochos hit Mydon, the charioteer who served him, Atymnios' fine son – he was wheeling the strong-footed horses round, and Antilochos hit him with a stone right on the elbow: the reins, white with ivory pieces, fell from his hands into the dust on the ground. Then Antilochos sprang forward and struck him on the temple with his sword: gasping, he tumbled headlong from the well-made chariot to land head and shoulders in the dust. For some time he stuck there – he had fallen in deep sand – until the horses kicked him over and trampled him down in the dust. Antilochos whipped them on and drove them back to the Achaian camp.

Hektor caught sight of them through the ranks and set off to attack them, shouting loud. With him there followed the Trojan battalions in strength, led by Ares and the goddess Enyo, she attended by Confusion the ruthless in battle, while Ares wielded in his hands a monstrous spear, and strode now in front of Hektor, now behind him.

Diomedes, master of the war-cry, shuddered at the sight of Ares. As when a man crossing a great plain stops and stands baffled at the edge of a river flowing fast in its course to the sea, looks at it surging into foam, and runs back the way he came, so then Diomedes began to give way, and said to his people: 'My friends, how we used to look on Hektor with awe as a great spearman and brave fighter! But there is always one of the gods at his side, to keep him from destruction: and now that is Ares there beside him, in human form. Keep facing the Trojans, then, but gradually retreat, and do not try to do full battle with the gods.'

So he spoke, and the Trojans came on very close. Then Hektor killed two men, skilled fighters, both together in one chariot, Menesthes and Anchialos. When they fell huge Aias, Telamon's son, felt pity for them. Going in close he took his stand and cast with his shining spear, and he hit Amphios, son of Selagos, who lived in Paisos, a man rich in property and rich in farmland – but fate had led him on to join Priam and his sons as their ally. Telamonian Aias hit him in the belt, and the long-shadowed spear fixed deep in the base of his belly, and he fell with a crash. Glorious Aias ran forward to strip his armour, but the Trojans showered him with spears, sharp and glinting, and his shield took many of them. He braced his foot against the corpse and pulled out his bronze spear. But he could not go on to take the fine armour from its shoulders, as the spears were overwhelming him, and he was frightened of the fierce defence the high-hearted Trojans would make over the body – many brave Trojans pressed in on him with spears in their hands, and for all his size and strength and pride pushed him away from them: and he was shaken back in retreat.

So they laboured in the fighting's fury. Then Tlepolemos, the son of Herakles, huge and brave, was roused by the power of his fate to attack godlike Sarpedon. When these two had advanced to close range, the son and the grandson of Zeus the cloud-gatherer, Tlepolemos spoke first and said to Sarpedon: 'Sarpedon, counsellor of the Lycians, what prompted you to come and do your cowering here – you, a man with no knowledge of fighting? They lie when they say you are a son of Zeus who holds the aegis, since you are far inferior to those men who were born to Zeus in earlier times. The mighty Herakles they say was quite a different man – my father, bold of spirit and with the heart of a lion. He once came here to claim Laomedon's horses, and with only six ships and fewer men than these he sacked the city of Ilios and widowed her streets. But yours is a coward's heart, and your people are dying. And I do not think your coming from Lycia will be any protection for the Trojans – no, you will be brought down at my hands and cross the gates of Hades.'

Then Sarpedon, leader of the Lycians, said to him: 'Tlepolemos, yes, your father did destroy sacred Ilios, but it was through one man's folly, proud Laomedon's, who repaid his good service with words of insult, and refused to give him the horses for which he had come from far away. But your achievement here, I tell you, will be death and black doom at my hands: you will be brought down under my spear and give me my triumph and a life to Hades the horseman.'

So Sarpedon spoke, and Tlepolemos raised his ash spear: and both their long spears flew from their hands at the same moment. Sarpedon hit in the middle of Tlepolemos' neck, and the cruel point passed right through, and black night covered over his eyes. Tlepolemos' long spear hit Sarpedon in the left thigh, and the point ran ravening through, driven on to touch the bone: but his father kept destruction from him for the time.

His noble companions started to carry godlike Sarpedon out of the fighting. The long spear burdened him, dragging at his side, but in their haste none of them noticed or thought to pull the ash spear out of his thigh, so he could stand – such was the work they had in attending him.

On the other side the well-greaved Achaians were carrying Tlepolemos out of the fighting. Godlike Odysseus saw it, and bore the sight steadfastly, but his heart raged within him. He pondered then in heart and mind whether to go on in pursuit of the son of loud-thundering Zeus or to take the lives from more of the Lycians instead. But it was not fated for great-hearted Odysseus to kill the mighty son of Zeus with the sharp bronze, so Athene turned his anger on the mass of the Lycians. Then he took Koiranos and Alastor and Chromios and Alkandros and Halios and Noëmon and Prytanis. And now godlike Odysseus would have killed yet more of the Lycians, if great Hektor of the glinting helmet had not seen it. He strode through the front ranks helmeted in gleaming bronze, bringing terror to the Danaans. Sarpedon, Zeus' son, was glad at his approach, and spoke plaintively to him: 'Son of Priam, help me, do not leave me lying here as prey for the Danaans. Then let my life go from me in your city, since it seems I was not destined after all to return to my home in my dear native land and bring joy to my dear wife and baby son.'

So he spoke, and Hektor of the glinting helmet gave him no answer, but rushed past him, eager to push back the Argives without delay, and take the life from many. His noble companions set godlike Sarpedon down under a lovely oak-tree sacred to Zeus who holds the aegis, and strong Pelagon, his dear companion, forced the ash spear clear out of his thigh. His spirit left him, and mist spread down over his eyes. Then he came back to his senses, as the breath of the north wind blowing round him gathered back the life he had breathed out in his pain.

Meanwhile the Argives, pressed by Ares and bronze-armoured Hektor, never turned in flight to their black ships nor offered battle, but gradually gave ground in retreat, when they learnt that Ares was with the Trojans.

Then who was the first, and who the last slaughtered by Hektor, Priam's son, and brazen Ares? Godlike Teuthras first, and then Orestes the horseman, and Trechos the Aitolian spearman, and Oinomaos, and Helenos son of Oinops, and Oresbios with the glinting skirt-piece, a man who used to live in Hyle much busied with his wealth, down by the shore of the Kephisian lake: and beside him there lived other men of Boiotia, owners of a fertile land.

Now when the white-armed goddess Hera saw the Argives being destroyed in the battle's fury, straightaway she spoke winged words to

Athene: 'Shame on it, Atrytone, daughter of Zeus who holds the aegis – the promise that we made to Menelaos, that he would return after sacking the well-walled city of Ilios, that was empty talk indeed, if we are to allow murderous Ares to rage like this. Come then, let us too recall our fighting spirit.'

So she spoke, and the bright-eyed goddess Athene did not fail to obey. Hera then, queenly goddess, daughter of great Kronos, busied about the harnessing of the horses with their golden head-pieces. And Hebe quickly fitted the curved wheels to the chariot-frame, bronze wheels with eight spokes, at each end of the axle made of iron. Their felloes are of imperishable gold, and all round them are fixed tyres of bronze, a wonderful sight. The naves that revolve on either side are of silver: and the platform is made of gold and silver straps stretched tight, and twin rails run round it. From it there extends a pole of silver: at the end of this Hebe lashed a beautiful yoke of gold, and fitted it with lovely golden yoke-straps. And Hera brought the swift-footed horses under the yoke, eager for the clash and shout of battle.

And Athene, daughter of Zeus who holds the aegis, let slip to the floor of her father's house her soft embroidered robe, which she herself had made and worked with her hands. And she put on Zeus the cloud-gatherer's own tunic in its place, then dressed in her armour for the misery of war. Round her shoulders she hung the tasselled aegis, a fearful weapon, set with Panic all round it in a circle: and on it there is Strife, and Power, and chilling Rout, and set there too is the head of the fearful monster Gorgon, a thing of fright and terror, a potent sign from Zeus who holds the aegis. And on her head she placed a golden helmet, set round with horns, four-bossed, and decorated with a hundred cities' men-at-arms. She stepped into her flaming chariot, and took up her spear, the huge, heavy, massive spear with which she brings low the ranks of men, the heroes who stir the mighty-fathered goddess into anger. Hera quickly touched the horses with the whip: and of their own accord the gates of heaven groaned open, the gates kept by the Seasons, who have been given charge over the vast heaven and Olympos, both to push aside the heavy cloud and to close it to. This way, then, they held their whipped horses through the gates. And they found the son of Kronos sitting apart from the other gods on the highest peak of ridged Olympos. There the white-armed goddess Hera pulled in the horses, and spoke to Zeus the most high, the son of Kronos, asking him: 'Father Zeus, are you not angry at Ares for the violence he is doing, for the number and worth of the Achaian men he has killed – reckless, unjustified slaughter which is anguish to me, while Kypris and Apollo of the silver bow sit happily by, enjoying this madman they have let loose, who has no notion of right? Father Zeus, will you be at all angry with me, if I beat Ares off with painful blows and drive him out of the fighting?'

Then Zeus the cloud-gatherer answered her: 'To your work, then. Set Athene at him, the goddess of spoil – she is the one who most often brings him to inglorious pain.'

So he spoke, and the white-armed goddess Hera did not fail to obey. She whipped on the horses, and they flew eagerly on their way between earth and the starry heaven. As far as a man's eyes can see into the haze, when he sits on a high point and looks out over the sparkling sea – such is the vaulting stride of the gods' high-ringing horses. But when they reached the land of Troy and the two rivers that flow in it, at the point where Simoeis and Skamandros join together their streams, there the white-armed goddess Hera pulled in the horses, unyoked them from the chariot, and rolled thick mist round them. And Simoeis sprang a field of ambrosia for them to feed on.

The goddesses walked out stepping like trembling doves, eager to bring aid to the Argive soldiers. They came to the place where the largest number and the best of them had taken their position, packed close round the mighty Diomedes the horse-tamer, like lions who eat raw flesh, or wild boars whose strength is inexhaustible. There the white-armed goddess Hera stood and shouted loud, taking the form of great-hearted Stentor, the bronze-voiced, whose call had the power of fifty other men: 'Shame, you Argives, you sorry disgraces, nothing but show and looks! In the time when godlike Achilleus was coming into the fight, the Trojans would never venture beyond the Dardanian gates, in terror of his mighty spear. But now they are fighting far from their city, right by our hollow ships.'

So speaking she spurred the strength and heart in each of them. The bright-eyed goddess Athene made quickly for the son of Tydeus, and found the king by his horses and chariot, airing the wound that Pandaros' arrow had dealt him. The sweat was chafing him under the broad strap that held his round shield: chafed there, and with his arm aching, he was lifting up the strap and wiping away the dark blood. The goddess put her hand on the horses' yoke and spoke to him: 'Oh, the son that was born to Tydeus is little like his father! Tydeus was a small man in build, but he was a fighter. Even when I forbade him to fight or make any display, when he came with a message to Thebes, a lone Achaian among a crowd of Kadmeians – I had told him to sit quietly at the banquet in the palace – even so with that bold spirit which was always his he challenged the young men of the Kadmeians to a contest, and won every event with ease – such was the help I gave him. But as for you, I stand at your side and protect you, and urge you to fight the Trojans with a will. Yet either the weariness of long labour has come over your body, or perhaps fear has gripped you and taken the heart from you – then you cannot be the child of Tydeus, warrior Oineus' son.'

Strong Diomedes answered her: 'I know you, goddess, daughter of Zeus who holds the aegis: so I will readily tell you, and not hide it from you. No fear or cowardice has gripped me and taken the heart from me, but I am still keeping in mind the instructions you gave me. You would not have me make open fight with the immortal gods, with any of them except Aphrodite, daughter of Zeus: if she entered the fighting, I was to stab her with the sharp bronze. That is why I am now falling back and have ordered all the other Argives to mass round me here – I can see that Ares is mastering the field.'

Then the bright-eyed goddess Athene answered him: 'Diomedes, son of Tydeus, pleasure of my heart, have no fear on that account of Ares or any other of the immortals – such is the help I will give you. Come then, hold your strong-footed horses against Ares first, go close and strike him: do not be afraid of raging Ares, this madman, this masterwork of evil, this many-faced monster, who just now gave his pledge to me and to Hera, saying he would fight against the Trojans and bring aid to the Argives – but now he is siding with the Trojans, and his promises are forgotten.'

So speaking she put a hand to Sthenelos and hauled him out from behind the horses, pushing him to the ground – and he quickly jumped clear. And she, determined goddess, mounted the chariot beside godlike Diomedes: the oak axle creaked loud under the weight, carrying a fearful goddess and the noblest of men. Pallas Athene caught up the whip and the reins, and held the strong-footed horses straight against Ares first of all. He was stripping the enormous Periphas, far the best of the Aitolians, the splendid son of Ochesios. Ares the murderer was stripping him: but Athene put on the helmet of Hades the invisible, so that monstrous Ares should not see her.

When Ares, curse of men, saw godlike Diomedes, he left the enormous Periphas lying on in the spot where his blow had taken the life from him, and strode straight for Diomedes the tamer of horses.

When they had advanced to close range, Ares lunged first with his bronze spear over the yoke and the horses' reins, eager to rob his life. And the bright-eyed goddess Athene caught the spear in her hand and pushed it aside, to waste its thrust above the chariot. Then Diomedes, master of the war-cry, made his attack with his bronze spear: and Pallas Athene leaned on the spear and forced it into the base of Ares' belly, where the skirt-piece was belted. Here, then, Diomedes hit home, and wounded him, and tore through his fine flesh, and pulled the spear out again. And brazen Ares screamed, loud as the shout of nine thousand men or ten thousand men on a battle-field, when they join the clash of war. And the Achaians and Trojans were struck with terror, and trembling came over them, so loud was the scream of Ares the war-glutton.

Like the air which spouts black from the clouds, when the heat is burning and a violent wind blows up, such was the sight to Diomedes, Tydeus' son, as brazen Ares whirled up to the wide heaven wrapped in cloud. Quickly he reached the gods' home, steep Olympos, and sat down beside Zeus the son of Kronos in anguish of heart, and showed him the immortal blood dripping from the wound, and spoke fretfully to him with winged words: 'Father Zeus, are you not angry at the sight of this violence? We gods have always had to endure the most horrible suffering through each other's malice, when we do favours to men. It is you we all blame – you gave birth to the witless girl, this curse, whose mind is always set on mischief. All the rest, all the gods on Olympos, obey your will and every one of us is subject to you. But this one has no criticism from you, in word or action – no, you let her go free, because you yourself gave birth to this ruinous daughter. Just now she set Tydeus' son, proud Diomedes, in raging onslaught against the immortal gods. First he closed with Kypris and stabbed her hand in the wrist, then he even flung himself at me, attacking like a god. But my quick feet carried me away: otherwise I would be lying there suffering long agony among the grim dead, or living on robbed of strength by the bronze spear's blow.'

Then Zeus the cloud-gatherer scowled at him and said: 'You two-faced creature, do not sit here and whine at me. You are the most hateful to me of all the gods that hold Olympos: always your delight is in strife and war and fighting. Your mother Hera has an ungovernable spirit in her, loth to give way, and it is hard for me to bend her will to what I say – so I think it is her instigation that has led to your suffering. But I will not have you in pain for any longer – you are my child, and your mother bore you to me. But if such a plague had been born to any other of the gods, you would long ago have found yourself kept lower than the sons of Ouranos.'

So he spoke, and told Paiëon to heal him. And Paiëon spread pain-killing medicines on him and cured him, since he was not of mortal make. As when fig-juice is added to white milk and rapidly coagulates the liquid, and the milk quickly curdles as it is stirred, so speedy was his healing of raging Ares. Hebe then washed him, and put lovely clothing on him: and he took his seat beside Zeus the son of Kronos, glorying in his splendour.

And the two goddesses returned to great Zeus' house, Hera of Argos and Alalkomenaian Athene, after they had put a stop to the killings of Ares, curse of men.

BOOK 6
HEKTOR IN TROY

So the grim battle of Trojans and Achaians was left to them alone. And the fighting swayed many times this way and that over the plain, as they aimed their bronze-tipped spears at each other, between the streams of Simoeis and Xanthos.

It was Aias, Telamon's son, bulwark of the Achaians, who first broke the Trojan line and brought the light of triumph to his company, striking the man who was the best among the Thracians, Eüssoros' son, Akamas the tall and brave. Casting first, he struck him on the ridge of his horse-plumed helmet, and the bronze point lodged in his forehead, driving in through the bone: and darkness covered over his eyes.

Then Diomedes, master of the war-cry, killed Axylos, son of Teuthras. He lived in well-founded Arisbe, a man rich in substance, and hospitable to all men – his house was by the road, and he would entertain all who passed. But none of them faced Diomedes for him then, and saved him from a miserable death, but he took the life from both of them, Axylos and his lieutenant Kalesios, his charioteer on that day: and both went down to the world below.

Euryalos killed Dresos and Opheltios. Then he went in pursuit of Aisepos and Pedasos, who were borne by the water-nymph Abarbareë to the excellent Boukolion. Boukolion was a son of proud Laomedon, the oldest born, but his mother gave birth to him in secret. He lay with the nymph in love's union while shepherding his flocks, and she conceived and bore him twin sons. And these now had their strength and their bodies' brightness undone by the son of Mekisteus, and he set to stripping the armour from their shoulders.

Astyalos was killed by the staunch fighter Polypoites, and Odysseus killed Pidytes, a man from Perkote, with his bronze spear, and Teukros killed godlike Aretaon. Ableros fell to the shining spear of Antilochos, Nestor's son, and Elatos to Agamemnon, lord of men: he lived in steep Pedasos, by the banks of the lovely stream of Satnioeis. The hero Leïtos caught Phylakos as he ran from him: and Eurypylos cut down Melanthios.

Then Menelaos, master of the war-cry, took Adrestos alive. His pair of horses, bolting in panic across the plain, had tangled in the shoots of a tamarisk and broken off the curved chariot at the end of the pole. They ran on by themselves towards the city, where the others were fleeing terror-struck, and he was tumbled headlong from the car over the wheel, into the dust face down: and Menelaos, son of Atreus, stood over him, holding a long-shadowed spear. Then Adrestos took him by the knees and begged with him: 'Take me alive, son of Atreus, and win a ransom of proper worth. My father is rich, there are many treasures stored in his house, bronze and gold, and iron laboriously worked. My father would give you unlimited ransom from this store, if he learnt that I was alive by the ships of the Achaians.'

So he spoke, and began to have effect on Menelaos' heart within him: and Menelaos was about to give him to his lieutenant to take back to the Achaians' fast ships. But Agamemnon came running to face him, and loudly berated him: 'Menelaos, dear brother, why this concern for men's lives? Did you get the very best treatment from the Trojans in your house? Not one of them must escape stark destruction at our hands, even the boys still carried in their mothers' wombs – not even they must escape, but all be extinguished together, wiped from Ilios without sight or ceremony.'

With these words the hero turned his brother's mind, winning him with right advice. Menelaos pushed the hero Adrestos away from him with his hand, and lord Agamemnon stabbed him in the side. He collapsed on his back, and the son of Atreus braced his foot against his chest and pulled out the ash spear.

Then Nestor called in a great shout to the Argives: 'My friends, Danaan heroes, Ares' men-at-arms: let us have none of you now hanging back in desire for spoils, hoping to return to the ships with as much as you can carry – no, let us be killing men! Then afterwards you can have that too, and go over the plain stripping the bodies of the dead at your leisure.'

So speaking he spurred the strength and heart in each of them. Then soon the Trojans would have fled back into Ilios, driven broken and spiritless before the Achaian warriors, if Helenos, Priam's son and far the best of augurs, had not come up beside Aineias and Hektor and said: 'Aineias and Hektor, it is on you two more than any of the Trojans and Lycians that the burden of battle falls, since in every venture you are the best at both fighting and planning. So make a stand here. Go right through the army and rally the troops outside the gates, before they run on home and throw themselves into the arms of their womenfolk, and bring joy to our enemies. When you have spurred all the ranks to the fight, we will stand our ground here and do battle with the Danaans, for all our great exhaustion – necessity compels us. And you, Hektor, make your way to the city, and then give instructions to your mother and mine. She should gather the old women and go with them to the temple of bright-eyed Athene on the city's height, open the doors of the holy dwelling with the key, and place a robe on the knees of the lovely-haired goddess Athene, choosing the finest and largest robe in her house and the one that she herself delights in most. And she should promise to sacrifice twelve heifers in her temple, yearlings never touched by the goad, if she will take pity on our town and the Trojans' wives and their little children – so she may hold the son of Tydeus away from sacred Ilios, this savage spearman, this powerful creator of panic. I think him the greatest fighter of the Achaians. Not even Achilleus, leader of men, ever struck such fear in us as this, and they say he is son of a goddess: but this man rages beyond measure, and no-one can match his strength.'

So he spoke, and Hektor did not fail to obey his brother. He immediately jumped down to the ground from his chariot with all his armour, and shaking a pair of sharp spears in his grip he ranged all through the army, spurring them to fight and rousing their spirit for grim battle. They rallied and turned to stand against the Achaians: and the Argives gave way and stopped their slaughter, thinking that one of the immortals had come down from the starry heaven to help the Trojans, so strong was their rally. Hektor called with a great shout to the Trojans: 'You high-hearted men of Troy, and you our far-famed allies, be men, my friends, and fill your minds with fighting spirit, while I go to Ilios and tell the old men of the council and our own wives to pray to the gods, and promise them full sacrifices.'

So speaking Hektor of the glinting helmet left them. And as he went the dark leather of the rim that ran round the edge of his bossed shield kept tapping top and bottom, at his ankles and his neck.

Then Glaukos, son of Hippolochos, and Tydeus' son came together into the ground between the two sides, eager for battle. When these two had advanced to close range, Diomedes, master of the war-cry, was first to speak: 'Which of mortal men are you, my friend? I have never seen you before in the battle where men win glory: though now you have shown yourself far superior to all others in your bravery, to stand up to my long-shadowed spear – misery comes to the parents of those who face my strength. But if you are one of the immortals come down from heaven, I would not want to fight against the heavenly gods. Even the son of Dryas, strong Lykourgos, even he lived no long life, for clashing with the heavenly gods. He once chased the nurses of wild Dionysos down from the sacred mountain Nysa. They all scattered their holy wands on the ground, under the blows of murdering Lykourgos' ox-goad: and Dionysos in terror dived into the sea's swell, and Thetis took him to her breast, fearful and trembling hard at the man's threat. Then the gods who live at their ease were angry with Lykourgos, and the son of Kronos struck him blind: and he did not live long after that, hated as he was by all the immortal gods. I would not want either to fight with the blessed gods. But if you are a mortal, of those who eat the crop of plough and field, come closer now, to meet your doomed end the sooner.'

Then Hippolochos' glorious son replied: 'Great-hearted son of Tydeus, why do you ask of my birth? The generation of men is just like that of leaves. The wind scatters one year's leaves on the ground, but the forest burgeons and puts out others, as the season of spring comes round. So it is with men: one generation grows on, and another is passing away. But if you do want to hear of it, and learn the history of my family, it is something that many men know. There is a city, Ephyre, set in the corner of horse-rearing Argos. There lived Sisyphos, who was the most cunning of men, Sisyphos son of Aiolos. He had a son Glaukos, and Glaukos fathered the excellent Bellerophontes. The gods granted Bellerophontes beauty and all that is lovely in manhood. But Proitos intended him harm, and drove him out of the land of the Argives – his was the greater power, since Zeus had subjected Bellerophontes under his kingship. Proitos' wife, godlike Anteia, had become mad with desire to lie with him and make secret love: but the good Bellerophontes had a virtuous heart, and she could not seduce him. She then spoke lyingly to king Proitos: "Die yourself, Proitos, or kill Bellerophontes! He has tried to lie with me in love against my will." So she spoke, and anger took hold of the king at what he had heard. He shrank from killing him – awe of that touched his heart and he could not – but he sent him away to Lycia, and sent with him signs of disastrous meaning, many lethal marks that he wrote in a folded tablet, and told him to show them to his father-in-law, to ensure his death. So Bellerophontes went on his way to Lycia, under the gods' safe speeding. And when he reached Lycia and the stream of Xanthos, the king of broad Lycia honoured him with ready welcome: nine days were given to hospitality, and nine cows slaughtered in sacrifice. But when rosy-fingered dawn appeared on the tenth day, then he began to question him, and asked to see the token that he brought with him from his son-in-law Proitos. Then when his son-in-law's cruel token was in his hands, he first of all told Bellerophontes to kill the Chimaira, a creature none could conquer, born of gods, not of men: she was a lion in front, a snake behind, and a goat in the middle, and her fearful breath was a blast of blazing fire. He killed her, following signs from the gods. Then next he fought against the renowned Solymoi: this, he said, was the hardest battle with men that he ever entered. Then thirdly he slaughtered the Amazons, women the equal of men. And as he returned, the king set another cunning snare for him. He chose the best men from the breadth of Lycia and set them in ambush for him: but they made no return to their homes – all of them were killed by the excellent Bellerophontes. But when the king came to realise that he was a god's noble issue, he kept him there with him, and offered his daughter in marriage, and granted him half of all his royal honours: and the people of Lycia set aside the finest piece of land for him, rich in vineyard and ploughland, to be his own domain. And the king's daughter bore three children to the good Bellerophontes, Isandros and Hippolochos and Laodameia. Zeus the counsellor lay with Laodameia, and she gave birth to Sarpedon, the bronze-armoured warrior. But when even Bellerophontes became hated by all the gods, he went wandering alone over the Aleïan plain, eating out his heart and avoiding the path of men. His son Isandros was killed by Ares the war-glutton, as he fought against the renowned Solymoi: and Laodameia was killed by Artemis in her anger, the goddess of the golden reins. But Hippolochos fathered me, and he is the man I spring from. He sent me to Troy, and gave me constant instructions, always to be bravest and best and excel over others, and not bring disgrace on the stock of my fathers, who were far the best men in Ephyre and in the breadth of Lycia. This is the family and blood I am proud to call mine.'

So he spoke, and Diomedes, master of the war-cry, was overjoyed. He fixed his spear fast in the nourishing earth, then spoke with friendly warmth to the shepherd of the people: 'Well then, you are a guest-friend of mine from far back in our families! Godlike Oineus once entertained the excellent Bellerophontes in his house, and kept him for twenty days: and they also gave each other fine gifts of friendship. Oineus gave a belt brilliant with purple, and Bellerophontes a two-handled cup of gold – I left it in my house when I came to the war.

Tydeus I do not remember, because he left me when I was still small, when the army of the Achaians was destroyed at Thebes. So now you have me as your loyal host in the heart of Argos, and I have you in Lycia, whenever I come to that country. Let us keep away from each other's spears, even in the thick of the fighting. There are many of the Trojans and their famous allies for me to kill, any of them that god sets in my way and my legs can catch: and again many Achaians for you to cut down, all those you can. And let us exchange armour with each other, so the others too can see that we are proud to claim guest-friendship from our fathers' time.'

So they spoke to each other, and they jumped down from their chariots, and took each other's hand and pledged their friendship. Then Zeus son of Kronos took Glaukos' wits away from him: he exchanged with Diomedes son of Tydeus gold armour for bronze, a hundred oxen's worth for nine.

Now when Hektor came to the Skaian gates and the oak tree, the wives and daughters of the Trojans came running to surround him, asking after their sons and brothers and kinsmen and husbands. He told each one of them to pray to the gods: but sorrow was there in store for many.

Hektor then came to the beautiful house of Priam, furnished with porticoes of polished stone. In it there were fifty rooms of polished stone, built close by each other: there Priam's sons slept beside the wives of their marriage. His daughters' rooms were facing on the opposite side within the courtyard, twelve roofed rooms of polished stone, built close by each other: there Priam's sons-in-law slept beside their honoured wives. At the house his generous mother met him, coming in with Laodike, the most beautiful of her daughters. She took his hand, and spoke to him: 'Child, why have you left the hard battle and come here? The sons of the Achaians – a curse on their name! – must be wearing you down with their fighting right up to the city, and your heart has moved you to come here and hold up your hands in prayer to Zeus from the city's height. But wait for me to bring you some honey-sweet wine, so that you can first pour a libation to father Zeus and the other immortals, and then enjoy it yourself, if you will drink. When a man is tired wine is a great restorer of strength, and you have tired yourself in the defence of your kinsmen.'

Then great Hektor of the glinting helmet answered her: 'Do not offer me cheering wine, dear mother, or you may sap the strength from my limbs and make me lose my courage for the fight. My hands are unwashed, and I am ashamed to pour out gleaming wine to Zeus like this: and no-one can offer prayers to the son of Kronos, lord of the dark clouds, all spattered with blood and filth. No, you must go to the temple of Athene, goddess of spoil: bring offerings, and gather the old women with you. And take a robe, the finest and largest in your house and the one that you yourself delight in most, and place it on the knees of the lovely-haired goddess Athene. And promise to sacrifice twelve heifers in her temple, yearlings never touched by the goad, if she will take pity on our town and the Trojans' wives and their little children – if she will hold the son of Tydeus away from sacred Ilios, this savage spearman, this powerful creator of panic. So you go to the temple of Athene, goddess of spoil, and I will go after Paris to call him back – if he will listen to what I say. Oh, that the earth would gape under him where he stands! It was a great curse the Olympian was rearing, when he let him grow, a curse to the Trojans and to great-hearted Priam and his children. If I could see that man dead and gone to Hades, I could say my heart had forgotten its misery.'

So he spoke, and his mother went into the house and gave her instructions to the serving-women: and they went through the city gathering the old women. She herself went down into the sweet-smelling storeroom where her robes were kept – the intricate work of Sidonian women, who had been brought from Sidon by godlike Alexandros himself, as he sailed over the breadth of the sea on that same voyage which carried back Helen, daughter of a noble house. Hekabe lifted out one of the robes and took it as a gift for Athene – it was the finest in its woven decoration and the largest, gleaming like a star, and it lay beneath all the others. She then went on her way, and many old women flocked with her.

When they came to the temple of Athene on the city's height, Theano opened the doors for them, the beautiful daughter of Kisseus, and wife of Antenor the horse-tamer: the Trojans had made her priestess of Athene. All the women lifted up their hands with wailing to Athene, and beautiful Theano took the robe and placed it on the knees of the lovely-haired goddess Athene, then spoke in prayer to the daughter of great Zeus: 'Lady Athene, guardian of our city, queen among goddesses, break now Diomedes' spear, and grant that the man himself be brought down on his face in front of the Skaian gates – so that we may sacrifice here and now twelve heifers in your temple, yearlings never touched by the goad, if you will take pity on our town and the Trojans' wives and their little children.'

Such was her prayer, but Pallas Athene shook her head in refusal.

Now while the women were making their prayers to the daughter of great Zeus, Hektor had gone to Alexandros' house – a beautiful house, that he had built himself together with the men who at that time were the finest master-builders in all the fertile land of Troy, and they had made him a bedroom and a hall and courtyard, close to Priam and Hektor, on the city's height. Hektor, loved of Zeus, entered the house, and in his hand he held a spear eleven cubits in length – the spear's bronze point gleamed before him, and a gold band ringed it round. He found Alexandros in the bedroom, fussing over his exquisite armour, the shield and the corselet, and handling his curved bow. And Argive Helen was sitting there among her servant-women and supervising her maids' magnificent handcraft.

When Hektor saw him, he attacked him with shaming words: 'Strange man! This resentment you have conceived in your heart does you no honour. Our people are dying, fighting right by the city and its steep wall – and it is because of you that the clamour of battle is blazing round this city. You would quarrel with any other man you saw hanging back from the hateful fighting. Up then, or the city will soon be burning with fire to destroy it.'

Then godlike Alexandros said to him: 'Hektor, your charge is not unfair, and there is justice in it, so I will tell you the truth, and you mark what I say and listen to me. It is not so much anger or resentment at the Trojans that has kept me sitting in my room, but I wanted to give way to my distress. But just now my wife talked me round with gentle persuasion and urged me back to war: and I think that would be best myself – victory switches from man to man. So come now, wait for me while I put on the armour of war: or you go on, and I shall follow – I think I shall catch you.'

So he spoke, and Hektor of the glinting helmet made no answer. But Helen spoke softly to him: 'My brother – brother of the bitch, the scheming horrible creature that I am! How I wish that on that first day when my mother bore me some vile storm-wind had taken me and whirled me up to the mountains or into the swell of the sounding sea, where the waves would have washed me away before all this could happen. But since the gods have decreed that these miseries must be so, then I wish I had been the wife of a better man than this, one who had sense for men's outrage and all the shaming things they say. But this one has no wits in his head now, and never will in the future: and I think he will meet the reward for that. But come now, come in, brother, and sit here on this chair – since it is your mind more than any that the war's work besets, all for the sake of the bitch that I am and the blind folly of Alexandros. On us two Zeus has set a doom of misery, so that in time to come we can be themes of song for men of future generations.'

Then great Hektor of the glinting helmet answered her: 'Do not ask me to sit, Helen, for all your kindness – you will not persuade me. My heart is eager now to bring help to the Trojans, who miss me greatly when I am away from them. But you can rouse this one to action, and he should hurry himself too, so he can catch me while I am still inside the city. I am going now to my own home, to see my servants and my dear wife and baby son. I cannot know whether I shall ever return again and come back to them, or it is now that the gods bring me down at the hands of the Achaians.'

So speaking Hektor of the glinting helmet left her. He went straight to his own pleasant house, but did not find white-armed Andromache at home – she had gone with her child and a fine-dressed maid and was standing on the tower in wailing and lamentation. When Hektor found that his excellent wife was not at home, he went and stood at the door-way and said to his maids: 'Come, maids, tell me truly. Where has white-armed Andromache gone from the house? Has she gone to one of my sisters or my brothers' fine-dressed wives, or to Athene's temple, where the other lovely-haired women of Troy are offering appeasement to the fearful goddess?'

His busy housekeeper replied: 'Hektor, you ask me to tell you the truth. She has not gone to any of your sisters or your brothers' fine-dressed wives, nor to Athene's temple, where the other lovely-haired women of Troy are offering appeasement to the fearful goddess. But she has gone to the great tower of Ilios, because she had heard that the Trojans were failing, and the Achaians winning a great victory. So she has gone running to the wall, like a woman in frenzy: and the nurse is with her, carrying the baby.'

This is what the housekeeper said, and Hektor ran from his house back along the way he had come through the well-laid streets of Troy. When he had crossed the great city and reached the Skaian gates, where he would make his way out to the plain, there came running to meet him his dowered wife Andromache, daughter of great-hearted Eëtion – Eëtion, who had lived under wooded Plakos, in Thebe-under-Plakos, ruling over his people the Kilikes: he it was whose daughter was wife to Hektor of the bronze helmet. She then came up to him, and with her there went a maid carrying at her breast their innocent child, no more than a baby, Hektor's only beloved son, shining lovely as a star. Hektor's name for him was Skamandrios, but the others called him Astyanax, Lord of the City, because Hektor was Ilios' sole protection. Hektor looked at his son and smiled in silence. Andromache came close to him with her tears falling, and took his hand and spoke to him: 'Poor dear man, your own brave spirit will destroy you, and you have no pity for your baby son and for me your doomed wife, who will soon be your widow. Soon the Achaians will mass an attack on you and kill you. And for me then, when I lose you, it would be better to sink down under the earth. There will be no other comfort left for me, when you meet your fate, only misery – I have no father now or honoured mother. My father was killed by godlike Achilleus, when he sacked Thebe with its high gates, the Kilikes' lovely town. He killed Eëtion, but did not strip him of his arms – respect touched his heart and he could not – but he burnt him with his crafted armour, and piled a barrow over him: round it elms grow, planted there by the nymphs of the mountains, daughters of Zeus who holds the aegis. The seven brothers I had in my home, all of them went down to Hades on the same one day: all were killed by swift-footed godlike Achilleus, as they tended our shambling cattle and our white-fleeced sheep. As for my mother, who was queen under wooded Plakos, Achilleus brought her here with all our other goods, but then released her for a countless ransom, and she died in her father's house, struck down by Artemis the archer-goddess. But Hektor, you are father and honoured mother and brother to me, as well as my strong husband. Please, feel pity for us, stay here on the battlements, so you do not make an orphan of your child and your wife a widow. Have the army take up position by the fig-tree, where the city is most open to assault and the wall can be scaled. Three times their leading fighters have come and made an attempt there, under the two Aiantes and the renowned Idomeneus, and under the sons of Atreus and the brave son of Tydeus. Either someone skilled in prophecies must have told them, or it may be their own hearts' prompting.'

Then great Hektor of the glinting helmet answered her: 'Wife, all that you say is surely in my mind also. But I would feel terrible shame before the men of Troy and the women of Troy with their trailing dresses, if like a coward I skulk away from the fighting. Nor is that what my own heart urges, because I have learnt always to be brave and to fight in the forefront of the Trojans, winning great glory for my father and for myself. One thing I know well in my heart and in my mind: the day will come when sacred Ilios shall be destroyed, and Priam, and the people of Priam of the fine ash spear. But the pain I feel for the suffering to come is less for the people of Troy, less even for Hekabe and king Priam and my brothers, the many brave brothers who will fall in the dust at the hands of our enemies, than my pain for you, when one of the bronze-clad Achaians carries you away in tears and takes away the day of your freedom: and you will live in Argos, weaving at the loom at another woman's command, and carrying water from a foreign spring, from Messeïs or Hypereia, much against your will, but compulsion will lie harsh upon you. And someone seeing you with your tears falling will say: "This is the wife of Hektor, who was always the best warrior of the horse-taming Trojans, when they were fighting over Ilios." That is what they will say: and for you there will be renewed misery, that you have lost such a husband to protect you from the day of slavery. But may I be dead and the heaped earth cover me, before I hear your screams and the sound of you being dragged away.'

So speaking glorious Hektor reached out to take his son. But the child shrank back crying against the breast of his girdled nurse, terrified at the sight of his own father, frightened by the bronze and the crest of horse-hair, as he saw it nodding dreadfully from the top of the helmet. His dear father and his honoured mother laughed aloud at this, and glorious Hektor took the helmet straight from his head and laid it gleaming bright on the ground. Then he kissed his dear son and dandled him in his arms, and said in prayer to Zeus and the other gods: 'Zeus and you other gods, grant that this my son may become, as I have been, preeminent among the Trojans, as strong and brave as I, and may he rule in strength over Ilios. And let people say, as he returns from the fighting: "This man is better by far than his father." May he carry home the bloody spoils of the enemy he has killed, and bring joy to his mother's heart.'

So speaking he placed his son in his dear wife's arms. She took him to her scented breast, smiling with tears in her eyes. Her husband saw the tears and was moved to pity. He stroked her with his hand, and spoke to her, saying: 'Poor wife, please do not let your heart be too distressed. No man will send me down to Hades before my fated time – and fate, I tell you, is something no man is ever freed from, whether brave man or coward, from the first moment of his birth. No, go back to the house and see to your own work, the loom and the distaff, and tell your maids to set about their tasks. War will be the men's concern, all the men whose homeland is Ilios, and mine above all.'

So speaking glorious Hektor took up his helmet with the horse-hair crest. And his dear wife went back towards their home, turning often as she went, the heavy tears falling. Soon she came to the pleasant house of Hektor the killer of men, and all the many servant-women she found inside she set to lamentation. So they mourned Hektor, while he still lived, in his own house: because they thought he would never again return from the fighting, and escape the fury of the Achaians' hands.

And Paris did not dally long in his high house, but once he had put on his glorious armour of intricate bronze, he dashed through the city, sure of the speed of his legs. As when some stalled horse who has fed full at the manger breaks his halter and gallops thudding across the plain, eager for his usual bathe in the lovely flow of a river, and glorying as he runs. He holds his head high, and the mane streams back along his shoulders: sure of his own magnificence, his legs carry him lightly to the haunts where the mares are at pasture. So Paris, son of Priam, came down from the height of Pergamos, bright in his armour like the beaming sun, and laughing as he came, his quick legs carrying him on. Then he soon came up with godlike Hektor, his brother, just as he was about to turn from the spot where he talked with his wife. Godlike Alexandros spoke first to him: 'Brother, you are in a hurry, and I am sure I must have delayed you with my dawdling, and not coming on time as you told me.'

Then Hektor of the glinting helmet answered him: 'Strange man! No-one in all fairness could belittle your success in battle, as you are a brave fighter. But you deliberately hang back and refuse to fight: and my heart within me is pained at that, when I hear shaming things said of you by the Trojans, who have much hardship to endure on your account. Let us be going, then. We will make all this good later, if ever Zeus grants that we may set up in our houses the feasting-bowl of freedom, in thanks to the heavenly ever-living gods, when we have driven the well-greaved Achaians out of Troy.'

BOOK 7
DUEL OF HEKTOR AND AIAS

So speaking glorious Hektor rushed out through the gates, and with him went Alexandros his brother: both of their hearts were eager to do battle and join the fighting. Like a breeze that god sends to sailors in their need, when they are worn out with striking their polished oars into the sea, and their bodies are limp with exhaustion, this was how these two appeared to the Trojans in their need.

Then both took their man. Alexandros killed the son of king Areïthoös, Menesthios who lived in Arne, born to Areïthoös the mace-man and ox-eyed Phylomedousa. And Hektor with his sharp spear hit Eïoneus in the neck, under his helmet's strong bronze rim, and his body went slack. And Glaukos, Hippolochos' son, leader of the men of Lycia, hit Iphinoös, son of Dexios, with a spear-cast in the battle's fury. He struck him as he jumped up behind his fast horses, in the shoulder: and he fell to the ground from his chariot, and his body went slack.

Now when the bright-eyed goddess Athene saw them destroying the Argives in the battle's fury, she came darting down from the peaks of Olympos to sacred Ilios: and Apollo, looking out from Pergamos, moved to meet her, as his wish was victory for the Trojans. These two then met each other by the oak-tree. Lord Apollo, son of Zeus, spoke first to Athene: 'What is your interest this time, daughter of great Zeus, in coming down from Olympos at your great heart's prompting? Is it to turn the fortune of battle and give victory to the Danaans? – because you have no pity for the Trojans when they are destroyed. Far better would be to do as I suggest. For the moment let us put a stop to the fighting and the conflict, for this day – they will fight on afterwards, until they reach their goal in Ilios, since that is the heart's desire of you goddesses, the sacking of this town.'

Then the bright-eyed goddess Athene said to him: 'So be it, far-worker. That was my thought too in coming down from Olympos to visit the Trojans and Achaians. Come then, how do you want to put an end to the men's fighting?'

Then lord Apollo, son of Zeus, said to her: 'Let us rouse the strong spirit in Hektor the tamer of horses, and see whether perhaps he will challenge one of the Danaans to face him alone and fight him one to one in grim combat: and then the bronze-greaved Achaians' pride will be touched, and they will send out someone on his own to do battle with godlike Hektor.'

So he spoke, and the bright-eyed goddess Athene did not fail to obey. And Helenos, Priam's dear son, had understood their plan in his mind, the plan the gods had settled on as they conferred. He came and stood by Hektor, and said to him: 'Hektor, son of Priam, Zeus' equal in your mind's resource, do something now that I tell you, as I am your brother. Make the rest of the Trojans and all the Achaians sit down, and you challenge the best of the Achaians to fight you one to one in grim combat. It is not yet the fated time for you to die and meet your doom. I have heard the talk of the ever-living gods, and that is what they say.'

So he spoke, and Hektor then was delighted at what he heard. He stepped into the open, and kept back the Trojan lines, holding his spear at the middle: and they all settled on the ground. Agamemnon likewise made the well-greaved Achaians sit down. And Athene and Apollo, god of the silver bow, settled down too, in the form of vultures, on a tall oak-tree sacred to father Zeus who holds the aegis, taking their pleasure in the doings of men. The ranks of men sat there packed close in a shiver of shields and helmets and spears. Like the shiver which spreads over the sea at the west wind's fresh rising, and the water darkens under it, such were the ranks of the Achaians and Trojans as they sat in the plain. Hektor then spoke out to both sides: 'Listen to me, Trojans and well-greaved Achaians, so I can tell you what my heart within me urges. The oaths we made were not given fulfilment by Zeus who sits on high. Rather he plans misery for both our peoples and is working it on us until either you capture the strong walls of Troy or are yourselves beaten down beside your seafaring ships. Now you have among you the leading men of all the Achaians. Let the one whose heart urges him to fight me come out here now in front of all to be your champion against godlike Hektor. And I say this, and let Zeus be our witness to it. If he kills me with the long-pointed bronze, let him strip my armour and take it to the hollow ships, but he must give my body back to my home, so that the Trojans and the wives of the Trojans can give me in death my due rite of burning. And if I kill him, and Apollo grants my prayer, I shall strip his armour and carry it back to sacred Ilios, and hang it in dedication at the temple of Apollo the far-shooter, but his body I shall return to the well-benched ships, so that the long-haired Achaians can give him the rites of burial and heap a mound for him by the broad Hellespont. And people will say, even men of generations not yet born, as they sail by over the sparkling sea in their many-benched ships: "This is the mound of a man who died long ago. He was the greatest of men, and glorious Hektor killed him." That is what they will say: and my glory will never die.'

So he spoke, and the Achaians all stayed silent. They were ashamed to refuse, but afraid to accept. But then finally Menelaos stood up and spoke among them, scorning them to shame, and groaning in the sorrow of his heart: 'Oh you braggarts, mere women of Achaia now, no longer men! Oh, this will be ruin and disgrace indeed, the horror of horrors, if not one of the Danaans will now go to face Hektor. Well, may you all rot into water and earth, each one of you who sits on here in stark ignominy, spiritless. I myself shall arm against this man – the threads of victory are not in our hands, they are held above, among the immortal gods.'

So speaking he put on his fine armour. And then, Menelaos, there would have been revealed the ending of your life at Hektor's hands, since he was much the stronger man, if the kings of the Achaians had not leapt up and held you, and Agamemnon himself, the wide-ruling son of Atreus, not taken you by the right hand and spoken to you, saying: 'You are mad, my lord Menelaos, and there is no call for this madness. Bear with it for all your distress, and do not try to fight a rival's battle with a better man than you, Hektor son of Priam, a man that others shrink from. Even Achilleus shudders to meet this man in the fighting where men win glory, and he is a much better man than you. No, you go now and sit with your band of companions, and the Achaians will put up another champion against this man. Even if he is without fear and cannot have his fill of fighting, I think he will be right glad to take his rest, if he comes out alive from the grim conflict of furious battle.'

With these words the hero turned his brother's mind, winning him with right advice, and he was persuaded. So then Menelaos' servants joyfully took the armour from his shoulders. But Nestor stood up then and spoke out to the Argives: 'Oh, shame! Great sorrow is coming to the land of Achaia! How the old horseman Peleus would groan aloud, the great counsellor and speaker of the Myrmidons! A man who once took great joy in questioning me when I was in his house, asking me for the family and birth of every Argive. If he now heard that these men, every one of them, were cowering in fear before Hektor, he would lift up his hands in ceaseless prayer to the immortals that his spirit should leave his body and sink down into Hades. Oh, father Zeus and Athene and Apollo, if only I were young as I was at the battle by the fast water of Keladon, when the men of Pylos had gathered and were fighting the Arcadian spearmen, by the walls of Pheia, along the stream of Iardanos. Then Ereuthalion stood up as their challenger, a man like a god, wearing on his shoulders the armour of king Areïthoös, the godlike Areïthoös, whom men and girdled women used to call by the name Mace-man – because his fighting was not done with bow or long spear, but he used to smash through the ranks of men with a club made of iron. He was killed by Lykourgos – by cunning, not by strength – in a narrow pathway, where his iron club could not keep the destruction from him: before he could wield it Lykourgos struck first, and pinned him through the middle with his spear, and he crashed to the earth on his back and lay still. Lykourgos stripped his armour, which brazen Ares had given him, and thereafter used to wear it himself into the fray of battle. Then when Lykourgos was growing old in his house, he gave it to Ereuthalion, his loyal attendant, for him to wear. This was the armour he had on him when he challenged all of our leading men. They began to tremble with terror, and not one of them had the courage. But my hardy spirit in its boldness prompted me to do battle with him – and I was the youngest in birth of all of them. And I did fight him, and Athene granted me my triumph. That was the tallest and mightiest man I ever killed – he was a giant, and lay there sprawled hugely this way and that. Would that I were as young now, and the power was still in me! Then Hektor of the glinting helmet would soon meet his battle. But some of you are the leading men of all the Achaians, and not even you have any will or desire to go against Hektor.'

So the old man berated them, and nine men in all stood forward. Far the first to rise was Agamemnon, lord of men, then Tydeus' son strong Diomedes rose after him, then the two Aiantes, clothed in fighting spirit, then Idomeneus and Idomeneus' follower Meriones, the equal of the murdering war-god, then Eurypylos, Euaimon's splendid son: and Thoas rose up, Andraimon's son, and godlike Odysseus. All these were ready to do battle with godlike Hektor. Then Nestor the Gerenian horseman spoke to them once more: 'Now you must shake lots, thoroughly, to see who is chosen. This man will bring gladness to the well-greaved Achaians, and gladness too to his own heart, if he comes out alive from the grim combat of furious battle.'

So he spoke, and each man put his mark on a lot, and dropped it into the helmet of Agamemnon, son of Atreus. And the people made their prayers, holding up their hands to the gods. And this is what they would say, looking up into the broad heaven: 'Father Zeus, let Aias win the lot, or Tydeus' son, or the king of golden Mykene himself.'

So they spoke, and the Gerenian horseman Nestor shook the helmet, and out jumped the lot the men were all hoping for, Aias'. A herald carried it all through the gathering, and showed it, moving from left to right, to all the leading men of the Achaians. And each one of them in turn did not recognise it and denied it. But when the herald came, as he carried it all through the gathering, to the one who had put his mark on it and dropped it into the helmet, glorious Aias, he put out his hand, and the herald stood in front of him and placed the lot in his hand: he saw the mark on the lot and recognised it, and felt joy in his heart. Then he threw the lot to the ground at his feet, and said: 'Yes, friends, the lot is mine, and I am glad in my own heart, as I think I shall have the victory over godlike Hektor. Come then, while I put on the armour of battle, you make your prayers to lord Zeus, son of Kronos, but pray quietly, to yourselves, so the Trojans cannot hear – or no, pray out loud, since there is no-one we fear in any case. No man is going to force his will against mine and drive me from the field by strength, nor by fighting skill either, since I hope it is not quite such a greenhorn that I was born and reared in Salamis.'

So he spoke, and they made their prayers to lord Zeus, son of Kronos. And this is what they would say, looking up into the broad heaven: 'Father Zeus, ruling from Ida's height, greatest and most glorious, give Aias the victory and the bright success of his prayer. But if you love Hektor too, and care for him, grant equal strength to both, and equal glory.'

So they spoke, and Aias began to arm himself in gleaming bronze. And when he had clothed his body in all its armour, he set out then like monstrous Ares going out to war, when he goes to attend the battle of men whom the son of Kronos has set to fighting in the fury of a quarrel that eats their hearts. Such was the monstrous Aias, the bulwark of the Achaians, as he rose to battle, and his face bristled in a grim smile: he went on, his legs striding huge beneath him, gripping a long-shadowed spear. The Argives were joyful as they watched him, but fearful trembling came over every Trojan's body, and Hektor's own heart knocked in his breast. But there was no chance now of shrinking back or retreating into the mass of the army, since it was he in his eagerness for battle who had made the challenge. Aias came close carrying a shield like a tower, made of bronze and seven ox-hides, the work of Tychios' labour, who was far the best of the workers in leather and had his home in Hyle. He had made him a glinting shield with seven layers of hide from full-grown bulls, and had beaten over it an eighth layer of bronze. Carrying this shield in front of his chest Telamonian Aias took his stand right close to Hektor, and warned him with a threat: 'Hektor, now you are going to find out for certain, one man against one, what sort of leaders the Danaans too have among them, even after lion-hearted Achilleus, the breaker of men. Achilleus is keeping by his beaked seafaring ships in his fury at Agamemnon, shepherd of the people – but in the rest of us there are men good enough to stand up to you, and many of them. So you start the fighting and the combat.'

Then great Hektor of the glinting helmet said to him: 'Aias, royal son of Telamon, leader of your people, do not try to frighten me as if I were some feeble child or a woman without knowledge of war's work. No, I know about fighting and the killing of men well enough. I know how to swing the tanned ox-hide of my shield to the right, I know how to swing it to the left – that I call true shield-fighting. I know how to charge into the fury of speeding chariots. I know the steps of Ares' deadly dance in the close fighting. But on your guard now – great man that you are, I do not want to hit you with a sneaking shot, with an eye for my chance, but in open fight, like this, if this strikes home.'

So he spoke, and steadying his long-shadowed spear he let it fly, and he hit Aias' fearful shield of seven ox-hides on the very edge of the bronze that was its eighth layer. Through six layers the bronze head tore on unwearied, but the seventh ox-hide held it. Then after him royal Aias let fly his long-shadowed spear, and hit the even circle of the son of Priam's shield. Through the bright shield the strong spear went, and on through the worked corselet, forcing its way: pushing straight on it tore through the tunic at his side – but he swerved away and escaped black doom. Both of them pulled out the long spears with both hands, then flung themselves on each other like lions who eat raw flesh, or wild boars, whose strength is inexhaustible. Then Priam's son stabbed with his spear at the centre of the shield, but the spear's bronze did not break through, and its point was turned. Aias leapt on him and speared his shield. The spear went right on through, and slammed him back in his onslaught: it reached on to cut his neck, and the dark blood welled out. Yet even so Hektor of the glinting helmet would not leave off fighting, but he stepped back and picked up in his massive hand a stone that was lying on the plain, a black stone, huge and jagged: with this he hit Aias' fearful shield of seven ox-hides right in the middle, on the boss, and the bronze rang out loud. Then Aias after him took up a much larger stone, swung it round and hurled it, forcing immense power into the throw: and the blow from the rock like a mill-stone smashed the shield in on him, and took the strength from his knees. He was flung sprawled on his back, the shield rammed down over him – but Apollo quickly set him on his feet. And now they were ready to strike at each other with swords, hand to hand, if the heralds, messengers of Zeus and of men, had not intervened, one from the Trojans and one from the bronze-clad Achaians, Idaios and Talthybios, wise men both. They held their staves between the two, and the herald Idaios spoke to them in the wisdom of his thinking: 'Stop your fighting now, dear children – no more battle. Zeus the cloud-gatherer has love for both of you, and both are fine fighters – we all know this. And night is coming on now. It is good to give way to the night.'

Then Aias son of Telamon answered him: 'Idaios, you should ask Hektor to say the word on this – it was he who in his eagerness for battle made the challenge to all our leading men. Let him speak first: and I will gladly follow his choice.'

Then great Hektor of the glinting helmet said to him: 'Aias, there is no doubt that god has granted you great size and strength and intelligence, and you excel the Achaians in power with the spear – so let us now stop our fighting and the conflict for this day. We shall fight on afterwards, until god settles our issue and gives one side the victory. And night is coming on now. It is good to give way to the night, so that you can bring gladness to all the Achaians by your ships, and most of all to your kinsmen and companions: and I shall bring gladness throughout the great city of king Priam to the men of Troy and the women of Troy with their trailing dresses, who will gather in holy procession with vows of thanksgiving for my sake. But come, let us both give each other glorious gifts, so that people will say, both Achaians and Trojans: "These two fought together in rivalry that ate at their hearts, and then when they parted they were joined in friendship." '

So speaking he fetched a sword with a silver-nailed hilt and gave it to Aias, together with its sheath and baldric of well-cut leather: and Aias gave him a belt brilliant with purple. And so they parted. Aias went back to the Achaian army, and Hektor back to the hubbub of the Trojan throng – they were overjoyed when they saw him walking alive and unharmed towards them, escaped from the fury of Aias' invincible hands: and they escorted him to the city, hardly believing that he was safe. And on the other side the well-greaved Achaians escorted Aias to godlike Agamemnon, with the joy of victory on him.

When they were gathered inside the son of Atreus' hut, Agamemnon lord of men sacrificed among them a male ox, five years old, to the almighty son of Kronos. They flayed it and prepared the carcass, and jointed the whole animal. Then they chopped it deftly into pieces and threaded them on spits, roasted them carefully, and then drew all the meat off. When they had finished their work and prepared the meal they set to eating, and no man's desire went without an equal share in the feast: and the hero son of Atreus, wide-ruling Agamemnon, honoured Aias with the whole length of the chine. When they had put away their desire for eating and drinking, the old man Nestor first of all began to weave the web of his thoughts before them – his advice had proved best at earlier times too. In all good will he spoke and addressed the company: 'Son of Atreus and you other leading men of all the Achaians, many long-haired Achaians have been killed, and their dark blood now lies shed by fierce Ares along the lovely stream of Skamandros, and their souls gone down to Hades. Therefore at dawn you should put a stop to the Achaians' fighting, and we should gather together to wheel the bodies back here with oxen and mules: and then let us burn them a little way off from the ships, so that we can all take a man's bones back home to his children, when we return again to our native land. And let us pile a single funeral mound by the pyre, a common grave for all stretching back from the plain: and from it let us quickly build a high towered wall, as a defence for us and our ships, and let us make close-fitting gates in the wall, so that there is room for chariots to drive through them. And close outside it we should dig a deep ditch all the way round, which could keep back chariots and men, should the proud Trojans' fighting ever press hard on us.'

So he spoke, and all the kings applauded his proposal. And the Trojans also held an assembly in Ilios, on the city's height, meeting in fear and confusion by the doors of Priam's house. The first to speak was Antenor in his wisdom: 'Listen to me, Trojans and Dardanians and allies, so I can tell you what my heart within me urges. Come now, let us hand over Argive Helen and all her possessions with her to the sons of Atreus, for them to take away. We are fighting now with our sworn oaths broken: so I can see no good coming for us, unless we act as I say.'

So speaking Antenor sat down. Then there stood up godlike Alexandros, husband of lovely-haired Helen, and he spoke winged words in answer: 'Antenor, what you say now is not to my liking. You are capable of conceiving better advice than this. But if this is a serious proposal you are making, then the very gods themselves have destroyed your wits. I will speak out now to the horse-taming men of Troy: I refuse, absolutely – I will not give back my wife. But I am prepared to give up all the possessions I brought from Argos to our house, and add more of my own.'

So speaking Alexandros sat down. Then there stood up Priam, of Dardanos' line, the gods' equal in his wisdom. In all good will he spoke and addressed the assembly: 'Listen to me, Trojans and Dardanians and allies, so I can tell you what my heart within me urges. Now you should take your supper in the city, as before: remember to set guards, and every one of you stay awake. Then in the morning let Idaios go to the hollow ships, to tell the sons of Atreus, Agamemnon and Menelaos, the offer made by Alexandros, the man who gave rise to our quarrel. And he should make a further proposal of good sense, asking if they will be willing to stop the grim clash of war until we have burned our dead. We shall fight on afterwards, until god settles our issue and gives one side the victory.'

So he spoke, and they listened well and agreed: then they took their supper at their posts throughout the army. In the morning Idaios went to the hollow ships. He found the Danaans, Ares' men-at-arms, in assembly by the stern of Agamemnon's ship. The loud-voiced herald took his position at their centre and spoke to them: 'Son of Atreus and you other leading men of all the Achaians, Priam and the other proud Trojans have ordered me to tell you, if it should be to your liking and pleasure, the offer made by Alexandros, the man who gave rise to our quarrel. The possessions that Alexandros brought with him in his hollow ships to Troy – how we wish he had died before that! – he is prepared to give back in all their number and add yet more of his own. But as for the wife of glorious Menelaos' marriage, he says he will not give her back – though the Trojans certainly urge him to do so. And they told me to make this further proposal, asking if you will be willing to stop the grim clash of war until we have burned our dead. We shall fight on afterwards, until god settles our issue and gives one side the victory.'

So he spoke, and they all stayed silent. But then finally Diomedes, master of the war-cry, spoke out to them: 'Let no-one now accept possessions from Alexandros, nor Helen either. Even a very fool can see that now the threads of death are fastened on the Trojans.'

So he spoke, and all the sons of the Achaians roared their approval, delighted at the speech of Diomedes the horse-tamer. And then lord Agamemnon spoke to Idaios: 'Idaios, you hear for yourself what the Achaians say, what answer they give you: and my pleasure is the same. As for the burning of the dead, I make no objection. There can be no grudging the bodies of the dead their swift appeasement by the fire, once they have died. Let Zeus, loud-thundering husband of Hera, be witness of our oaths.'

So speaking he held up his sceptre for all the gods to see, and Idaios went back on his way to sacred Ilios. The Trojans and Dardanians were sitting in assembly, all gathered together waiting for Idaios to return. He came in and took position in their centre, and told them his message: and they made hasty preparations for the two tasks, to bring in the dead, and others to go for firewood. And the Argives on the other side hurried out from their well-benched ships to bring in the dead, and others to go for firewood.

The sun then was just beginning to touch the fields, rising from the gentle flow of Ocean's deep stream and climbing up to the sky, when the two sides met each other. Then it was hard for them to recognise the individual dead: but they washed away the clotted blood with water, and lifted them on to wagons with warm tears falling. And great Priam would not let the Trojans cry aloud – so in silence they kept heaping the bodies on the pyre in anguish of heart, and when they had burnt them in the fire they went back to sacred Ilios. And in the same way on the other side the well-greaved Achaians kept heaping the bodies on the pyre in anguish of heart, and when they had burnt them in the fire they went back to the hollow ships.

When it was not yet dawn the next day, but still twilit darkness, a chosen company of the Achaians rose and went to the pyre. Then by it they made a single funeral mound, a common grave for all stretching back from the plain, and from that they built a wall with high towers, as a defence for them and their ships: and they made close-fitting gates in the wall, so that there could be room for chariots to drive through them. And outside close by it they dug a deep ditch, large and wide, and fixed stakes in it.

So the long-haired Achaians laboured on. And the gods were sitting beside Zeus, the lord of the lightning, and looking on at the great work built by the bronze-clad Achaians. Poseidon the earthshaker was the first of them to speak: 'Father Zeus, is there now any mortal on the limitless earth who will still declare his mind and intention to the immortals? Do you not see this further act by the long-haired Achaians? They have built a wall to defend their ships, and drawn a ditch along its length, without offering splendid hecatombs to the gods. The fame of this wall will reach as far as the dawn spreads her light: and they will forget the wall that I and Phoibos Apollo laboured to build for the hero Laomedon.'

Zeus the cloud-gatherer answered him in vexation: 'Shame on you, mighty Earthshaker, for what you are saying! Some other god might feel fear for this contrivance, some god much feebler than you in strength of hand and power. It is your fame that will reach as far as the dawn spreads her light. Look now – when the long-haired Achaians have gone back again in their ships to their own dear country, you break down the wall and sweep it all into the sea, and bury the whole wide shore again in sand, so that you can see the Achaians' great wall reduced to nothing.'

Such were their words to each other. And the sun set, and the Achaians' work was done. Then they slaughtered oxen in their huts and took their supper. And ships had come from Lemnos bringing wine, many of them, sent there by Iason's son Euneos, borne by Hypsipyle to Iason, shepherd of the people. The son of Iason had given a special cargo of wine, a thousand measures, for the sons of Atreus, Agamemnon and Menelaos. From these ships the long-haired Achaians bought their wine. Some paid in bronze, some in gleaming iron, some in hides, some in live oxen, some in slaves: and they made a generous feast. Then all night long there was feasting for the long-haired Achaians, and for the Trojans and their allies throughout the city. And all night long Zeus the counsellor planned evil for them, thundering fearfully. Terror took its pale grip on them, and their wine flowed from their cups to the ground – no man dared drink until he had poured a libation to the almighty son of Kronos. Then they went to their beds and took the benison of sleep.

BOOK 8
TROJAN SUCCESS

Now Dawn in her yellow robe was spreading over all the earth: and Zeus who delights in thunder held an assembly of the gods on the highest peak of ridged Olympos. He began to address them, and all the gods gave him their attention: 'Listen to me, all you gods and all you goddesses, so I can tell you what my heart within me urges. Now let no female god or male either attempt to frustrate my stated will, but I want agreement from all of you, so I can bring this business to a speedy end. And any of you I find prepared to flout the gods and go bringing help to either Trojans or Danaans, he will be blasted without regard and sent running back to Olympos. Or I will take him and throw him into murky Tartaros, far down, into the deepest abyss below the earth, where the gate is iron and the threshold bronze, as far below Hades as the heaven is above earth – then he will realise how much I am the strongest of all the gods. Or come, try it, gods – then all of you will know. Hang a gold cord down from heaven, and all you gods and goddesses take hold of it: but you could not pull Zeus, the counsellor most high, down from heaven to the ground, however long and hard you laboured. But whenever I had a mind to pull in earnest, I could haul you up, earth and sea and all – then I could hitch the cord round a peak of Olympos, so that everything was then left hanging in mid-air. That is how superior I am to gods and men.'

So he spoke, and they all stayed silent, shocked by his words and the great force of his threat. But then finally the bright-eyed goddess Athene spoke out: 'Son of Kronos, our father, highest of the mighty, we do know well that your strength cannot be resisted – but all the same we are sad for the Danaan spearmen, who will fill the measure of a miserable fate and perish. Yes, we will keep ourselves out of the fighting, as you command: but we will put saving advice in the minds of the Argives, so that not all of them perish under your anger.'

Then Zeus the cloud-gatherer smiled at her and said: 'Do not worry, Tritogeneia, dear child. I do not speak with my heart in full earnest, and my intention to you is kind.'

So speaking he harnessed a pair of bronze-hoofed horses to his chariot – wing-swift horses, with flowing manes of gold – and dressed himself in gold, and took up his whip which was finely made of gold, and mounted his chariot. He whipped the horses on, and they flew eagerly on their way, between earth and the starry heaven. He came to Ida with the many springs, the mother of wild creatures, to Gargaron, where he has his precinct and his altar fragrant with sacrifice. There the father of men and gods reined in his horses, unyoked them from the chariot, and rolled thick mist over them. He then sat down on the peak of the mountain glorying in his splendour, and looking out over the Trojans' city and the ships of the Achaians.

Meanwhile the long-haired Achaians took their meal quickly in their huts, and straight after it they began to arm themselves. Likewise the Trojans on the other side prepared for war throughout the city. They were fewer men, but ready even so to engage the fury of battle, under force of necessity, for their children's sake and for their wives. All the gates were opened, and the army streamed out, foot-soldiers and horsemen, and the din rose loud.

When they had advanced together to meet on common ground, then there was the clash of shields, of spears and the fury of men cased in bronze: bossed shields met each other, and the din rose loud. Then there were mingled the groaning and the crowing of men killed and killing, and the ground ran with blood.

For as long as it was morning and the holy day was waxing, the weapons thrown by both sides reached their mark, and men kept falling. But when the sun had straddled the centre of the sky, then the Father opened out his golden scales. In the pans he put two fates of death's long sorrow, one for the horse-taming Trojans and one for the bronze-clad Achaians, and he took the scales in the middle and lifted them up: and the Achaians' day of doom sank down. The Achaians' fates settled on the nourishing earth, and the Trojans' were lifted up into the broad heaven. And Zeus himself thundered loud from Ida, and sent a burning flash down into the Achaian army. They saw it with horror, and fear took its pale grip on all of them.

Then neither Idomeneus nor Agamemnon had the courage to stand firm, nor the two Aiantes, Ares' men-at-arms. Nestor alone stayed on, the Gerenian, the warden of the Achaians – and that was not of his will, but one of his horses was wounded, hit with an arrow by godlike Alexandros, husband of lovely-haired Helen, which struck right at the top of its head, where the first hairs of a horse's mane grow from the skull, an especially mortal place. The horse reared up with the pain, as the arrow had sunk into its brain, and brought confusion to the other horses as it rolled and twisted under the arrow's bronze point. While the old man was lunging with his sword to cut away the traces that held the horse, Hektor's quick horses came on through the mêlée carrying their brave master, Hektor. And then the old man would have lost his life, if Diomedes, master of the war-cry, had not quickly seen it. He gave a fearful shout to urge Odysseus to his aid: 'Royal son of Laertes, resourceful Odysseus, where are you off to, turning your back and fleeing like a coward in battle? Take care that no-one fixes a spear in your back as you run! No, stand with me, to beat back this savage fighter from the old man.'

So he spoke, and much-enduring godlike Odysseus had no ear for him, but ran on past towards the hollow ships of the Achaians. And the son of Tydeus, alone though he was, went to engage the front-fighters, and stood in front of the chariot of the old man, the son of Neleus, and spoke winged words to him: 'Old man, these young fighters press you too hard. Your strength is broken, and grim old age is at your heels. Your lieutenant is a weakling, and your horses are slow. Come then, mount my chariot, so you can see the mettle of these horses of Tros' stock, and their skill in speeding up and down through the plain in pursuit or retreat – I took them from Aineias, and they are horses that drive men to flight. Our lieutenants can see to your pair, while you and I steer these two against the horse-taming Trojans, so that Hektor can find out whether my spear too has power to rage in my hands.'

So he spoke, and the Gerenian horseman Nestor did not fail to obey him. Then their strong lieutenants, Sthenelos and heroic Eurymedon, took charge of Nestor's mares: and the two of them mounted Diomedes' chariot. Nestor took the shining reins in his hands and whipped on the horses. They quickly came within range of Hektor, and the son of Tydeus hurled a spear at him as he rushed straight for them. He missed Hektor, but hit his charioteer and lieutenant, Eniopeus the son of great-hearted Thebaios, striking him in the chest by the nipple as he held the horses' reins. He crashed from the chariot, and his swift-footed horses shied at his loss: life and strength collapsed where he lay. Terrible pain for his charioteer clouded Hektor's heart. But then for all his grief for his companion he let him lie there, and went to find another brave charioteer: and his horses were not long without a man to direct them – Hektor quickly found the brave

Archeptolemos, Iphitos' son, and mounted him behind his swift-footed horses, and put the reins in his hands.

Then there would have been havoc and doings beyond all remedy, and the Trojans would have been penned back in Ilios like lambs, if the father of men and gods had not quickly seen it. He thundered fearfully, and let fly a vivid lightning-bolt, and hurled it to the ground in front of Diomedes' horses. The burning sulphur gave off a terrible flare, and the horses shied back in panic in their harness. The shining reins dropped from Nestor's hands, and he felt terror in his heart and said to Diomedes: 'Son of Tydeus, come, turn your strong-footed horses back in flight. Can you not see that Zeus' aid to victory is not with you? Now Zeus the son of Kronos is granting Hektor the glory for today – another time he will give it to us, if that is his will. No man, not even the strongest, can resist the purpose of Zeus, since his power is far greater than ours.'

Then Diomedes, master of the war-cry, answered him: 'Yes, all that you say, old man, is right and true. But this grievous thought touches my heart and spirit with pain – that Hektor will say one day when speaking with the Trojans: "I put Tydeus' son to flight and sent him back to the ships." That will be his boast: and then may the wide earth gape for me.'

Then the Gerenian horseman Nestor answered him: 'Oh, son of warrior Tydeus, what a thing to say! Even if Hektor calls you a coward and a weakling, yet he will have no belief from the Trojans and the Dardanians, and the wives of the great-hearted Trojan shield-fighters, whose strong husbands you have flung in the dust.'

So speaking he turned the strong-footed horses in flight back through the mêlée. And Hektor and the Trojans, raising a tremendous clamour, hurled showers of pain-fraught weapons after them. Great Hektor of the glinting helmet called in a great shout after Diomedes: 'Son of Tydeus, the fast-horsed Danaans used to show you special honour, with pride of place, the best of the meat, the wine-cup always filled. But now they will scorn you – you turn out to be no better than a woman. Off with you, you poor puppet! You will never find me giving way to let you scale our walls, or carry off our women in your ships. Before that I will deal you your doom.'

So he spoke, and the son of Tydeus was torn in thought, whether to turn his horses and fight him face to face. Three times he thought it over in his mind and heart, and three times Zeus the counsellor thundered from the peaks of Ida, giving a sign to the Trojans of battle's turn to their victory. And Hektor called with a great shout to the Trojans: 'Trojans and Lycians and close-fighting Dardanians, be men, my friends, and fill your minds with fighting spirit. I can see that the son of Kronos has willed and granted me the victory and great glory – and to the Danaans disaster. Poor fools, they have contrived this wall of theirs, a feeble thing of no account – it will not keep back my fury: my horses will easily leap over the ditch they have dug. And when I am there by their hollow ships, then let me have you mindful of the fire to consume them, so that I can set fire to the ships and cut down the Argives as they panic in the smoke.'

So speaking he called out to his horses: 'Come, Xanthos, and you, Podargos, and Aithon and splendid Lampos! Now you can repay me for your keep, all the care that Andromache, daughter of great-hearted Eëtion, has given you, serving you with heartening wheat, and mixing wine for you to drink at your will – and all before feeding me, her own strong husband. Come on with me, then, and show your speed, so we can capture Nestor's shield, a thing whose fame now reaches to the sky for being all of gold, both cross-bars and the shield itself: and then strip from the shoulders of Diomedes the horse-tamer his crafted corselet which is the work of Hephaistos' labour. If we could take these two prizes, I would think the Achaians would get aboard their fast ships this very night.'

So he spoke, boasting words, and queen Hera was angry. She tossed on her throne, and shook the heights of Olympos, and spoke out to the great god Poseidon: 'Shame on you, mighty Earthshaker: not even your heart feels any sadness for the Danaans as they perish. And yet they bring you many pleasing gifts to Helike and Aigai: and you used to will them victory. If we were to decide, all of us who favour the Danaans, to beat back the Trojans and keep wide-seeing Zeus away, he would then have to sit on there on Ida alone with his fury.'

The Earthshaker, powerful lord, answered her in vexation: 'Hera, what is this you are saying? This is reckless talk. I would not want the rest of us to fight against Zeus son of Kronos, since his power is far greater than ours.'

Such were their words to each other. Meanwhile in front of the ships the whole space between the wall and the ditch's boundary was filled with Achaians penned in there, horses and fighters with the shield alike: and penning them was Hektor, Priam's son, the equal of swift Ares himself, now that Zeus had given him the glory. And he would have fired the balanced ships with burning flame, if queen Hera had not put it into Agamemnon's mind to stir into action himself and urge on the Achaians with all speed. He went along by the huts and ships of the Achaians, holding his great purple cloak in his massive hand, and stopped beside Odysseus' black huge-bellied ship, which lay in the very middle, so that a shout could be heard on both sides, right to the huts of Aias son of Telamon and to Achilleus' station on the other side – both of these had beached their balanced ships at the far ends, confident in their bravery and the strength of their hands. Then he called in a great carrying shout to all the Achaians: 'Shame, you Argives! You sorry wretches, nothing but show and looks! Where have those boasts of ours gone, when we said we were the bravest of men – those empty pratings you made in Lemnos, as you ate great quantities of meat from straight-horned cattle and drank whole bowls brim-full with wine, claiming that each one of you would take his stand in battle against a hundred Trojans, or two hundred? And now all of us are not even a match for one of them – Hektor, who will soon fire our ships with burning flame. Father Zeus, is there any other great king you have ever cursed with such delusion as mine, and robbed him like this of his great glory? I declare that there was no lovely altar of yours that I passed by in my benched ship on this doomed voyage here, but on every one of them I burnt the fat and thigh-bones of oxen, in my great desire to sack the well-walled city of Troy. Yet, Zeus, grant me this one prayer: allow us to escape with our lives and get away, and do not let the Achaians be brought down in this destruction by the Trojans.'

So he spoke, and the Father pitied him as his tears fell, and granted his consent that his people be safe, and not destroyed. And he immediately sent an eagle, surest omen of all flying things, with a fawn in its talons, the young of a quick-running deer: and it dropped the fawn beside the lovely altar of Zeus, where the Achaians made their sacrifices to Zeus the lord of all omens. Now when they saw that the bird had come from Zeus, they leapt at the Trojans with a new will, and their spirits filled for battle.

Then not one of the Danaans, for all their number, could boast that he was ahead of Tydeus' son in steering his quick horses to cross over the ditch and engage in close battle. He was far the first to kill a Trojan warrior, Agelaos son of Phradmon: he had wheeled his horses to flight, and when he was turned Diomedes fixed his spear in his back between the shoulder-blades, and drove it on out through the chest. He crashed from the chariot, and his armour clattered about him.

After him came the sons of Atreus, Agamemnon and Menelaos, then the two Aiantes, clothed in fighting spirit, then Idomeneus and Idomeneus' follower, Meriones, the equal of the murdering war-god, then Eurypylos, Euaimon's splendid son. And the ninth to come was Teukros, stringing his curved bow, and he took up position under the covering of Aias the son of Telamon's shield. Then Aias would move his shield a little to one side: and the hero Teukros would look sharply around him, shoot and hit a Trojan in the mass of men, and then, leaving the man to fall and die where he was shot, he would dodge back again to Aias' protection, like a child running to its mother: and Aias would cover him with his bright shield.

Then which of the Trojans did the excellent Teukros kill first? Orsilochos first, and Ormenos and Ophelestes and Daitor and Chromios, and godlike Lykophontes, and Amopaon son of Polyaimon, and Melanippos – all these, one after another, he brought down to the nourishing earth. Agamemnon, lord of men, was delighted when he saw him destroying the ranks of Trojans with his powerful bow. He came and stood by him, and said to him: 'Teukros, dear head, son of Telamon, leader of your people, keep shooting like this, so you can bring the light of their desire to the Danaans, and to your father Telamon, who brought you up when you were small, and though you were a bastard son looked after you in his own house. Set him in his glory now, though he is far away. And I tell you something which will certainly be done as I say. If Zeus who holds the aegis and Athene grant me the sacking of the well-founded city of Ilios, yours will be the first hands after mine to receive from me the prize of honour – a tripod, or two horses with their chariot, or a woman to climb to your bed and share it.'

Then the excellent Teukros answered him: 'Most glorious son of Atreus, why spur me on when I am keen enough in my own mind? I tell you I have not stopped working with all the strength that is in me, but ever since the moment we drove them back towards Ilios I have been looking for victims and killing them with my bow. I have shot eight long-barbed arrows, and every one has sunk into the flesh of a quick young warrior – but this one I cannot hit, this mad dog.'

So he spoke, and sent another arrow from the string straight at Hektor, and his heart longed to hit him. And he missed Hektor, but his arrow hit the excellent Gorgythion in the chest, a noble son of Priam, born to a mother who married from Aisyme, lovely Kastianeira, beautiful as the goddesses. He dropped his head to one side like a poppy in a garden, bent by the weight of its seed and the showers of spring: so his head sank drooping to one side under the weight of the helmet.

Teukros sent another arrow from the string straight at Hektor, and his heart longed to hit him. But again he missed, as Apollo foiled his shot: but he hit Archeptolemos, Hektor's brave charioteer, in the chest by the nipple as he came speeding into battle. He crashed from the chariot, and his swift-footed horses shied at his loss: life and strength collapsed where he lay. Terrible pain for his charioteer clouded Hektor's heart. But then for all his grief for his companion he let him lie there, and called to his brother Kebriones, who was nearby, to take the horses' reins: and he did not fail to do as he had heard. Hektor himself jumped to the ground from his glittering chariot shouting fearfully. He took up a boulder in his hand and went straight for Teukros, his heart urgent to hit him. Teukros had taken a bitter arrow out from the quiver and had fitted it to the string. Then as he drew it back past his shoulder, with Hektor his aim, Hektor of the glinting helmet struck him with the jagged stone, hitting where the collar-bone separates neck and chest, an especially dangerous spot, and broke his string: his arm went numb at the wrist, and he dropped to his knees and stayed there, and the bow fell from his hand. Aias did not fail to look after his fallen brother, but ran to bestride him and covered him with his shield. Then two loyal companions bent under him, Mekisteus son of Echios and godlike Alastor, and carried him groaning heavily back to the hollow ships.

Then the Olympian once more spurred strength into the Trojans, and they drove the Achaians back straight towards the deep ditch: and Hektor went among the first of them, revelling in his strength. As when a dog in the speed of its chase catches a wild boar or a lion from behind, on the haunches and hind-quarters, and watches closely for its every turn, so Hektor pressed close on the long-haired Achaians, constantly killing the hindmost: and they fled in terror. When they had crossed the stakes and the ditch in their flight, and many had been brought down at the Trojans' hands, they came to a halt alongside the ships and stayed there, calling to each other: and every man held up his hands to all the gods and prayed aloud, while Hektor kept wheeling his lovely-maned horses up and down, glaring with the eyes of Gorgo or of Ares the curse of men.

Now when she saw them, the white-armed goddess Hera felt pity for them, and straightaway spoke winged words to Athene: 'Shame on it, daughter of Zeus who holds the aegis, are we two to show no more care now for the Danaans as they die, even at this last hour? They will fill the measure of a miserable fate, and perish under the sweep of one man – Hektor, Priam's son, is raging now with a fury that none can resist, and already he has done much havoc.'

Then the bright-eyed goddess Athene answered her: 'Yes, how I wish that he would lose his life and strength, killed at the Argives' hands in his own land! But my father is raging with his mind on evil – hard god that he is, a constant blight, the foiler of my plans! And he has no memory for the many times I kept saving his son when the tasks set by Eurystheus were breaking him – he would cry aloud to the heaven, and Zeus sent me down from the sky to bring him aid. If my mind's bent had been like his now, when Eurystheus sent his son down to the house of Hades the Keeper of the Gate, to bring up from Erebos the dog that loathsome Hades keeps, then he would never have come away safe from the rushing flow of Styx's water. But now Zeus hates me, and has brought about the designs of Thetis, who kissed his knees and took his chin in her hand, begging him to show honour to Achilleus, sacker of cities. But the time will come when he calls me his darling Bright Eyes once again. So now you harness the strong-footed horses for us, while I go into the house of Zeus who holds the aegis and arm myself for war, so that I can see whether Priam's son, Hektor of the glinting helmet, will be glad at our appearance in the avenues of battle, or whether some Trojan too will glut the dogs and birds with his fat and his flesh, lying fallen by the ships of the Achaians.'

So she spoke, and the white-armed goddess Hera did not fail to obey. Hera then, queenly goddess, daughter of great Kronos, busied about the harnessing of the horses with their golden head-pieces. And Athene, daughter of Zeus who holds the aegis, let slip to the floor of her father's house her soft embroidered robe, which she herself had made and worked with her hands. And she put on Zeus the cloud-gatherer's own tunic in its place, then dressed in her armour for the misery of war. She stepped into her flaming chariot, and took up her spear, the huge, heavy, massive spear with which she brings low the ranks of men, the heroes who stir the mighty-fathered goddess into anger. Hera quickly touched the horses with the whip: and of their own accord the gates of heaven groaned open, the gates kept by the Seasons, who have been given charge over the vast heaven and Olympos, both to push aside the heavy cloud and to close it to. This way, then, they held their whipped horses through the gates.

When Zeus the father saw this from Ida, terrible anger came over

him, and he sent Iris the golden-winged speeding to give his message:
'Away with you, swift Iris, turn them back and do not let them come
to face me – it will not be well for us to clash in battle. I tell them this,
and it will certainly be done as I say. I shall lame their quick horses in
their harness, and hurl them out of the car and smash their chariot:
and not even ten circling years will be enough for them to be healed of
the wounds that the lightning's bite will deal them – so that the
bright-eyed goddess can learn what it is to fight with her father. With
Hera I am not so indignant or angry – it is always her way to cross my
every order.'

So he spoke, and stormswift Iris sped to give his message, rising
from the mountains of Ida to the heights of Olympos. She met them
at the outer gates of valleyed Olympos and stopped them there, and
told them Zeus' words: 'Where are you storming? What is this madness
in your hearts? The son of Kronos has forbidden help to the Argives.
This is what the son of Kronos has threatened, what he will do. He
will lame your quick horses in their harness, and hurl you out of the
car and smash your chariot: and not even ten circling years will be
enough for you to be healed of the wounds that the lightning's bite
will deal you – so that you, bright-eyed goddess, can learn what it is to
fight with your father. With Hera he is not so indignant or angry – it is
always her way to cross his every order. But you are fearsome indeed,
shameless bitch, if you will truly dare to raise your monstrous spear
against Zeus.'

So speaking swift-footed Iris left them, and Hera spoke to Athene:
'Oh now, daughter of Zeus who holds the aegis, I can no longer agree
that we should fight against Zeus for mortals' sake. Let them die or
live as fortune has it: and he can keep his own plans in his heart, and
make whatever decision is right between Trojans and Danaans.'

So speaking she turned back their strong-footed horses. And the
Seasons unyoked their lovely-maned horses and tied them at their
divine mangers, and leaned the chariot against the polished wall of
the yard. The goddesses took their seats on golden chairs in the
company of the other gods, with pain at their hearts.

And Zeus the father drove his fine-wheeled chariot and horses from
Ida to Olympos, and came to the place where the gods were sitting.
The famous earthshaker unyoked his horses for him, and set his
chariot on its stand, covering it with cloth. Wide-seeing Zeus took his
seat on his golden throne, and great Olympos was shaken under his
feet. Athene and Hera were sitting alone, away from Zeus, and they

gave him no word or question. But he understood them in his mind, and spoke to them: 'Why so pained, Athene and Hera? It cannot be that you have exhausted yourselves in the battle where men win glory, with all that destruction of the Trojans, those objects of your terrible anger! As for me, such is my strength and the invincible power of my hands, there is no way that all the gods on Olympos could turn me from my purpose. But with you two, the shiver of fear took hold of your bright bodies before you had any sight of war and war's grim workings. I tell you this, and it would certainly have been as I say. You would have been blasted by lightning, and not come back in your own chariot to Olympos, where the immortals have their home.'

So he spoke, and Athene and Hera muttered at his words – they were sitting close by each other, and plotting hardship for the Trojans. Athene stayed silent and said nothing, furious at her father Zeus, and gripped by savage anger. But Hera's breast could not contain her rage, and she spoke out: 'Dread son of Kronos, what is this you are saying? We do know well that your strength cannot be resisted – but all the same we are sad for the Danaan spearmen, who will fill the measure of a miserable fate and perish. Yes, we will keep ourselves away from the fighting, if you command it: but we will put saving advice in the minds of the Argives, so that not all of them perish under your anger.'

Then Zeus the cloud-gatherer answered her: 'In the morning, ox-eyed queen Hera, if you have the mind for it, you will see the son of Kronos in yet greater power, destroying the Argive spearmen in great numbers. Because mighty Hektor will not cease from his fighting before the swift-footed son of Peleus is roused to action beside the ships, on that day when they will fight in desperate confinement by the sterns over dead Patroklos – this is the way of fate. But as for you and your anger, it is of no concern to me, even if you go to the uttermost limits beneath earth and sea, where Iapetos and Kronos sit without enjoyment of the beams of Hyperion the Sun or of the winds, but all round them is the abyss of Tartaros – even if your wandering takes you that far, your resentment does not concern me, since there is nothing more shameless than you.'

So he spoke, and white-armed Hera made him no answer. And the bright light of the sun sank into Ocean, drawing black night over the grain-giving ploughland. The Trojans were sorry to see the daylight set, but for the Achaians the coming of night's welcome darkness was their most fervent prayer.

Then glorious Hektor held an assembly of the Trojans, taking them away from the ships to gather beside the swirling river, in a clear space, where room could be seen free of corpses. They dismounted to the ground from their chariots and listened to the speech made by Hektor, loved of Zeus. In his hand he held a spear eleven cubits in length: the spear's bronze point gleamed before him, and a gold band ringed it round. He leaned on this spear as he spoke to the Trojans: 'Listen to me, Trojans and Dardanians and allies. Today I thought that I would return to windy Ilios with the ships and all the Achaians destroyed – but before that darkness came, and it is that above all which has now saved the Argives and their ships on the shore. Well, for the present we should give way to dark night and prepare our supper. Unyoke your lovely-maned horses from your chariots and throw fodder by them. And bring oxen and sturdy sheep from the city quickly, and take cheering wine and bread from your houses, and gather piles of wood as well, so that we can burn many fires all night long until the early-born dawn, and their light can strike up to the sky – in case the long-haired Achaians perhaps try to escape during the night over the sea's broad back. No, they must not be allowed to board their ships as they please, without struggle, but let some of them take a wound back with them to nurse at home, hit by an arrow or sharp spear as they jump to their ships – so that others too can shrink from bringing the misery of war against the horse-taming Trojans. And let the heralds, loved of Zeus, proclaim throughout the city that the boys in their early youth and the grey-headed old men should camp on the god-built walls around the city. And as for the womenfolk, let each man's wife burn a great fire in the house: and there must be a constant watch, so that no enemy band can enter the city while the fighting men are away. Let these things be done, great-hearted men of Troy, as I tell you. So much for my orders to suit the present need. Now I will give you horse-taming Trojans some words for the morrow. I hope, and I pray to Zeus and the other gods, that I shall chase away from here these doom-driven dogs, carried here in their black ships by the fates of death. So for the night we must keep guard on our position. But early in the morning, before the showing of dawn, let us arm in our weapons and wake war's anger by the hollow ships. And I shall know whether Tydeus' son, strong Diomedes, will drive me back from the ships to the wall, or whether I will cut him down with the bronze and carry away my bloody spoils. Tomorrow we shall come to know his courage, whether he can stand against the onslaught of my spear – but I think he will lie there stabbed among the first to die, and many companions round him, as the sun rises for tomorrow. Oh, if only I could be deathless and ageless for all time, and honoured as Athene and Apollo are honoured, as surely as this coming day brings disaster to the Argives!'

So Hektor spoke to the assembly, and the Trojans shouted in response. They released their sweating horses from the yoke, and tethered them with straps, each by his own chariot. And they brought oxen and sturdy sheep from the city quickly, and took cheering wine and bread from their houses, and gathered piles of wood as well. And the winds carried the smell of sacrifice from the plain up into the sky.

So all night long they sat on the avenues of battle, with high thoughts in their minds: and their fires burned in their numbers. As when the stars show brilliant in the sky around the shining moon, when the air is windless calm: all the hill-tops and sharp headlands and mountain glens spring clear into sight, and brightness bursts infinite down from the sky: every star is seen, and the shepherd's heart is glad. So many were the Trojans' fires, burning clear in front of Ilios, between the ships and the stream of Xanthos. A thousand fires were burning in the plain, and round each there sat fifty men in the gleam of the blazing fire. And the horses stood beside their chariots munching their white barley and wheat, and waiting for the throned dawn.

BOOK 9
THE EMBASSY TO ACHILLEUS

So the Trojans kept their watch. But the Achaians were gripped by monstrous panic, the workmate of chilling flight, and all the leading men were struck down with unbearable sorrow. As when two winds come suddenly and whip the fish-filled sea, the north wind and the west wind, blowing down from Thrace: the mass of the dark swell rears into crests, and piles the seaweed thick along the shore. So the Achaians' spirits were troubled in their breasts.

The son of Atreus, heart-struck with deep anguish, went ranging up and down, telling his clear-voiced heralds to summon the people to an assembly – to call each man by name, and not to shout out loud – and he himself worked at the task among the first of them. The men sat down in assembly dispirited. Agamemnon rose to speak, letting his tears fall like a spring of black water which trickles its dark stream down a sheer rock's face. So, with heavy groans, Agamemnon spoke to the Argives: 'Friends, leaders and lords of the Argives, Zeus the son of Kronos has snared me wholly in grievous delusion. Cruel god – before now he promised me, with solemn assent, that I would sack the well-walled city of Ilios before my return. But now he has planned a vile deception, and tells me to go back to Argos in dishonour, after I have lost many of my people. So it seems must be the pleasure of Zeus the almighty, who has already shattered the crowns of many cities, and will break yet more, such is his matchless power. Come then, let us all do as I say – let us away with our ships to our dear native land. We shall never now take the broad streets of Troy.'

So he spoke, and they all stayed silent. For a long time the sons of the Achaians sat silent and dispirited. But then finally Diomedes, master of the war-cry, spoke out: 'Son of Atreus, this is folly, and it is you I will take issue with first of all – such is the right of custom, my lord, in the assembly, and you must not be angry. It was my courage you decried before now in front of the Danaans, saying I was a coward and a weakling – all this is known by the Achaians, young and old alike. But your gifts from the son of devious-minded Kronos go both ways: he has given you the preeminent honour of the sceptre, but courage he did not give you, and this is the true power. Strange man, do you really think that the sons of the Achaians are such cowards and weaklings as your words say? If your own heart is eager for return, then go – the way is open, your ships are standing by the sea, all those many ships which followed you from Mykene. But the rest of the long-haired Achaians will stay here until we sack Troy. Or they too can run home in their ships to their dear native land: and the two of us, I and Sthenelos, will fight on until we reach our goal in Ilios, since god is with us in our mission here.'

So he spoke, and all the sons of the Achaians roared their approval, delighted at the speech of Diomedes the horse-tamer. Then Nestor the horseman stood up and spoke to them: 'Son of Tydeus, in battle you are a man of great power, and in counsel too you are the best among all of your age. Not one of the Achaians will disparage what you have said, or speak against it: but you did not bring your argument to its conclusion. But of course you are young – you could be my own son, and the youngest born. And yet you spoke with good sense to the kings of the Argives, and what you said is right. But look, let me speak on – I claim myself older than you – and I shall cover everything. And no-one can want to reject my words, not even lord Agamemnon. The man who wills the chill horror of war within his own people is an outlaw, banished from clan and law and hearth. Now for the present we should give way to dark night and prepare our supper: and guards should camp outside the wall along the ditch we have dug, each party at its own post. These are my instructions for the young men. But then you, son of Atreus, should take the lead, as you are the greatest king among us. Give a feast for the elders: it is right for you to do this, and quite what is proper. Your huts are full of the wine that the Achaians' ships bring daily over the broad sea from Thrace: all hospitality rests with you, as you are the king over many people. And when many are gathered together you will follow the man who proposes the best plan – and all the Achaians have great need of a plan that is good and well-laid, since our enemies have their many fires burning right close to our ships. Who could take pleasure in this? This night will prove the shattering of our army or its saving.'

So he spoke, and they listened well and agreed. The guards set out in their armour under Nestor's son Thrasymedes, shepherd of the people, and under Askalaphos and Ialmenos, sons of Ares, and under Meriones and Aphareus and Deïpyros, and under the godlike Lykomedes, son of Kreion. There were seven commanders of the guards, and a hundred young men went with each of them with long spears in their hands. They went and settled into position between the ditch and the wall. There they lit fires, and each man prepared his supper.

The son of Atreus led the elders of the Achaians in a body into his hut, and placed before them a feast to please their hearts: and they put their hands to the food set prepared beside them. When they had put away their desire for eating and drinking, the old man Nestor first of all began to weave the web of his thoughts before them – his advice had proved best at earlier times too. In all good will he spoke and addressed the company: 'Most glorious son of Atreus, Agamemnon, lord of men, you will be the beginning of my words, and you will be their end, since you are the king of many peoples and Zeus has entrusted to you the sceptre and the ways of law, to make judgments for your people. Therefore you more than any other man should speak the thoughts of your mind and listen too, and act even on another's advice, whenever a man's heart prompts him to speak for the good – yours will be the credit for all that he begins. Now I shall tell you what seems best to me. There can be no better thought than what has long been the thought of my mind, and still is now, ever since the time, my lord, when you went and took the girl Briseïs from Achilleus' hut, for all his anger – quite against our feeling: I certainly tried long to dissuade you. But you gave in to your heart's high passion and brought dishonour on the greatest of men, a man whom the very immortals have honoured – you have taken his prize and keep it for yourself. But even at this late day let us consider how we may appease him and win him over with soothing gifts and kind persuasion.'

Then Agamemnon, lord of men, answered him: 'Old man, your talk of my blindness is no lie: I was blinded, I do not deny it myself. A man loved from the heart by Zeus is worth many armies – just as now Zeus has honoured this man, and broken the army of the Achaians. But since I was blinded and listened to my heart's wretched persuasion, I am ready to take it back and offer the appeasement of limitless reparation. Let me name now, before you all, the glorious gifts I will give. Seven tripods untouched by the fire, ten talents of gold, twenty gleaming cauldrons, twelve horses – strong racers, prize-winners with their speed: a man who owned all that my strong-footed horses have won me in prizes would not be short of booty or poor in precious gold. And I will give seven women skilled in excellent handcraft, women from Lesbos: when he himself captured well-founded Lesbos I chose them out for their beauty surpassing all the company of women. These I will give him and with them the girl I took from him in the beginning, Briseus' daughter. And I will swear a great oath as well, that I never mounted her bed and lay with her, as is the way of mankind between men and women. All these gifts will be his on the instant. And then later, if the gods grant that we sack Priam's great city, he may go in there when we Achaians are dividing the spoil and heap his ship high as he will with gold and bronze: and he may choose for himself twenty Trojan women, the most beautiful of all after Argive Helen. And if we reach the udder-rich soil of Achaian Argos, he can become my son-in-law: and I will honour him as much as Orestes, my loved young son growing there in abundant prosperity. I have three daughters in my strong-built house, Chrysothemis and Laodike and Iphianassa. He may take whichever of these he wishes back to Peleus' house as his own wife, and pay no bride-price: and I will add a dowry of many gifts, more than any man has yet given with his daughter. I will give him seven well-founded cities, Kardamyle and Enope, and grassy Hire, and holy Pherai, and Antheia with its deep meadows, and lovely Aipeia and Pedasos where the vines grow. All these are close by the sea, at the edge of sandy Pylos, and in them live men rich in sheep and rich in cattle, who will honour him with gifts like a god and bring his rule to prosperity under his sceptre. All this I will do for him if he moves from his anger. Let him yield – Hades is the one who never pities or yields, and for that he is of all gods the most hated by men – and let him submit to me, in that I am the greater king and can claim to be his senior in age.'

Then the Gerenian horseman Nestor answered him: 'Most glorious son of Atreus, Agamemnon, lord of men, no-one can now find fault with the gifts you offer to lord Achilleus. Come then, let us pick men and send them on their way to go quickly to the hut of Achilleus son of Peleus. Or come, let the ones I choose now accept the task. First of all let Phoinix, loved of Zeus, take the lead: and then huge Aias and godlike Odysseus. And let the heralds accompanying them be Odios and Eurybates. Bring water for our hands, and call for holy silence, so that we can pray to Zeus the son of Kronos and ask for his mercy.'

So he spoke, and his words were approved by all. The heralds quickly poured water over their hands, and the young men filled the mixing-bowls to the brim with wine, and poured a libation into each man's cup and then served them all. When they had made their libations and drunk what their hearts desired, they set out from the hut of

Agamemnon son of Atreus. And the Gerenian horseman Nestor gave them constant instructions, fixing his eye on each, and on Odysseus most of all, to make every effort to win over the excellent son of Peleus.

So they went along the shore of the sounding sea, praying long to Poseidon the encircler and shaker of the earth that it would be easy for them to win over the great heart of Achilleus, of Aiakos' stock. They came to the huts and the ships of the Myrmidons, and found Achilleus giving pleasure to his heart with a clear-voiced lyre, a beautiful finely-worked thing with a cross-piece of silver, which he had won from the spoils when he destroyed Eëtion's city. He was delighting his heart with this, and singing tales of men's glory. Patroklos alone sat opposite him in silence, waiting for when Achilleus would end his singing. They walked further forward, with godlike Odysseus leading, and stopped in front of him. Achilleus left his seat and jumped up in astonishment, still holding his lyre. And Patroklos likewise stood up, when he saw the men there. And swift-footed Achilleus showed his greeting and said to them: 'Welcome! Oh, you are dear friends that have come! – so there is great need of me – yes, even in my anger you are those I love most of the Achaians.'

So speaking godlike Achilleus led them in, and sat them on seats spread with purple rugs. And he spoke straight to Patroklos who was close by him: 'Set up a larger bowl, son of Menoitios, and mix the wine stronger, and make a cup for each of them. These are my dearest friends that have come under my roof.'

So he spoke, and Patroklos obeyed his dear companion. Then he put down a great meat-block in the light of the fire, and placed on it the backs of a sheep and a fat goat, and a hog's chine rich in lard. Automedon held the meat for him, while Achilleus cut it into joints. He then chopped it fine and threaded the pieces on spits, and the son of Menoitios, a man like the gods, made the fire into a great blaze. Then when the fire had burned down and the flames had died, he spread the embers and laid the spits' length above the fire, placing them up on their blocks, and he sprinkled the meat with holy salt. Then when he had roasted it and piled it on trenchers, Patroklos took bread and set it out on the table in fine baskets, and Achilleus served the meat. Then Achilleus sat down by the opposite wall facing godlike Odysseus, and told his companion Patroklos to offer sacrifice to the gods: and Patroklos threw the gods' portions in the fire. They then put their hands to the food set prepared beside them. When they had put away their desire for eating and drinking, Aias nodded to Phoinix. But godlike Odysseus noticed the sign, and filled his cup with wine and drank to Achilleus: 'Your health, Achilleus! We have not lacked our share in the feasting both in the hut of Agamemnon son of Atreus and now here with you – here is food in abundance to please our hearts. But our concern is not with the delights of the feast; no, we are looking on a great disaster, my lord, and we are afraid. There is doubt whether we can save our well-benched ships or they are lost, if you do not clothe yourself in your fighting power. The high-hearted Trojans and their far-famed allies have made camp right close to our ships and the wall, they have lit countless fires throughout their army, and they think there will be no holding them now, but they will hurl themselves on our black ships. And Zeus the son of Kronos is showing them signs of his favour with lightning on the right. Hektor is revelling high in his strength and raging hideously, with his trust in Zeus and no thought for men or gods – a mighty madness has entered him. He is praying for holy dawn to come quickly, as he threatens to cut the poop-ends from our ships, then burn the ships themselves with devouring fire and cut the Achaians down beside them as the smoke drives them madding in confusion. There is a dreadful fear in my heart that the gods may see his threats fulfilled, and then it would be our fate to perish here in Troy, far from the horse-pasture of Argos. Up then, if, late though it is, you want to save the sons of the Achaians in their affliction and rescue them from the Trojans' clamour. Or you will feel pain yourself in the future, and there will be no way to find the cure once the harm is done – no, long before that give your mind now to protecting the Danaans from the evil day. My dear friend, your father Peleus gave you his advice on the day when he sent you from Phthia to join Agamemnon. "My child", he said, "strength will be given to you by Athene and Hera, if such is their wish, but you must hold down your heart's high passion in your breast – good will between friends is a better thing. And if a quarrel begins its mischief, you should abandon it – this way the Argives, young and old alike, will show you greater honour." That was the old man's advice, and you are forgetting it. Yet even now please stop, let go the anger that pains your heart. Agamemnon is offering you full recompense if you move from your anger. Come, listen, while I tell you all the gifts in his huts which Agamemnon has promised. Seven tripods untouched by the fire, ten talents of gold, twenty gleaming cauldrons, twelve horses – strong racers, prize-winners with their speed: a man who owned all that

Agamemnon's horses have won him in prizes would not be short of booty or poor in precious gold. And he will give seven women skilled in excellent handcraft, women from Lesbos: when you yourself captured well-founded Lesbos he chose them out for their beauty surpassing all the company of women. These he will give you and with them the girl he took from you in the beginning, Briseus' daughter. And he will swear a great oath as well, that he never mounted her bed and lay with her, as is the way, my lord, between men and women. All these gifts will be yours on the instant. And then later, if the gods grant that we sack Priam's great city, you may go in there when we Achaians are dividing the spoil and heap your ship high as you will with gold and bronze: and you may choose for yourself twenty Trojan women, the most beautiful of all after Argive Helen. And if we reach the udder-rich soil of Achaian Argos, you can become his son-in-law: and he will honour you as much as Orestes, his loved young son growing there in abundant prosperity. He has three daughters in his strong-built house, Chrysothemis and Laodike and Iphianassa. You may take whichever of these you wish back to Peleus' house as your own wife, and pay no bride-price: and he will add a dowry of many gifts, more than any man has yet given with his daughter. He will give you seven well-founded cities, Kardamyle and Enope, and grassy Hire, and holy Pherai, and Antheia with its deep meadows, and lovely Aipeia and Pedasos where the vines grow. All these are close by the sea, at the edge of sandy Pylos, and in them live men rich in sheep and rich in cattle, who will honour you with gifts like a god and bring your rule to prosperity under your sceptre. All this he will do for you if you move from your anger. But if hatred for the son of Atreus has grown too strong in your heart, for the man and for his gifts, then still have pity on all the other Achaians of the army in their affliction, and they will honour you like a god. You could win the very greatest glory in their eyes, because now you could kill Hektor. With this fatal madness on him he would come up close to face you, since he thinks there is no match for him among all the Danaans carried here in our ships.'

Then swift-footed Achilleus answered him: 'Royal son of Laertes, resourceful Odysseus, what I say I must say outright, and tell you bluntly how I think and what will happen, so that you do not sit here and coo your blandishments at me one after another. I hate like the gates of Hades the man who hides one thing in his mind and speaks another. But I will tell you what seems right to me. I do not think that Agamemnon son of Atreus will win me over, nor the rest of the

Danaans, since it now appears that there is no thanks if a man fights the enemy relentlessly on and on. Stay at home or fight your hardest – your share will be the same. Coward and hero are honoured alike. Death does not distinguish do-nothing and do-all. And it has done me no profit to have suffered all that pain in fighting on ceaselessly with my life at constant risk. Like a bird that brings back to her unfledged chicks every morsel she can find, and has to go without herself, so it has been with me. I have spent many sleepless nights, and won through days of blood and battle, fighting with men over their wives. I have sacked twelve of men's cities from my ships, and I claim eleven more by land across the fertile Troad. From all of these I took many fine treasures, and every time I brought them all and gave them to Agamemnon son of Atreus: and every time, back there by the fast ships he had never left, he would take them in, share out a few, and keep the most for himself. All the other prizes he gave to the kings and leading men stay safe with their owners. I am the only Achaian he has robbed. He has taken my wife, my heart's love – let him lie with her and take his pleasure. Why is it that the Argives must fight the Trojans? Why did the son of Atreus raise an army and sail it here? Was it not because of lovely-haired Helen? Are the sons of Atreus the only ones of humankind to love their wives? No, any good man of sense loves his own wife and cares for her – as I too loved this girl from my heart, even though I won her by my spear.

'Now that he has taken my prize from my hands and cheated me, let him not try me. I know him well now – he will not persuade me. No, Odysseus, let him consider with you and the other kings how to keep the enemy fire away from the ships. Oh, he has laboured hard in my absence, and built a wall, and run a ditch in front, large and wide, and fixed stakes in it. Yet even so he cannot hold back the strength of murderous Hektor. But while I was fighting with the Achaians, Hektor was never willing to push the battle away from the wall, but would come out no further than the Skaian gates and the oak-tree. There he once stood up to me alone, and barely escaped my attack. But now, since I do not wish to fight with godlike Hektor, tomorrow I shall make sacrifice to Zeus and the other gods, I shall load my ships full, I shall drag them down to the water – and you will see, if you wish, if you have the mind for it, in the early morning you will see my ships sailing out over the fish-filled Hellespont, and men in them eager at their oars. And if the glorious Earthshaker grants us fair sailing, on the third day I shall reach fertile Phthia. I have much wealth there that I left behind on this doomed voyage here. And I shall take with me more gold from here, and red bronze, and fine-girdled women and grey iron, all that I have won. But my prize of honour – he gave it, and he, lord Agamemnon, son of Atreus, has taken it back to my insult. Tell him all that I say, and openly, so that the rest of the Achaians can feel anger too, if he is hoping still to cheat some other Danaan, clothed as ever in shamelessness – yet, dog that he is, he would not dare to look me in the face. I will not join him in plan or in action. He has cheated me and wronged me. He will not work his cheating tongue on me again. Enough already. No, he can take himself to ruin at his own pace – Zeus the counsellor has robbed his wits. I abominate his gifts, I care not a splinter for the man. Not even if he offered me ten times or twenty times all he possesses now, and others' wealth besides, not even all the riches that pour into Orchomenos, or Thebes in Egypt, where the houses are piled high with treasure, and the city has a hundred gates, and through each gate two hundred men drive out with horses and chariots: not even if he offered me gifts unnumbered like the sand or dust – not even so could Agamemnon yet turn my mind, until he pays me the full price for all this wrong that pains my heart. I will marry no daughter of Agamemnon son of Atreus, not even if her beauty rivals golden Aphrodite, and her hands equal the craft of bright-eyed Athene – not even so will I marry her. Let him choose some other of the Achaians, a man like himself, a higher king than I. If the gods preserve me and I reach home, Peleus himself will then marry me a wife. There are many Achaian women across Hellas and Phthia, daughters of leading men and rulers of cities, and whichever of them I want I shall make my dear wife. It is my proud heart's strong desire to take a wife in marriage over there, the partner of my liking, and live in enjoyment of the wealth that old Peleus has won. Because nothing equals the worth of my life – not even all the riches they say were held by the well-founded city of Ilios, in earlier times, in peace, before the sons of the Achaians came, nor all that the Archer's stone threshold guards inside, in Phoibos Apollo's temple in rocky Pytho. Men can raid cattle and sturdy sheep, and men can win tripods and bay horses by the head – but there is no raiding or winning a man's life back again, when once it has passed the guard of his teeth. My mother, the silver-footed goddess Thetis, says that I have two fates that could carry me to the end of death. If I stay here and fight on round the Trojans' city, then gone is my home-coming, but my glory will never die: and if I come back to my dear native land, then gone is my great glory, but my life will stretch long and the end of death will not overtake me quickly. And I would advise the rest of you too to sail back home, since you will not now reach your goal in steep Ilios – wide-seeing Zeus has held his hand firm above the city, and its people have taken strength. So you go now, and make plain this message to the leading men of the Achaians – such is the right of elders – that they must conceive in their minds a better plan to save their ships and the Achaian army beside the hollow ships, since this plan they have thought of in the time of my anger will bring them no success. But let Phoinix stay with us and sleep here, so that tomorrow he can join us in our voyage to our dear native land, if that is his wish – I will not force him to come.'

So he spoke, and they all stayed silent, shocked by his words and the great force of his refusal. But then finally the old horseman Phoinix spoke out, with his tears welling up in his great fear for the Achaians' ships: 'If return home, glorious Achilleus, is really what your mind is thinking, and you refuse absolutely to keep the destroying fire away from our fast ships, because anger has come over your heart, how then, dear child, could I be left here without you, alone? The old horseman Peleus sent me out with you on the day when he sent you from Phthia to join Agamemnon – you were a child, with no knowledge yet of levelling war or of debate, where men win distinction. So he sent me out to teach you all these things, to make you a speaker of words and a doer of deeds. So then, dear child, I would never want to be left away from you, not even if god himself were to promise to slough off my old age and make me a young man and vigorous as I was when I first left Hellas where the women are handsome, running from the anger of my father Amyntor, son of Ormenos. He was enraged at me over his lovely-haired concubine. He was giving his love to her and scorning his wife, my mother: and my mother constantly took me by the knees and entreated me to lie with the concubine first, to make her hate the old man. I agreed and did it. And my father realised at once and heaped curses on me, calling up the hateful Erinyes, that he should never sit on his knees a dear son born to me: and his curses were given fulfilment by the gods, Zeus of the underworld and terrible Persephone. My thought was to kill him with the sharp bronze. But one of the immortals stopped my fury, putting in my mind the talk of my people and all the shaming things that men would say, so that I would not have the name of parricide among the Achaians. Then my heart within me could in no way be constrained any longer to live on in the house with my father's anger. Yet my cousins and kinsmen who lived around tried to keep me there in the house with many entreaties – many sturdy sheep and shambling twist-horned cattle were slaughtered, and many hogs rich in fat were laid to singe across the flames of Hephaistos, and much wine was drunk from the old man's jars. For nine nights they spent the nights close by me. They took turns to keep watch, and the fires never died, one under the colonnade in the strong-walled yard, and another in the hallway in front of the bedroom doors. But when I had seen the tenth night's darkness come, then I burst the close-fitting doors of my room and came out, and jumped over the yard-wall with ease, unseen by the men on watch or the servant-women. And then I went running away through the broad spaces of Hellas, and came to fertile Phthia, the mother of flocks, to king Peleus' house. He welcomed me gladly, and loved me as a father loves his son who is an only child, late-born, the heir to many possessions. And he made me a rich man, and made over a numerous people to me: and I lived on the edge of Phthia, ruling over the Dolopes. And I brought you up to your manhood, godlike Achilleus, with heartfelt love. You would never want to go with anyone else to a feast, or eat in your own house, until I sat you on my knees and fed you, cutting up the first of the meat for you and holding wine to your lips. And many times you soaked the shirt on my chest with the wine you dribbled out in your baby helplessness. So I went through much trouble and much hard work over you, thinking how the gods were not going to bring about any child of my own – but I was making you my son, godlike Achilleus, so that in time you can protect me from shameful destruction.

'Come then, Achilleus, master your great passion. You should not have a heart that does not forgive. Even the gods themselves can be turned, and they are greater than us in standing and honour and power. And yet men turn aside the gods' anger with the penitence of sacrifices and humble prayers, and offerings poured and burnt, whenever a man has transgressed and sinned. You see, the Repents are the daughters of great Zeus. They are lame and wrinkled and squint-eyed, and their business is to come behind the course of Folly. Folly is strong and sound of foot: she outruns them all by far, and is first to do her harm in every land where men live – and they come behind with their healing. When a man shows respect as the daughters of Zeus approach, they prosper him and hear his prayers. But if he refuses them and spurns them in the hardness of his heart, then they go to Zeus the son of Kronos and beg him that Folly should visit that man, so that he pays with his own hurt. You too, Achilleus, should give the daughters of Zeus that respect which bends the minds of other men, even the greatest. Now if the son of Atreus was not bringing gifts, and naming more to come, but was keeping up the fury of his resentment, I would not ask you to put away your anger and defend the Argives, for all their need. But now he is offering much to be given immediately, and has promised more to come, and he has chosen the best men in the Achaian army to send here in entreaty, men who are your own dearest friends among the Argives: do not scorn their words or the steps of their journey – though before this there could be no blame for your anger.

'This is what we have heard in tales of the past heroes too, when furious anger came on one of them – they could be won by gifts and words' persuasion. I myself remember this story from long ago, no recent thing: you are all friends, and I will tell you how it happened. The Kouretes and the brave Aitolians were fighting round the city of Kalydon and killing each other, the Aitolians defending lovely Kalydon and the Kouretes intent on sacking it in war. You see, Artemis of the golden throne had sent a plague on the Aitolians, in her anger that Oineus had not offered the first-fruits to her on the crown of his garden – the other gods had their sacrifices to feast on, and it was only to the daughter of great Zeus that he made no offering. Either he forgot or he ignored her – but it was a great blindness in his heart. The archer-goddess grew angry, and sent against him a monster from the gods, a huge wild boar with white tusks, which kept on doing great damage in Oineus' orchards: it uprooted many tall trees and flung them whole on the ground, roots and ripe fruits and all. Oineus' son Meleagros killed the boar, when he had gathered huntsmen and dogs from many cities – since a small band of men could not have brought the beast down, it was so huge, and had set many men on the pyre of sorrow. But Artemis raised a great clamour of fighting over it, over the boar's head and bristling hide, between the Kouretes and the great-hearted Aitolians. Now as long as the warrior Meleagros was fighting, it went badly for the Kouretes, and for all their numbers they could not make a stand outside their city walls. But when the anger entered Meleagros, that anger that swells the heart in the breast of others too, even men of good sense, then in his heart's fury against his own mother Althaia he took to lying idle beside the wife of his marriage, lovely Kleopatra. She was the daughter of Marpessa, lovely-ankled child of Euenos, and of Idas, who was the strongest of all men living on earth at that time – he even took up his bow against the lord

Phoibos Apollo in contest for the lovely-ankled girl: then her father and her honoured mother in their home used to call Kleopatra by the name of Alkyone, because her mother once shared the life of the sorrowing halcyon, the king-fisher, and wept that Phoibos Apollo the far-worker had snatched her away. This was the wife that Meleagros lay with, and brooded on the anger that pained his heart, made furious at his mother for her curses. She prayed long to the gods, in anguish for the killing of her brother, and long she beat her hands on the nourishing earth, bent forward on her knees with the tears soaking her lap, calling on Hades and terrible Persephone to deal her son death: and out of Erebos the Erinys that walks in darkness, and has no pity in her heart, heard her. And soon the clamour and crash of the enemy rose around their gates and the walls were under storm. And the elders of the Aitolians began to entreat Meleagros, sending to him the noblest priests of the gods, to come out and help them, and they promised him a great gift – they told him he could choose the finest piece of land for his own domain, fifty acres in the richest part of the plain of lovely Kalydon, taking half from the plain in vineyards, and half in open ploughland. Many times the old horseman Oineus begged him, standing on the threshold of the high-roofed bedroom and shaking the close-shut doors, imploring his son. And many times his sisters and his honoured mother entreated him, but he refused all the more: and many times his companions, the closest and dearest of all his friends. But even so they could not move the heart in his breast, until the enemy weapons were hitting thick on his own room, and the Kouretes were beginning to climb over the walls and trying to fire the great city. Then his fine-girdled wife entreated Meleagros with tears, and described to him all the miseries that come on people when their city is captured – the men are slaughtered, fire razes the city, and other men carry away the children and the deep-girdled women. His heart was stirred as he listened to these horrors, and he went out, and clothed his body in its gleaming armour. So he gave way to his own feeling, and kept off the evil day from the Aitolians. But they did not go on to pay him those many lovely gifts – he kept away their destruction, but for nothing. Dear friend, please do not have the mind that he did. Do not let the gods turn you that way – it will be worse for you if you bring help when the ships are burning. No, come while the gifts are yours – the Achaians will honour you like a god. But if you enter the fighting which takes men's lives without the gifts, then your honour will be less, even though you do push the battle away from them.'

Then swift-footed Achilleus answered him: 'Phoinix, old father, my lord, I have no need of that honour. I think I am already held in honour by the will of Zeus, which will always be with me by the beaked ships, as long as there is breath in my chest and lift in my knees. I tell you another thing, and you mark it well in your mind. Do not upset my heart with your tears and anguish, to serve the will of the hero son of Atreus: you should not feel love for him, so that the love I have for you does not turn to hate. Your honour is to join me in hurting any man who hurts me – take half of my kingdom, share my royal honour. These two can take my message back: you stay with me here, and sleep here in a soft bed. Then with the showing of dawn we shall consider whether to return to our own land or to stay.'

So he spoke, and gave a silent signal to Patroklos with his eyebrows, to lay a thick bed for Phoinix, so that the others should think soon of leaving his hut. Then Aias, godlike son of Telamon, spoke out: 'Royal son of Laertes, resourceful Odysseus, let us go. I do not think there will be any achievement of our mission on this journey at least. We must take the news, bad though it is, to the Danaans as soon as we can – they must be sitting waiting for it now. But Achilleus has turned his heart's high passsion to savagery in his breast. Cruel man, he has no thought for the love of his companions, how we honoured him more than any other by the ships. He has no pity – and yet a man will accept recompense for his dead brother, or his own son, from the man who killed him: the killer pays a great blood-price and stays on in his country, and the other's heart and high anger are kept down when he takes the payment. But the heart the gods have put in your breast is implacable and perverse, all because of a girl, one girl – but now we are offering you seven, the very finest, and much more besides them. Then turn your heart to kindness, remember the welcome owed by your house: we are under your roof, we have come from the whole body of the Danaans, and we trust we are beyond all others the closest and dearest to you of all the Achaians.'

Then swift-footed Achilleus answered him: 'Aias, royal son of Telamon, leader of your people, all that you have said seems much after my own feeling. But my heart swells with anger whenever I think of that time, how the son of Atreus treated me with contempt in front of the Argives, as if I were some migrant without rights. No, you go back and tell this message. I will not think of bloody warfare until wise Priam's son, godlike Hektor, has killed his way through the Argives right up to the Myrmidons' huts and ships, and has set the ships smouldering with fire. But at my hut and my black ship I think that Hektor will be stopped, however much he lusts for battle.'

So he spoke, and they each took a two-handled cup and made libation, then went back along the line of ships: and Odysseus led the way. Patroklos gave orders to his men and his serving-women to lay a thick bed for Phoinix without delay. They obeyed and made up a bed as he told them, with fleeces and a rug and the finest linen. There the old man lay down and waited for the holy dawn. And Achilleus slept in the corner of his well-built hut, and beside him lay a woman he had brought from Lesbos, Phorbas's daughter, beautiful Diomede. Patroklos lay down on the opposite side. He too had a woman lying beside him, the fine-girdled Iphis – Achilleus had given her to him when he took steep Skyros, the city of Enyeus.

Now when the others reached the huts of Agamemnon, the sons of the Achaians rose to their feet and from all sides drank their welcome in gold cups, and began to question them. First to ask was Agamemnon, lord of men: 'Tell me, famed Odysseus, great glory of the Achaians – is he willing to keep the enemy fire from our ships, or did he refuse, and does the anger still rule his proud heart?'

Then much-enduring godlike Odysseus answered him: 'Most glorious son of Atreus, Agamemnon, lord of men, the man will not quench his anger, but he is filled all the more with fury, and rejects both you and your gifts. He tells you to think for yourself with the Argives of a way to save the ships and the Achaian army – and for himself he threatened that with the showing of dawn he would drag his well-benched balanced ships down to the water. And he said he would advise the rest of you too to sail back home, since you will not now reach your goal in steep Ilios – wide-seeing Zeus has held his hand firm above the city, and its people have taken strength. That is what he said – and there are the others who went with me to tell you the same, Aias and the two heralds, wise men both. But the old man Phoinix has lain down to sleep there, as Achilleus told him, so that tomorrow he can join them in their voyage to their dear native land, if that is his wish – he will not force him to go.'

So he spoke, and they all stayed silent, shocked by his words and the great force of his speaking. For a long time the sons of the Achaians sat silent and dispirited. But then finally Diomedes, master of the war-cry, spoke out: 'Most glorious son of Atreus, Agamemnon, lord of men, you should never have made entreaty to the excellent son of Peleus and offered him countless gifts. He is a proud man at any time

– and now you have sent him yet further into his pride. No, let us leave him be, to go or stay. He will fight again when the heart in his breast urges him and god sets him to it. Come then, let us all do as I say. Now you should go to bed, now that you have satisfied your hearts with food and wine, which give a man strength and courage. Then when rosy-fingered dawn appears in her beauty, you, Agamemnon, should quickly draw up your forces, men and chariots, in front of the ships and urge them on, then fight yourself among the leaders.'

So he spoke, and all the kings applauded his proposal, delighted at the speech of Diomedes the horse-tamer. And then after libations they went each to his own hut. There they lay down and took the benison of sleep.

BOOK 10
NIGHT OPERATIONS

The other leading men of the Achaians slept the night long beside the ships, mastered by soft sleep. But sleep did not keep its sweet hold on Agamemnon, son of Atreus, shepherd of the people, whose mind was filled with worry. As when the husband of lovely-haired Hera sends flashes of his lightning, a sign that he is preparing a huge downpour of rain or hail, or a snow-blizzard, when snow covers over the fields – or perhaps somewhere the great jaws of biting war: such were the frequent groans in Agamemnon's breast, coming from the depth of his heart, and his mind trembled within him. When he looked out over the Trojan plain, he was horrified by the many fires burning in front of Ilios, by the sound of their reed-flutes and pipes and the hubbub of the men. And when he looked back to the ships and the Achaian army, he would tear the hair from his head by the roots in supplication to Zeus on high, and his glorious heart groaned loud. This seemed the best plan to his thinking, to go first to Nestor, Neleus' son, before any other man, in the hope that Nestor could help him devise a sure strategy which might prove salvation for all the Danaans. He rose and dressed his body in a tunic: he bound his fine sandals under his shining feet, then slung round him the blood-red hide of a great tawny lion, reaching to his feet, and took up his spear.

Menelaos likewise was in the grip of fear, and sleep did not sit on his eyelids either – fear that harm would come to the Argives, who for his sake had come over much water to Troy with the bold design of war. First he covered his broad back with a spotted leopard-skin, then lifted his bronze helmet and put it on his head, and took up a spear in his massive hand. And he set on his way to rouse his brother, who was high king over all the Argives and honoured by his people like a god. He found him putting his fine armour over his shoulders by the stern of his ship: and Agamemnon was glad to see him come. Menelaos, master of the war-cry, spoke to him first: 'Brother, why this arming? Are you hoping to send one of your companions out to spy on the Trojans? But I very much fear that no-one will undertake this task for you, to go out alone through the immortal night and spy on the enemy – he would need a brave heart indeed.'

Then lord Agamemnon answered him: 'You and I need a plan, lord Menelaos, and a clever one, to protect and rescue the Argives and their ships, now that Zeus' heart has turned away from us. It seems that Hektor's offerings have won his heart more than ours. I have never yet seen or heard others tell of one man creating so much damage in a single day as Hektor, loved of Zeus, has done to the sons of the Achaians, and all by himself – he is no son of god or goddess. But he had done things to us which I think the Argives will remember for long, long to come – such is the harm he has dealt the Achaians. But go now, run quickly along by the ships and call Aias and Idomeneus: and I shall go to godlike Nestor and urge him up, to see if he is willing to visit the strong company of guards and give them instructions. They will listen to him most of all, as the captains of the guards are his own son and Idomeneus' follower Meriones – they are the ones we gave the greatest responsibility.'

Then Menelaos, master of the war-cry, answered him: 'I will do so, but what are your further instructions for me? Shall I stay there with them, and wait for you to come – or run back to join you after giving them their orders?'

Then Agamemnon, lord of men, answered him: 'Stay there, so we do not miss each other as we go – there are many paths across the camp. Call out wherever you pass, and tell the men to keep awake – give each man the honour of his titles, and call him by the names of his father and family. Do not let your heart be too proud – no, we too must work hard ourselves: such is the heavy burden of hardship Zeus must have laid on us at our birth.'

So speaking he sent off his brother with full instructions: and he went in search of Nestor, the shepherd of the people. He found him by his hut and his black ship on a soft bed. Beside him lay his crafted armour, his shield and a pair of spears and his shining helmet. By him too was the glittering belt which the old man buckled round him when he armed and led his people into the fighting which takes men's lives, since he would make no concession to cruel old age. He lifted his head and sat up on his elbow, and spoke to the son of Atreus with a question: 'Who are you, going alone along the ships and through the camp in the darkness of night, when other men are sleeping? Is it a mule you are looking for, or one of your companions? Speak, do not come on me in silence. What is your business?'

Then Agamemnon, lord of men, answered him: 'Nestor, son of Neleus, great glory of the Achaians, you must recognise Agamemnon son of Atreus – the man more than all others immersed by Zeus in troubles without end, for as long as there is breath in my chest and lift in my knees. I am brought here like this because sweet sleep will not sit on my eyes, but my thoughts are on the war and the Achaians' danger. I am terribly afraid for the Danaans, and my heart will not stay still, but I am in an agony of fear – my chest will not contain my heart's leaping, and my body is trembling under me. Come, if you are ready for action – and sleep is not visiting you either – come with me and let us go out to the guards and inspect them, in case weariness and lack of rest have exhausted them and they have fallen asleep, quite forgetting their watch-duty. The enemy are encamped right close to us: and we do not know – they could even decide to attack at night.'

Then the Gerenian horseman Nestor answered him: 'Most glorious son of Atreus, Agamemnon, lord of men, Zeus the counsellor will not bring all Hektor's thoughts to fulfilment, all that he must now be hoping. Rather I think he will be struggling with yet more troubles than you, if Achilleus turns his heart away from his ruinous anger. I shall certainly come with you. And let us wake some others too – Tydeus' son, the famous spearman, and Odysseus and Aias the runner and the brave son of Phyleus. And someone should go and call two more, godlike Aias and lord Idomeneus – their ships are the furthest and not within easy distance. But, love and respect him though I do, I must blame Menelaos, and I will not hide it from you, even if you are angry with me, for the way he sleeps on and has left the work to you alone. He should be at work himself now, going round all the leading men and begging their support – there is a need on us now which is urgent.'

Then Agamemnon, lord of men, answered him: 'Old man, at other times I would even encourage you to find fault with him. Often he hangs back and is not willing to enter the work – it is not fear that makes him reluctant, or weakness of mind, but he looks to me and waits for my initiative. But this time he was up well before me and it was he who came to me: and I sent him out to call the men you are asking for. So let us go. We shall meet them with the guards outside the gates, where I told them to gather.'

Then the Gerenian horseman Nestor answered him: 'This way none of the Argives will resent him or fail to obey when he urges them on and gives them orders.'

So speaking he dressed his body in a tunic, and bound his fine sandals under his shining feet, then pinned around him a purple cloak that spread wide in a double fold, with the wool nap thick on it. He took up a strong spear, sharp-edged with pointed bronze, and went on his way along the ships of the bronze-clad Achaians. Then the first man that the Gerenian horseman Nestor woke from sleep was Odysseus, Zeus' equal in his mind's resource. He called to him, and the sound reached through to his consciousness straightaway. Odysseus came out of his hut and spoke to them: 'What are you doing, wandering alone like this along the ships and through the camp in the immortal night? The need must be serious.'

Then the Gerenian horseman Nestor answered him: 'Royal son of Laertes, resourceful Odysseus, do not be angry – the misery that has overcome the Achaians is indeed that great. But come with us, so we can wake others too who should be with us when we debate the issue of flight or battle.'

So he spoke, and resourceful Odysseus went into his hut and slung his crafted shield round his shoulders, then joined them on their way. They went on to Diomedes, son of Tydeus, and found him with his armour outside his hut. His companions were sleeping around him, with their shields under their heads: their spears were stuck upright in the ground by the butt-spike, and the bronze points flashed out far like the lightning of father Zeus. The hero was sleeping, with the hide of a field ox spread beneath him and a bright rug laid out under his head. The Gerenian horseman Nestor came up to him and stirred him awake with his foot, and urged him up with a direct taunt: 'Wake up, son of Tydeus! Why this sleeping all night long? Have you not heard that the Trojans are encamped on the rise of the plain close to our ships, and only a little ground now separates us?'

So he spoke, and Diomedes jumped quickly up from his sleep and spoke winged words to Nestor: 'You are hard, old man: you never stop working. Are there not other sons of the Achaians younger than you who could be running up and down waking all the kings? But you, old man, are more than we can manage.'

Then the Gerenian horseman Nestor answered him: 'Yes, my friend, all that you say is right. I have fine sons, and I have many men too under my command – one of them could run and do the calling. But a crisis of great gravity has overcome the Achaians. Now the fate of all the Achaians stands balanced on a razor's edge – either death in utter misery or survival. Well, if you pity me, you go now and rouse Aias the runner and Phyleus' son – you are a younger man than I.'

So he spoke, and Diomedes slung round his shoulders the hide of a great tawny lion, reaching to his feet, and took up his spear. The hero went on his way, roused the men, and brought them with him from their huts.

When they all reached the place where the guards were gathered, they found that the captains of the guard were not sleeping either, but they were all sitting wakeful under arms. Like dogs who keep restless watch over the sheep in a farmyard, when they have heard some savage beast as he comes down through the forest on the mountains: behind him there is a great clamour of men and hounds, and sleep for the dogs is gone. So sweet sleep was gone from the eyelids of the guards as they watched through the dangerous night: they were turned always towards the plain, waiting for the sound of a Trojan attack. The old man was delighted when he saw them, and spoke encouragement to them in winged words: 'That is the way, dear children! Keep watching now like that – and let none of you fall prey to sleep, so that the enemy do not have their joy of us.'

So speaking he moved out over the ditch: and he was followed by all the kings of the Argives who had been called to the meeting. With them also went Meriones and Nestor's splendid son, invited by the kings to join their conference. When they had crossed over the deep ditch they settled in a clear space, where room could be seen free of fallen corpses. It was the place where monstrous Hektor had turned back from his slaughter of the Argives, when night had covered the field. Here they sat down, and their talk began. The Gerenian horseman Nestor was the first to speak: 'Friends, will not some man have the confidence in his own daring heart to go out among the great-hearted Trojans, to see if he can perhaps catch an enemy straggler, or even perhaps hear some of the Trojans' talk and the plans they are making among themselves – whether they are determined to stay far out here by the ships, or will move back to the city, now that they have worsted the Achaians? He might find all this out, and come back to us unscathed. And then he would win great glory among all men under the heavens, and honourable gifts will be his – all the leading men who have power in our fleet will each give him a black sheep, a ewe with her suckling lamb, the finest of possessions, and he will always have his place at our feasts and banquets.'

So he spoke, and they all stayed silent. But then Diomedes, master of the war-cry, spoke out: 'Nestor, my heart and proud spirit urge me to penetrate the camp of our enemies the Trojans who are lying so close to us. But if another man would go with me, that would be a comfort and bring greater confidence. When two go together, one is quicker than the other to see where advantage lies – a man on his own may see it, but even so his mind has less range than two, and his resource is not so strong.'

So he spoke, and many of the others were ready to go with Diomedes. The two Aiantes were ready, Ares' men-at-arms, and Meriones was ready; Nestor's son was ready and eager; the son of Atreus, Menelaos the famous spearman, was ready; and the hardy Odysseus was ready to steal among the mass of the Trojans – his heart within him was always full of daring. Then Agamemnon, lord of men, spoke out: 'Diomedes, son of Tydeus, pleasure of my heart, you must choose as your companion the man you want, the best of those you can see, since many are eager to join you. And do not let any respect felt in your heart make you pass by the better man and take the less good with you – do not be ruled by respect and look to a man's birth, even if one is a greater king than the others.'

So he spoke, as he was afraid for fair-haired Menelaos. Then Diomedes, master of the war-cry, spoke again: 'If it is your wish, all of you, that I choose my own companion, then how could I ignore godlike Odysseus? His heart and proud spirit are the readiest of all for every kind of danger, and Pallas Athene loves him. With this man beside me we could even go through blazing fire and both come back safe – the skill of his mind is without equal.'

Then much-enduring godlike Odysseus said to him: 'Son of Tydeus, there is no need for praise or blame – you are speaking among Argives, and they know me. Let us be going. The darkness is wearing fast, and dawn is close. The stars are far over in their course, and most of the night is gone – two thirds are spent, and only the third part is left us.'

So speaking the two of them dressed in fearful arms. The staunch Thrasymedes gave the son of Tydeus a two-edged sword – his own had been left by his ship – and a shield: and on his head he put a helmet made of bull's hide, without knob or crest, the helmet known as 'morion', which protects the heads of strong young fighters. And Meriones gave Odysseus a bow and a quiver and a sword, and on his head he put a helmet of leather, carefully made. It was stretched tight on the inside by many straps: and outside rows of white tusks from a shining-toothed boar ran round it this way and that, well and skilfully fastened: and a layer of felt was fixed between. Autolykos had once stolen it from Amyntor son of Ormenos, breaking through his strong house in Eleon: and he gave it to Amphidamas of Kythera to take to his home in Skandeia. Amphidamas gave it as a gift of friendship to Molos, and he gave it to his son Meriones to wear. And now it was put over Odysseus' head to cover it.

So when the two of them had dressed in their fearful arms, they went on their way, leaving behind all the leading men where they were. And Pallas Athene sent them a heron on the right close to the path. Their eyes could not see it in the darkness of the night, but they heard its cry. Odysseus was delighted at the omen of the bird, and prayed to Athene: 'Hear me, daughter of Zeus who holds the aegis. You always stand by me in every kind of danger, and you have seen my starting out. This time too show me your special love, Athene, and grant that we may come back to the ships in glory, with some great deed achieved that the Trojans will feel hard.'

And after him Diomedes, master of the war-cry, made his prayer too: 'Hear me now also, daughter of Zeus, Atrytone. Be with me now as you were with my father, godlike Tydeus, at Thebes, when he went ahead of the Achaians with a message. He left the bronze-clad Achaians at the Asopos, and went on there bringing proposals of peace to the Kadmeians. But on his journey back he won a grim triumph with your help, divine goddess, when you stood by him in your kindness. So now consent to stand by me, and protect me. And then I will sacrifice to you a heifer, a yearling broad across the brow, unbroken, and never yet brought beneath the yoke – this will be your sacrifice, and I will cover her horns with gold.'

So they spoke in prayer, and Pallas Athene heard them. When they had made their prayers to the daughter of great Zeus, they went on their way like two lions into the black night, through the slaughter and the dead bodies, through the armour and the black blood.

Nor indeed did Hektor allow the proud Trojans to sleep either, but he summoned all the leading men in a body, all the leaders and lords of the Trojans. He called them together and laid before them a plan of his devising: 'Is there any man who will undertake this task for me and carry it out for a great prize? The reward will be there ready for him to claim. I will give a chariot and two strong-necked horses, the finest horses there are by the fast ships of the Achaians, to any man who has the courage – and it will be glory won for him too – to go close to the speedy ships and discover whether their fast ships are guarded as they have been before, or whether now that they have been worsted at our hands they are planning flight among themselves, and utter weariness has exhausted their will to keep watch at night.'

So he spoke, and they all stayed silent. But there was a Trojan called Dolon, son of Eumedes the sacred herald, a man rich in gold and rich in bronze, who was ugly in appearance, but quick of foot: and he was the only son among five sisters. He then spoke to the Trojans and Hektor: 'Hektor, my heart and proud spirit urge me to go close to the speedy ships and spy on them. But come, hold up this sceptre and swear to me that you will give me the horses and the bronze-trimmed chariot that carry the excellent son of Peleus, and I will make you a spy that does not fail you or disappoint your hopes. I shall go right through their camp until I reach Agamemnon's ship, where their leading men must be debating the issue of flight or battle.'

So he spoke, and Hektor took the sceptre in his hands and swore an oath for him: 'Let my witness now be Zeus himself, loud-thundering husband of Hera, that no other Trojan man will be carried by those horses, but I promise they will be your pride for ever.'

So he spoke. He had sworn an oath which would be false, but Dolon was encouraged. Straightaway he slung a curved bow round his shoulders, and put on a grey wolf's pelt over it and a cap of marten skin on his head. And he took a sharp spear, and set on his way out of the camp towards the ships – but in fact he was never to return from the ships and bring his report back to Hektor. However, when he had left behind the gathered throng of men and horses, he set out eagerly along the path. Royal Odysseus saw him coming, and said to Diomedes: 'There is a man here, Diomedes, coming from the Trojan camp, perhaps to spy on our ships, or to strip one of the corpses of the dead – I do not know. Let us let him go past us a little way out into the plain – then we can rush quickly on him and catch him. But if his legs are fast enough to take him clear, keep pressing him towards the ships and away from their camp with lunges of your spear, so that he cannot escape back towards the city.'

With these words they both turned aside from the path and lay down among the dead bodies: and he ran quickly past in his ignorance. But when his distance from them was the width of a day's ploughing by mules – and mules are better than oxen at pulling the jointed plough through deep fallowland – they ran after him, and he stopped at the sound of feet. His heart's thought was that Hektor had changed his order, and these were friends from the Trojans coming to turn him back. But when they were a spear's carry away or even less, he recognised them as enemies and set his legs running fast to escape: and they started straight in pursuit. As when two saw-toothed dogs, experienced hunters, keep pressing relentlessly on after a young deer or a hare across a wooded countryside, and it runs squealing ahead of them, so the son of Tydeus and Odysseus, sacker of cities, ran in relentless pursuit of Dolon and cut him off from his people. But when he was just about to meet with the guards as he ran on towards the ships, Athene put strength into the son of Tydeus, so that no other bronze-clad Achaian should have first claim to the honour of hitting Dolon, and Diomedes reach him too late. Strong Diomedes sprang at him with his spear and said: 'Stop, or my spear will find you – and I do not think you will long escape stark destruction from my hand.'

So he spoke, and let fly his spear, deliberately missing the man. The point of the polished spear went over his right shoulder and stuck in the ground. He stood still and fell into gibbering terror – his teeth began to chatter in his mouth and he went white with fear. They came up with him, breathing hard, and took hold of his arms. He burst into tears and said: 'Take me alive – I shall ransom myself. There is bronze and gold in my, house and iron laboriously worked: my father would give you unlimited ransom from this store, if he learnt that I was alive by the ships of the Achaians.'

Then resourceful Odysseus answered him: 'Do not worry, do not let death weigh on your thoughts. But come, tell me this and tell me in clear truth. Where are you off to, going alone like this away from your camp to the ships in the darkness of night, when other men are sleeping? Is it to strip one of the corpses of the dead? Or did Hektor send you out to spy on everything at the hollow ships? Or was it your own heart's prompting?'

Then Dolon answered him, and his body was trembling: 'Hektor made my mind stray into blindness after blindness. He promised to give me the strong-footed horses and the bronze-trimmed chariot of the proud son of Peleus, and told me to go through the quick black night and come close to the enemy, and discover whether their fast ships are guarded as they have been before, or whether now they have been worsted at our hands they are planning flight among themselves, and utter weariness has exhausted their will to keep watch at night.'

Then resourceful Odysseus smiled at him and said: 'Oh, those are great gifts your heart was set on, the horses of the warrior Achilleus, of Aiakos' stock. Those horses are hard for any mortal man to control or drive, except for Achilleus, and he is the son of an immortal mother.

But come, tell me this and tell me in clear truth. Where did you leave Hektor, shepherd of the people, when you came here now? Where is his war-armour lying? Where are his horses? How are the other Trojans' guard-posts set, and where are they sleeping? And tell me of the plans they are making among themselves – are they determined to stay far out here by the ships, or will they move back to the city, now that they have worsted the Achaians?'

Then Dolon, Eumedes' son, answered him: 'I will tell you all that you ask in clear truth. Hektor is with the counsellors in debate, by the tomb of godlike Ilos, away from the din of the camp. As for the guard-posts you ask me about, hero, there is no special detail of sentries to protect and guard the camp. Each Trojan watch-fire has its appointed men who stay awake and keep each other on their guard. But then our allies called from many lands are sleeping – they leave the watch to the Trojans, as they do not have their children or their wives living close at hand.'

Then resourceful Odysseus answered him: 'Yes, but where are they sleeping? Together with the horse-taming Trojans, or apart from them? Tell me – I want to know.'

Then Dolon, Eumedes' son, answered him: 'I will tell you all this too in clear truth. Towards the sea are the Carians and the Paionians with their curved bows, and the Leleges and Kaukones and godlike Pelasgians. The positions towards Thymbra are taken by the Lycians and the high-hearted Mysians, and the Phrygians who fight from horseback and the Maionian charioteers. But why do you ask me all these details? If you want to get inside the Trojan encampment, over there are the Thracians, newly arrived and lying apart from the others at the very end: and among them is their king Rhesos, the son of Eïoneus. His are the finest horses I have seen and the largest – whiter than snow, and like the winds when they run. His chariot is a beautiful work of gold and silver. And he has come with prodigious armour made of gold, a wonderful sight – such things should not be worn by mortal men, but rather by the immortal gods. Well, take me now to your speedy ships, or tie me up and leave me here in cruel bondage until you have gone and put me to the test, whether the story I have told you is the truth or not.'

Strong Diomedes scowled at him and said: 'I would not want your mind to have any thought of escape, Dolon. Your news is valuable, but you have fallen into our hands. If I ransom you now, or let you go, you will come back again later to the fast Achaian ships either to spy on us or in open battle. But if you are brought down at my hands and lose your life, you will never again be a trouble to the Argives.'

So he spoke, and as Dolon was about to take his chin with his great hand and entreat him, Diomedes lunged with his sword and struck his neck in the middle, cutting through both the tendons – he was beginning to speak as his head dropped in the dust. They took the marten-skin cap from his head, and his wolf-skin and the curved bow and long spear. And godlike Odysseus held them up high in his hand to Athene, and spoke to her in prayer: 'These are yours, goddess, to gladden you – you are the first we will call to of all the immortals on Olympos. Now be with us once more and guide us to the Thracians' camp and their horses.'

So he spoke, and lifted the spoils up high and placed them on a tamarisk bush: and he added a clear mark for the spot, gathering together some reeds and sprouting tamarisk branches, so they should not miss it on their way back through the quick black night. So the two of them went further on through the armour and the black blood, and quickly came to the Thracians' position. They were asleep, worn out with exhaustion, and their fine armour was lying neatly piled beside them on the ground, in three rows: and beside each man was a pair of horses. Rhesos was sleeping in their centre, and beside him his fast horses were tethered by straps to the end of the chariot-rail. Odysseus saw him first, and pointed him out to Diomedes: 'Look, that is the man, Diomedes, and those are his horses which Dolon told us of, the man we killed. Come on then, exert all your great strength. This is no time to stand there with your weapons idle – no, untie the horses: or you start killing the men, and I will see to the horses.'

So he spoke, and bright-eyed Athene breathed strength into Diomedes, and he began killing all around him. Terrible groans arose from the men as they died under his sword, and the earth reddened with blood. As a lion comes on an unshepherded flock of goats or sheep and springs on them with his heart set on slaughter, so Diomedes kept attacking the Thracians until he had killed twelve. And every time the son of Tydeus stood over a man and struck him with his sword, resourceful Odysseus behind him would take the body by the foot and drag it clear, his mind thinking of a path for the lovely-maned horses, so they could pass through easily and not be frightened by treading on corpses – they were not used to them. But when the son of Tydeus came on the king, he was the thirteenth that he robbed of life's sweetness, and his breath came gasping from him. There was a nightmare at his head that night by Athene's devising – and it was Tydeus' son. Meanwhile the hardy Odysseus was releasing the strong-footed horses. He tied them together with the straps and drove them out of the camp, striking them with his bow, as he had not thought to take the shining whip from the crafted chariot. Then he whistled in signal to godlike Diomedes.

But he stayed on, wondering what the most harmful thing was that he could do – whether to take the chariot, which held all the king's crafted armour, and pull it away by the pole or lift it above his head and carry it off, or whether instead he should take the life from yet more Thracians. As godlike Diomedes was thinking this over in his mind, Athene stood by him and spoke to him: 'Think of going back now to the hollow ships, son of great-hearted Tydeus, so you do not have to return in full flight – some other god might well wake the Trojans.'

So she spoke, and he heard the goddess' voice and quickly mounted one of the horses. Odysseus whipped them with his bow, and they flew on towards the Achaians' fast ships.

And Apollo, god of the silver bow, was not keeping blind watch either. He saw Athene taking Diomedes in hand, and was furious at her. So he went down into the crowded Trojan camp and woke one of the Thracians' counsellors, Hippokoön, Rhesos' noble cousin. He jumped up from his sleep, and when he saw the empty place where the fast horses had stood, and his men gasping out their lives amid horrible carnage, then he cried out aloud and called on the name of his dear companion. There were shouts from the Trojans and a mighty uproar arose as they rushed crowding to the spot: and they looked on the dreadful work done by the two men now gone on their way to the hollow ships.

When these two came to the place where they had killed Hektor's spy, Odysseus, loved of Zeus, held back the fast horses while the son of Tydeus jumped to the ground and put the bloody spoils in Odysseus' hands, then mounted again. He whipped the horses, and they flew eagerly on towards the hollow ships with willing hearts. Nestor was the first to hear the thud of their approach, and he said: 'Friends, leaders and lords of the Argives, will I be wrong in this – my heart urges me to say it – or will it be the truth? The thud of horses' running feet is beating at my ears. May it be that Odysseus and strong Diomedes are driving home some strong-footed horses straight from the Trojan camp – but my heart is terribly afraid that the best of the Argives have met with trouble and the Trojans are clamouring after them.'

He had not finished speaking when the two men came in. They dismounted to the ground, and the others greeted them with delight, taking their hands and speaking warm words of welcome. The Gerenian horseman Nestor questioned them first: 'Tell me, famed Odysseus, great glory of the Achaians, how did you two come by these horses? Did you steal inside the Trojan camp, or did some god meet you and give them to you? They are fearfully like the rays of the sun, the way they shine. Day after day I meet the Trojans – old though I am for the fight, I can claim to do no shirking by the ships – but I have never yet seen or come across such horses as these. No, it was some god, I think, that met you and gave them to you – both of you are loved by Zeus the cloud-gatherer and the daughter of Zeus who holds the aegis, bright-eyed Athene.'

Then resourceful Odysseus answered him: 'Nestor, son of Neleus, great glory of the Achaians, a god, if he wished, could easily give even better horses than these, since gods' power is much greater than ours. These horses that you ask of, old man, are new arrivals, come from Thrace. Their master was killed by brave Diomedes, and with him twelve of his companions died also, nobles all of them. A thirteenth to be killed was a spy we caught close by the ships, sent out by Hektor and the other proud Trojans to pry about our camp.'

So speaking he drove the strong-footed horses across the ditch, laughing in triumph: and the other Achaians went joyfully with him. When they came to Diomedes' well-built hut, they tied the horses with straps of well-cut leather by the manger where Diomedes' own quick horses stood eating their honeyed wheat. And Odysseus placed the bloody spoils from Dolon in the stern of his ship, until they could get ready a dedication to Athene. Then the two men waded into the sea and washed away the heavy sweat from their legs and necks and thighs. When the sea's waves had cleansed the thick sweat from their skin and their hearts were refreshed, they stepped into polished tubs and took their bath. Then when they had bathed and rubbed themselves richly with oil, they sat down to a meal, and drawing honey-sweet wine from the full bowl they poured offerings to Athene.

BOOK 11
ACHAIAN RETREAT

Dawn now rose from her bed beside lordly Tithonos, to bring light to deathless gods and mortal men. And Zeus sent Strife down to the fast ships of the Achaians, the cruel goddess, holding in her hands a sign of war. She took her stand on Odysseus' black huge-bellied ship, which lay in the very middle, so that a shout could be heard on both sides, right to the huts of Aias son of Telamon and to Achilleus' station on the other side – both of these had beached their balanced ships at the far ends, confident in their bravery and the strength of their hands. There the goddess stood and uttered a great fearful shout, piercing loud, and in each Achaian's heart she put great strength for warfare and battle without ceasing. Then war became a sweeter thought to them than returning in their hollow ships to their own dear native land.

And the son of Atreus shouted his command to the Argives to buckle on their armour: and among them he himself armed in gleaming bronze. First he placed greaves on his legs, a fine pair, fitted with silver ankle-pieces. Next he put a corselet round his chest, which Kinyres once gave him as a gift of friendship. The great news had come to him in Cyprus that the Achaians were to sail a fleet against Troy: and so he made Agamemnon a gift of the corselet, to please the king. It had ten bands of dark blue enamel, and twelve of gold, and twenty of tin: and enamel snakes reached up to the neck, three on each side, like rainbows which the son of Kronos fixes in the cloud as a sign for humankind. Over his shoulders he slung his sword: there were gold nails shining on it, and the scabbard sheathing it was of silver, attached to a baldric of gold. And he took up his mighty covering shield, a beautiful piece of intricate work which was plated with ten circles of bronze, and there were twenty bosses round it, white with tin, and at the centre of the plates one boss of dark blue enamel. Crowning the shield was the grim mask of Gorgo, glaring fearfully, with Terror and Panic on either side. The shield-strap was made of silver, and along it there wound an enamel snake, with three heads growing from a single neck and twisting this way and that. And on his head he placed a four-bossed helmet, set round with horns, with a plume of horse-hair: and the crest nodded fearfully from its top. And he took up two strong spears, sharp-tipped with bronze, whose gleam struck bright far into the sky. And Athene and Hera thundered over him, showing honour to the king of golden Mykene.

Then each gave instructions to his charioteer to pull in the horses in proper order right by the ditch's edge, and they themselves swarmed over on foot, dressed in all their armour: and their shouts rose ceaseless in the early morning. They made formation along the other side of the ditch well before the chariot-drivers, who came some way behind. And the son of Kronos started a troubled commotion among them, and from the height of the sky he rained down over them drops of blood, since it was his intention to hurl down to Hades many mighty heads of heroes.

On the other side the Trojans gathered at the rise of the plain, around huge Hektor and the excellent Poulydamas, and Aineias who was honoured like a god by the Trojan people, and the three sons of Antenor, Polybos and godlike Agenor and Akamas, not yet married, a man like the immortal gods. And Hektor carried the even circle of his shield among the front ranks. Like the deadly star which appears clear out of the clouds in all its shining, then sinks back again behind the shadowing clouds: so Hektor would constantly appear now with the front ranks, now among the rearmost, urging them on. And his whole body shone with bronze like the lightning of father Zeus who holds the aegis.

As bands of reapers work towards each other on a rich man's land, cutting their swathes to meet across a field of wheat or barley: and the crop falls handful after handful to the ground. So the Trojans and Achaians leapt at each other and cut men down, and neither side had any mind for cruel flight. The battle held them even, and they savaged like wolves. And Strife, goddess of misery, looked on with joy: she was the only one of the gods attending the fighting – the other gods were not there, but sitting at their ease in their own homes, where each had his lovely house built along the folds of Olympos. They were all at issue with the son of Kronos, lord of the dark clouds, because it was his will to give glory to the Trojans. But the Father cared nothing for the gods: he drew away from the others and sat down apart, glorying in his splendour, and looking out over the Trojans' city and the ships of the Achaians, at the flash of bronze and men killing and being killed.

For as long as it was morning and the holy day was waxing, the weapons thrown by both sides reached their mark, and men kept falling. But when a woodcutter makes his dinner in the mountain glens – when his hands are tired with cutting the tall trees and weariness has touched his heart, and desire for the pleasure of food takes over his mind – then the Danaans showed their worth and, calling to each other down the ranks, they broke the enemy line. Agamemnon was the first to spring through and kill his man, Bienor, shepherd of his people – first him, then his fellow Oïleus the charioteer: he jumped down from the chariot to face Agamemnon, but as he rushed straight for him Agamemnon stabbed him in the forehead with his sharp spear, and the heavy bronze of his helmet's rim could not stop the spear, but it went through that and through the bone, and all his brains were spattered inside, and the man brought down in his fury. Agamemnon, lord of men, left them as they lay, bright now only with the gleam of their bare chests, where he had stripped their clothing. And he went on to kill Isos and Antiphos, two sons of Priam, bastard and true son, both riding in one chariot – the bastard son was charioteer and glorious Antiphos the fighting-man beside him. These two had once been caught by Achilleus as they were shepherding their sheep on the spurs of Ida: he had bound them with willow twigs, and then released them for ransom. But now the son of Atreus, wide-ruling Agamemnon, hit Isos with his spear in the chest above the nipple, and Antiphos he struck by the ear with his sword and hurled him out of the chariot. Then hurriedly he stripped the fine armour from them, and recognised them – he had seen them before by the fast ships, when swift-footed Achilleus had brought them in from Ida. As a lion easily crunches up the infant young of a quick-running deer, when he has come to their den and caught them in his powerful teeth, and takes the soft life from them: and even if their mother is close by, she can be no help to them. She herself is taken with panic-shivers: and she darts away fast through the dense growth of the forest, driven to a sweat of speed by the great beast's attack. So it was that none of the Trojans could keep these two from destruction – they were all running themselves in panic before the Argives.

Then Agamemnon caught Peisandros and brave Hippolochos, sons of the wise Antimachos, who in return for a splendid gift of gold from Alexandros was always most strongly opposed to the return of Helen to fair-haired Menelaos. His, then, were the two sons that lord Aga- memnon caught, both riding in one chariot: the two together were trying to manage their fast horses – the shining reins had dropped from their hands and the horses were in confusion. The son of Atreus sprang like a lion to face them, and they began to beg for his mercy, right there where they stood in the chariot: 'Take us alive, son of Atreus, and win a ransom of proper worth. There are many treasures stored in Antimachos' house – bronze and gold, and iron laboriously worked. Our father would give you unlimited ransom from this store, if he learnt that we were alive by the ships of the Achaians.'

So these two wept their appeal to the king – soft words, but the answer they heard was hard: 'If you are the sons of wise Antimachos – the man who, when Menelaos had once come on an embassy with godlike Odysseus, urged the assembled Trojans to kill him on the spot and not allow him passage back to the Achaians – then now you will pay for your father's abominable crime.'

So he spoke, and knocked Peisandros out of the chariot to the ground with a spear-blow to his chest: he crashed to the earth on his back and lay still. Hippolochos jumped down, and this one he killed on the ground: he sliced off arms and head with his sword, and sent the trunk rolling log-like through the mass of men. He let them lie, and leapt on to where the enemy ranks swarmed thickest, taking the other well-greaved Achaians with him. Then there was massacre and hacking bronze as soldiers cut down soldiers beaten into flight, and chariots fell on chariots – a cloud of dust rose under them from the plain, kicked high by the thundering feet of horses. And lord Agamemnon drove on in pursuit, shouting to the Argives and killing all the time. As when annihilating fire falls on a thick forest scrub, and the wind carries it billowing all over, and the bushes are brought down headlong in the flames' overwhelming onslaught, so the fleeing Trojans went down under Agamemnon, son of Atreus, and many strong-necked horses rattled empty chariots along the avenues of battle, missing the noble charioteers they knew: but they lay dead on the ground, a sight now to gladden the vultures, not their wives.

Now Zeus drew Hektor away out of the flying weapons and the dust, out of the slaughter and the blood and the clamour: and the son of Atreus pressed on his pursuit, shouting loud to the Danaans. The Trojans streamed back over the open plain, past the tomb of old Ilos, of Dardanos' line, and past the fig-tree, urgent to reach their city: and the son of Atreus, bellowing, pursued them on and on, with blood spatter-ing his invincible hands. When the first Trojans reached the Skaian gates and the oak-tree, they stopped there and waited for the others.

But they were still in the middle of the plain stampeding like cows, when a lion has come in the dead of night and panicked the whole herd – but one is faced with stark destruction: the lion first breaks her neck in the grasp of his strong jaws, then gulps her blood and all her inwards. So the son of Atreus, lord Agamemnon, kept harrying the Trojans, constantly killing the hindmost, and they ran on in panic. Many were flung crashing from their chariots on their backs or on their faces, as the spear raged furious in the son of Atreus' hands. But when he was close to reaching the city and its steep wall, then the father of men and gods came down from the sky and settled on the peaks of Ida of the many springs: and he held a thunderbolt in his hands. He sent Iris the golden-winged speeding to give his message: 'Away with you, swift Iris, and tell what I say to Hektor. As long as he can see Agamemnon, shepherd of the people, raging among the front-fighters and cutting down the ranks of men, he should keep back and urge the rest of his army to fight against the enemy in the battle's fury. But when a spear-hit or arrow-shot sends Agamemnon to mount his chariot, then I shall grant Hektor the power to go on killing until he reaches the well-benched ships and the sun sets and the holy darkness comes on.'

So he spoke, and swift Iris with feet quick as the wind did not fail to obey. She went down from the heights of Ida to sacred Ilios, and found wise Priam's son, godlike Hektor, standing behind his horses in the strongly-made chariot. Swift-footed Iris came close and spoke to him: 'Hektor, son of Priam, Zeus' equal in your mind's resource, father Zeus has sent me with this message for you. As long as you can see Agamemnon, shepherd of the people, raging among the front-fighters and cutting down the ranks of men, you should withdraw from the combat and urge the rest of your army to fight against the enemy in the battle's fury. But when a spear-hit or arrow-shot sends Agamemnon to mount his chariot, then Zeus will grant you the power to go on killing until you reach the well-benched ships and the sun sets and the holy darkness comes on.'

So speaking swift-footed Iris left him. Hektor jumped down to the ground from his chariot with all his armour, and shaking a pair of sharp spears in his grip he ranged all through the army, spurring them to fight and rousing their spirit for grim battle. They rallied and turned to stand against the Achaians, and the Argives on the other side strengthened their ranks. So the battle-lines were set, and they faced each other: and Agamemnon was the first to charge in, eager to lead the fighting ahead of all others.

Tell me now, you Muses who have your homes on Olympos, who was the first of the Trojans themselves or their famous allies to come out against Agamemnon? It was Iphidamas, the son of Antenor, huge and brave. He had grown up in fertile Thrace, the mother of flocks. His grandfather Kisseus had brought him up in his own house when he was small – the father of his mother, lovely-cheeked Theano. When he reached the time of manhood, when young men seek glory, Kisseus tried to keep him there, and offered him his daughter. He married her, then went straight from the marriage-room, drawn by the news of the Achaians' arrival, and came to Troy with twelve beaked ships accompanying him. He had then left his balanced ships in Perkote, and travelled on foot to Ilios: and now he came out to face Agamemnon, son of Atreus. When these two had advanced to close range, the son of Atreus missed with his cast and his spear flew wide. Iphidamas stabbed at his belt below the corselet, and pressed on the spear with all his weight, trusting in the strength of his hand: but it did not pierce through the shining belt – well before that the point met silver and was turned like lead. And wide-ruling Agamemnon grasped the spear with his hand, pulled it towards him with the rage of a lion, and wrenched it from his grip: then he struck him in the neck with his sword, and collapsed his strength. So he fell where he was and slept the bronze sleep – pitiable man, far from the wife he had won, bringing help to his countrymen – far from the bride of his marriage: he had known no benefit of her, and had given much to win her: he had given a hundred cattle first, and promised a further thousand, goats and sheep mixed, from his immense flocks at pasture. And now Agamemnon son of Atreus killed and stripped him, and went carrying his fine armour through the press of the Achaians.

Now when Koön saw him, a man of note and the eldest of Antenor's sons, overpowering sorrow for his fallen brother clouded his eyes. He came up unseen to one side of godlike Agamemnon with his spear, and stabbed him in mid-arm below the elbow, and the shining spear's point passed right through. Then Agamemnon, lord of men, shuddered in horror: yet even so he would not stop his fighting or leave the battle, but leapt at Koön with his spear of wind-toughened grain. He had his brother Iphidamas, his own father's son, by the foot and was intent on dragging him away, shouting for help to all the leading fighters. As he dragged him back through the press Agamemnon stabbed him under his bossed shield with his bronze-headed spear-shaft, and collapsed his strength: then he stepped close and hacked off Koön's head over the body of Iphidamas. So there Antenor's sons filled the measure of their fate at the hands of king Agamemnon, and sank down into Hades.

But the son of Atreus kept plying his attack along the rest of the Trojan line, with spear and sword and huge stones, as long as the blood still gushed warm from his wound. But when the wound started to dry and the flow ceased, then sharp pains began to overcome his strength of spirit. As when a woman in labour is taken with the sharp stab of piercing pain sent by the Eileithyiai, daughters of Hera, who bring the bitter pangs of childbirth, so sharp pains began to overcome the son of Atreus' strength. He jumped up into his chariot and told his charioteer to drive for the hollow ships, as he was sick at heart. And he called in a great carrying shout to all the Danaans: 'Friends, leaders and lords of the Argives, now it is you who must keep the grim battle from our sea-going ships, since Zeus the counsellor has not allowed me to fight the whole day long against the Trojans.'

So he spoke, and his charioteer whipped the lovely-maned horses back to the hollow ships, and they flew eagerly on their way. Their chests flecked with foam, and dust spread under their bellies, as they carried the suffering king away from the fighting.

When Hektor saw Agamemnon leaving the field, he called out to the Trojans and Lycians with a great shout: 'Trojans and Lycians and close-fighting Dardanians, be men, my friends, and fill your minds with fighting spirit. The best of their men is gone, and Zeus the son of Kronos has granted me great glory. Now drive your strong-footed horses straight for the might of the Danaans, so you can win a yet higher glory.'

So speaking he spurred the strength and heart in each of them. As when a huntsman sets his white-toothed hounds at a wild boar or a lion, so Hektor, Priam's son, set the great-hearted Trojans against the Achaians, and he drove them on like Ares, curse of men. He himself strode out in the forefront with high thoughts in his mind, and fell on the fight like a squally storm-wind that swoops down on the violet sea and sets it heaving.

Then who was the first, and who the last slaughtered by Hektor, Priam's son, when Zeus gave him the glory? Asaios first, and Autonoös and Opites, and Dolops son of Klytios, and Opheltios and Agelaos, Aisymnos and Oros and steadfast Hipponoös. These were the leaders of the Danaans that he killed. And then he fell on the soldiery, as when the west wind batters the clouds that a bright southerly has set white in the sky, lashing them with dense storm-blasts – huge waves roll multitudinous, and the spray is flung high under the errant wind's roar. So thick and fast were the men brought down headlong at Hektor's hands.

Then there would have been havoc and doings beyond all remedy, and the Achaians would have been turned to flight and hurled back on their ships, if Odysseus had not called to Diomedes, the son of Tydeus: 'Son of Tydeus, what has come over us to make us forget our fighting spirit? Come then, dear friend, and stand by me here. It will be our great shame if Hektor of the glinting helmet captures our ships.'

Strong Diomedes answered him: 'Yes, I shall stand firm and take the attack. But we can bring only short joy to our friends, since Zeus the cloud-gatherer is minded to give victory to the Trojans rather than to us.'

So he spoke, and knocked Thymbraios out of his chariot to the ground, hitting him with his spear-cast on the left nipple: and Odysseus killed the king's lieutenant, godlike Molion. They left them there where they lay, their fighting ended, and charged in among the press of the enemy spreading havoc, as when two boars round and hurl themselves in high fury on the dogs that hunt them – so these two turned to the attack and cut into the Trojans, and the Achaians gained welcome respite as they ran clear of godlike Hektor.

Then they caught a chariot and the men in it, leading men of their district, the two sons of Merops from Perkote, who had knowledge of seercraft beyond all others, and kept trying to stop his sons from going to war which takes men's lives. But they would not listen to him, as the fates of black death were leading them on. These the son of Tydeus, the great spearman Diomedes, robbed of life and breath, and took the glory of their armour. And Odysseus killed Hippodamos and Hypeirochos.

Then the son of Kronos, looking down from Ida, strained the battle taut and level, and there was killing on both sides. The son of Tydeus struck Agastrophos, the hero son of Paion, in the hip-joint with his spear. He did not have his chariot close by for escape – a fatal error. His lieutenant was holding the horses at a distance, while he raced on through the front-fighters on foot, until he lost the life that was in him. Hektor was quick to see this across the ranks of men, and set off to attack the two of them: with him there followed the Trojan battalions. Diomedes, master of the war-cry, shuddered to see him coming, and spoke quickly to Odysseus, who was close by: 'Here comes that horror, the massive Hektor, surging towards us. Come on, let us stay firm and beat him off where we stand.'

So he spoke, and steadying his long-shadowed spear he let it fly – his aim was the head, and he did not miss, hitting high on the helmet. Bronze glanced off bronze, and failed to reach the handsome flesh, turned by the masking helmet, three layers thick, that Phoibos Apollo had given him. Hektor quickly ran a great way back to join the mass of his men, then dropped to his knees and stayed there, leaning with his heavy hand on the earth: and black night covered over his eyes. While the son of Tydeus was following the flight of his spear, far through the front-fighters to the place where it had fallen to earth, Hektor came back to his senses: he jumped into his chariot and drove away back into the crowd, and escaped black doom. Strong Diomedes sprang after him with his spear, and called out: 'Dog, this time you have escaped death once more – but your end came very close. This time Phoibos Apollo protected you – doubtless you pray to him when you set out for the thud of spears. I promise I shall finish you next time we meet, if any god has aid for me too. For now, I shall attack any I can catch of the others.'

So he spoke, and turned to the stripping of Paion's spear-famed son. But Alexandros, husband of lovely-haired Helen, was bending his bow against the son of Tydeus, shepherd of the people, leaning against the gravestone on the burial mound that men had built for Ilos, of Dardanos' line, the elder of the land in former times. Diomedes was taking the armour from powerful Agastrophos, the shining corselet from his chest, the shield from his shoulders and the strong helmet, as Alexandros drew back against the grip of his bow and shot – the weapon did not fly wasted from his hand, but hit on the flat of his right foot, and the arrow went right through and fixed in the ground. Alexandros jumped out from his cover with a happy laugh, and spoke in triumph: 'You are hit – my arrow did not fly wasted. How I wish I had hit you in the base of the belly and taken the life from you! Then the Trojans would have had respite from their misery – they shiver with fear of you like bleating goats before a lion.'

Undismayed strong Diomedes replied: 'You sorry arrow-slinger, curled dandy, leering lecher, if you took me on face to face in armour, your bow and cluster of arrows would be no help to you. Now you crow on when you have just scratched the flat of my foot. It troubles me as much as if a woman had hit me, or a silly child – there is no edge to a worthless coward's shot. Far different is the bite of a weapon cast by me – even a slight touch strikes a man dead on the spot. Then his wife's cheeks are torn in grief, and his children made orphans: he reddens the ground with his blood and rots there, and birds flock round him then, not women.'

So he spoke, and Odysseus, the famous spearman, came close and stood covering him. Behind him Diomedes sat down and pulled the sharp arrow out of his foot, and fierce pain stabbed through his flesh. He jumped up into his chariot and told his charioteer to drive for the hollow ships, as he was sick at heart.

Now Odysseus, the famous spearman, was left by himself, and none of the Argives stood by him, as fear had taken hold of them all. In dismay he spoke to his own great heart: 'What will become of me now? A great dishonour if I turn and run in fear of their numbers: but worse if I am caught isolated – the son of Kronos has put the rest of the Danaans to flight. But what need for this debate in my heart? I know that it is cowards who keep clear of fighting, while the brave man in battle has every duty to stand his ground in strength, and kill or be killed.'

While he was pondering this in his mind and his heart, the ranks of the Trojan warriors came on and penned him in, surrounding him – but they were making trouble for themselves. As when hounds and strong young huntsmen are crowding a boar, and he comes at them out of a dense thicket, whetting the white tusks in the angle of his jaws: as they run to surround him there comes a gnashing of his tusks, but for all his fearsomeness they stand firm before him. So then the Trojans came crowding round Odysseus, loved of Zeus. He first leapt at the excellent Deïopites and caught him in the shoulder with a high thrust of his sharp spear, and then he killed Thoön and Ennomos. Then when Chersidamas jumped down from his chariot he stabbed him in the crutch with his spear, under his bossed shield: he crashed in the dust and his hand clawed earth. He let these lie, and stabbed Charops, Hippasos' son, with his spear – the full brother of Sokos, a man of great wealth. Sokos, godlike man, came up to protect his brother, and stood close by Odysseus and said to him: 'Famed Odysseus, glutton for scheming and hardship, today you will either boast over two sons of Hippasos, killing two fine men and stripping their armour, or my spear will strike you down and take the life from you.'

So speaking he stabbed at the even circle of Odysseus' shield. Through the bright shield the strong spear went, and on through the worked corselet, forcing its way. It stripped all the flesh from his ribs, but Pallas Athene would not let it go on to sink into the man's inwards. Odysseus realised that the weapon had reached no vital place, and stepping back he spoke to Sokos: 'Poor wretch, stark destruction is surely coming on you now. Yes, you have stopped my fighting with the Trojans: but for you, I tell you here and now this day brings death and black doom – you will be brought down under my spear and give me my triumph and a life to Hades the horseman.'

So he spoke. Sokos turned to flight and began running back. But as he turned Odysseus fixed his spear in his back between the shoulder-blades and drove it on out through the chest. He fell with a crash, and godlike Odysseus spoke in triumph over him: 'Sokos, son of wise Hippasos the horse-tamer, the end of death was quick to catch you – you could not escape. Poor wretch, you will not have your father and honoured mother to close your eyes in death – no, carrion birds will fold their wings thick over you and tear your flesh. But I, if I die, will have full burial from the godlike Achaians.'

So speaking he began to pull the warrior Sokos' strong spear out from his flesh and through the bossed shield. Blood shot up as the spear was pulled clear, and pained his heart. When the great-hearted Trojans saw Odysseus' blood, they called across their massed ranks and made for him all together. He moved back, and shouted for his companions. Three times he shouted with all the voice a man can hold, and three times the warrior Menelaos heard him calling. Quickly he spoke to Aias, who was nearby: 'Aias, royal son of Telamon, leader of your people, I can hear the shouts of enduring Odysseus, sounding as if the Trojans have cut him off and are overpowering him on his own. Come, let us go to him through the mass of fighting. We had better rescue him – I am afraid that, brave man that he is, he will come to some harm if left alone among the Trojans, and there will be a great loss for the Danaans.'

So speaking he led the way, and the godlike man went with him. Then they found Odysseus, loved of Zeus. The Trojans were crowding round him like blood-red mountain jackals round a horned stag that has been wounded, shot by a huntsman with an arrow from the string: his legs get him clear of the man, running for as long as the blood flows warm and there is lift in his knees: but when the swift arrow has overcome his strength, the flesh-eating jackals tear him in the mountains, in a shadowy wood. Then some god brings by a marauding lion: the jackals scatter, and the lion makes his meal. So it was then that many brave Trojans crowded round the resourceful warrior Odysseus, but with lunges of his spear the hero was keeping off the pitiless hour of death. But then Aias came close carrying a shield like a tower, and took his stand beside him: and the Trojans scattered in terror this way and that. The warrior Menelaos took Odysseus by the hand and led him out of the fighting, while his lieutenant drove his chariot close.

Aias leapt at the Trojans and killed Doryklos son of Priam, a bastard son, and then stabbed Pandokos and Lysandros and Pyrasos and Pylartes. As when a river swollen in winter spate courses down to the plain from the mountains, sped by rain from Zeus, and sweeps into its current many dead trees, oaks and pines, and washes a mass of driftwood into the sea, so then glorious Aias swept havoc over the plain, cutting down horses and men. But Hektor knew nothing of this yet, as he was fighting far on the left of the battle, by the banks of the river Skamandros, where men's heads were falling thickest, and the clamour rose ceaseless around huge Nestor and the warrior Idomeneus. These were the company Hektor was keeping, and he was doing grim work with spear and chariot-craft, and breaking the ranks of young fighters. But even so the godlike Achaians would not yet have yielded to his path, if Alexandros, husband of lovely-haired Helen, had not put an end to the brave exploits of Machaon, shepherd of the people, hitting him in the right shoulder with a three-barbed arrow. The Achaians who breathe boldness were terrified for him, in case the battle shifted and he was captured. Idomeneus quickly spoke to godlike Nestor: 'Nestor, son of Neleus, great glory of the Achaians, come on, mount your chariot and have Machaon get up beside you, and hold your strong-footed horses at full speed to the ships. A healer is a man worth many others, for his skill to cut out arrows and spread wounds with soothing medicines.'

So he spoke, and the Gerenian horseman Nestor did not fail to obey. He immediately mounted his chariot, and Machaon got up beside him, the son of the peerless healer Asklepios. He whipped the horses, and they flew eagerly on towards the hollow ships with willing hearts.

Now Kebriones, standing beside Hektor in his chariot, saw that the Trojans were being routed, and spoke to him: 'Hektor, we two are consorting here with the Danaans out on the margin of the grim clash of battle. But the rest of the Trojans, chariots and men, are being routed pell-mell. And it is Aias son of Telamon who is causing the havoc – I can tell him well from the broad shield he carries slung from his shoulders. Let us steer our horses and chariot straight over there to join them, where the grimmest struggle is set and the killing of horsemen and foot-soldiers is at its height, with the clamour rising ceaseless.'

So speaking he whipped on the lovely-maned horses with the whistling lash: and they hearing its crack carried the speedy chariot fast towards the Trojans and Achaians, trampling on bodies and shields as they ran – and all the axle beneath and the rails round the car were spattered with blood, flung up in gouts from the horses' hooves and the rims of the wheels. Hektor was urgent to enter the mass of men, to charge in and break them: and he set a terrible commotion among the Danaans, and his spear had little rest. He kept plying his attack along the rest of the Achaian line, with spear and sword and huge stones, but he kept clear of battle with Aias son of Telamon.

But then father Zeus who sits on high stirred fear in Aias. He stopped, scared, and slung his shield of seven ox-hides behind his back, and looking sharply round him turned in retreat towards his own army, like a wild beast, rounding often as he went, step by short step. As country farmers and their dogs drive a tawny lion from the inner yard where the cattle are: they keep night-long watch and will not let him tear the fat from their cows: in his hunger for meat he charges in, but gains nothing – spears fly thick against him from brave hands, and burning faggots, which frighten him back for all his eagerness: and at early morning he goes away in distress of heart. So then Aias went back from the Trojans, distressed at heart and much against his will, as he was fearful for the Achaians' ships. As when a donkey – a stubborn creature, who has had many sticks broken on both sides of him – ignores the efforts of the boys leading him alongside a field, and turns in to crop the deep corn: the boys beat him with their sticks, but their strength is feeble, and they only drive him out with much effort, when he has had his fill of food. So then the great-hearted Trojans and their allies drawn from many places kept crowding the huge Aias, Telamon's son, stabbing with their spears at the centre of his shield. And every so often Aias would recapture his fighting spirit, swing round, and hold back the ranks of the horse-taming Trojans: and then again he would turn in retreat. So he kept the whole force of them from their advance on the fast ships, making a furious stand alone in the space between Trojans and Achaians. And of the spears thrown by brave hands and eager to taste flesh, some flew on and fixed themselves in his great shield, and many stuck in the earth between, before they could reach his white flesh.

Now when Euaimon's splendid son Eurypylos saw that Aias was beset by dense volleys of weapons, he came up and stood at his side, and let fly with his shining spear, and hit Apisaon, Phausias' son, shepherd of the people, in the liver under the midriff, and instantly collapsed his strength. Eurypylos leapt forward and began to take the armour from his shoulders. Now when godlike Alexandros saw him taking Apisaon's armour, he immediately drew his bow at Eurypylos and hit him with an arrow in the right thigh: the shaft snapped off, and pain burdened his thigh. He moved back into the mass of his companions to avoid destruction, and called in a great carrying shout to all the Danaans: 'Friends, leaders and lords of the Argives, rally now and stand your ground, and keep the pitiless hour of death from Aias – he is beset by flying spears, and I do not think he can escape from the grim clash of war. So stand and front them round huge Aias son of Telamon.'

So spoke the wounded Eurypylos, and they closed round him, sloping their shields against their shoulders and holding their spears out at the ready. Aias came to join them, then turned and stood firm when he had reached the mass of his companions.

So they fought on like burning fire. Meanwhile his sweating horses, mares of Neleus' breed, were carrying Nestor out of the battle and bringing out Machaon also, shepherd of the people. Now swift-footed godlike Achilleus noticed and saw him – he was standing on the stern of his great-bellied ship, watching the war's stark work and the painful rout. Quickly he spoke to his companion Patroklos, calling from the ship. Patroklos heard him inside the hut, and came out looking like Ares the god of war: and this was to be the beginning of his doom. The brave son of Menoitios spoke first: 'Why do you call me, Achilleus? What do you want of me?' Then swift-footed Achilleus answered him: 'Godlike son of Menoitios, pleasure of my heart, now I think the Achaians will crowd at my knees in supplication – there is a need on them now which is urgent. But for the moment, Patroklos loved of Zeus, go and ask Nestor who this man is he is bringing wounded out of the battle – all of his back view looks like Machaon the son of Asklepios, but I did not see the man's face, as the horses were pressing onward and shot by me.'

So he spoke, and Patroklos obeyed his dear companion, and went running along by the huts and the ships of the Achaians.

When those two reached the hut of Nestor, son of Neleus, the men dismounted on to the nourishing earth, while his lieutenant Eurymedon unyoked the old man's horses from the chariot. They dried off the sweat from their tunics, standing in the breeze by the sea-shore, then went into the hut and sat down on the chairs. And lovely-haired

Hekamede prepared them a toddy – the old man had won her at Tenedos when Achilleus sacked the town: she was the daughter of great-hearted Arsinoös, and chosen by the Achaians as a special gift for Nestor, for his supremacy over all in the giving of advice. She first moved up a table for them, a beautiful polished table with feet of dark blue enamel, and on it she placed a bronze dish with an onion as accompaniment for the drink, and fresh honey, and beside it bread of sacred barley-meal. Next a most beautiful cup, which the old man had brought from home – it was studded with rivets of gold, and there were four handles to it: on each handle a pair of golden doves was feeding, one on either side: and there were two supports below. Another man would strain to move it from the table when it was full, but Nestor, the old man, could lift it with ease. It was in this cup that the woman, beautiful as the goddesses, mixed them their drink out of Pramnian wine, over which she grated goat's cheese on a bronze grater, and sprinkled white barley: and when the toddy was prepared, she told them to drink. Now when both had drunk and quenched their parching thirst, and were enjoying the pleasure of their conversation, Patroklos came and stood in the doorway, a godlike man. Seeing him the old man rose from his shiny chair, and led him in by the hand, and asked him to sit down. But Patroklos declined where he stood, and said: 'No time for sitting, old king, and you will not persuade me. He is a forbidding man, and quick to anger, the one who sent me out to ask who this man is you are bringing in wounded – but I can recognise him for myself, and see that it is Machaon, shepherd of the people. Now I shall go back to tell the news to Achilleus. You know well enough, old king, what a terrible man he is: he is likely to blame even the blameless.'

Then the Gerenian horseman Nestor answered him: 'Now why does Achilleus show such concern for those sons of the Achaians who have been wounded by flying weapons – when he knows nothing of the great distress that has afflicted the whole army? Our leading men are lying wounded in their ships, shot or stabbed. Tydeus' son, strong Diomedes, has been hit: Odysseus, the famous spearman, and Agamemnon have been stabbed: Eurypylos too has been hit by an arrow in the thigh: and now here is another I have just brought in from the battle hit by an arrow from the string. No, Achilleus is a great fighter but he has no thought or pity for the Danaans. Is he waiting until the Argives can do nothing to stop their fast ships burning by the sea with fire to destroy them, and we are all slaughtered in heaps? Because my strength is not what it once was in the flex of my body. Would that I were as young, and the power was still in me, as when a quarrel arose between us and the Eleans over a cattle raid, when I killed Itymoneus, the brave son of Hypeirochos, who lived in Elis. I was driving off his herds in reprisal, and he was fighting for his cattle at the head of his men when he was hit by a spear from my hand, and fell to the ground, and his country troops scattered. Then we rounded up a huge amount of spoil from the plain – fifty herds of cattle, as many flocks of sheep, as many droves of pigs, as many ranging flocks of goats, one hundred and fifty bay horses, all of them mares, and many with foals under them. And we drove them all, through the night, into Neleus' city of Pylos: and Neleus was happy at heart that as a youngster going into battle I had met such success. Then with the showing of dawn the heralds made their clear summons for all to come who had debts owed them in holy Elis. And the leading men of Pylos gathered together and began the division of spoils – there were many owed debts by the Epeians, as we in Pylos had been weakened and reduced in numbers. The mighty Herakles had come and weakened us in previous years, and all the best men had been killed. There had been twelve of us sons of the excellent Neleus, and I was the only one left – all the others had perished. Growing confident at this the bronze-clad Epeians carried out horrors of aggression against us. So now the old man Neleus took a herd of cattle from the spoils and a huge flock of sheep, picking out three hundred of them and their shepherds too. Because he also was owed a great debt in holy Elis – four prize-winning horses together with their chariot, which had gone to the games and were to run for the prize of a tripod: but Augeias, lord of men, kept them there, and sent back their driver distraught at the loss of the horses. So the old man, in his anger at what Augeias had said and done, chose a vast quantity of spoils for himself, and gave the rest for division among the people, so that he should have none of them leaving without his fair share.

'We then were settling all this, and making sacrifices to the gods around the city. Then on the third day the Epeians invaded in all their numbers, and they came at full speed: and armed in their company went the two Moliones, still boys then, and not yet well versed in fighting. There is a steep hill-town called Thryoëssa, far away beside the Alpheios, at the edge of sandy Pylos. They laid siege to this town, intent on breaking it apart. But when they had overrun the whole plain, Athene came speeding to us in the night from Olympos with the news that we must arm, and throughout Pylos she raised an army of men who were in no way reluctant, but full of eagerness for battle. Neleus would not let me arm for the fight, and hid away my horses – he said I did not yet know enough about war's work. But even so I distinguished myself among our chariot-fighters, even though I went on foot, since this was how Athene directed the battle. There is a river called Minyeïos emptying into the sea near Arene: here we horsemen of the Pylians waited for the holy dawn, while the companies of foot-soldiers streamed in. From there we marched at speed in full armour, and at mid-day we reached the holy stream of Alpheios. There we sacrificed fine victims to almighty Zeus, a bull to Alpheios and a bull to Poseidon, and to bright-eyed Athene a cow from the herd. Then we took our supper at our posts throughout the army, and lay down to sleep, every man in his armour, along the banks of the river. Meanwhile the great-hearted Epeians were surrounding the town, intent on breaking it apart – but before they could do that, they witnessed a great feat of arms. When the sun rose glowing over the earth, we joined in battle, making our prayers to Zeus and Athene. Now when the fighting began between Pylians and Epeians, I was the first to kill a man, and I took over his strong-footed horses. He was Moulios the spearman, a son-in-law of Augeias and married to his eldest daughter, fair-haired Agamede, who knew all the drugs that the broad earth grows. As he came at me I hit him with my bronze-tipped spear, and he crashed in the dust. I jumped into his chariot and took my place with the front-fighters. But the great-hearted Epeians scattered in terror this way and that, when they saw the man fall, the leader of their horsemen and the best of their fighters. And I charged on like a black storm-wind, and caught fifty chariots, and each time two men sank their teeth into the ground, one on either side, brought down under my spear. And now I would have broken the two young Moliones, of Aktor's line, if their father, the wide-ruling Earthshaker, had not covered them in thick mist and taken them safe from the battle. Then Zeus granted the Pylians a great victory. We kept chasing them across the wide plain, killing the men and picking up their fine armour, until we had brought our horses to the wheatfields of Bouprasion and the rock of Olenos and the hill called the hill of Alesion – there Athene turned our people back. Then I killed my last man and left him there: and the Achaians drove their fast horses back from Bouprasion to Pylos, and all gave the glory to Zeus among gods and Nestor among men.

'That is the man I was, if ever I was, among my fellow-men. But

Achilleus will be the only one to profit from his bravery. Indeed I think profit will turn to long weeping afterwards, when his people have perished. My dear friend, this is the advice Menoitios gave you on the day when he sent you from Phthia to join Agamemnon. We were in the house, I and godlike Odysseus, and we heard all the advice that he gave you. We had come to Peleus' pleasant house on our journey through fertile Achaia, gathering troops. There we found the hero Menoitios in the house, and you, and Achilleus beside you. The old horseman Peleus was burning the fat-wrapped thigh-bones of an ox to Zeus who delights in thunder, out in the enclosed yard: he was holding a golden cup and pouring gleaming wine in libation as the offerings burned. You two were busy with the meat of the ox, when the two of us came and stood in the gateway. Achilleus jumped up in astonishment, and led us in by the hand, and told us to sit down, and laid proper hospitality before us, as is the way with strangers. When we had taken our pleasure in food and drink, I began the talking, and urged you both to come with us. You two were fully willing, and your fathers both gave you much advice. The old man Peleus instructed his son Achilleus always to be bravest and best and excel over others, then this was the advice given to you by Menoitios, son of Aktor: "My child, by birth Achilleus is superior to you, but you are the older. He is far stronger than you, but your proper task is to give him words of wisdom and advise him and guide him – and he will listen to you for the best." That was the old man's advice, and you are forgetting it. But even now you could speak like this to the warrior Achilleus, in the hope of winning him. Who knows if, with god's help, you might move his heart with your persuasion? There is power in a friend's persuasion. But if there is some prophecy known in his heart which prevents him, or some word from Zeus told him by his honoured mother, then let him at least send you out, and all the rest of the Myrmidon army behind you, and you could bring saving light to the Danaans. And let him give you his own fine armour to wear into battle, so the Trojans might take you for him and hold off their fighting, and the warrior sons of the Achaians gain relief in their weariness – there is little respite in war. You men are fresh, and the Trojans exhausted in the clamour of battle – you could easily drive them back on their city away from our ships and huts.'

So he spoke, and moved the heart in Patroklos' breast: and he went running along by the ships towards Achilleus of Aiakos' stock. But when his running brought him by godlike Odysseus' ships, where they had their meeting-place and court (and there too they had built their altars to the gods), there he was met by Eurypylos, royal son of Euaimon, wounded in the thigh by an arrow, and limping out of the battle. The sweat ran in streams from his head and shoulders, and dark blood was gushing from his painful wound, but the spirit was still strong in him. Seeing him, the brave son of Menoitios felt pity for him, and spoke winged words to him in distress: 'You poor men, leaders and lords of the Danaans, so it was your fate then to glut the quick dogs of Troy with the white fat of your bodies, far from your families and fatherland! But tell me, Eurypylos, royal hero, will the Achaians still perhaps be able to hold the monstrous Hektor, or will they now be brought down in destruction under his spear?'

Then the wounded Eurypylos answered him: 'My lord Patroklos, there can be no defence now for the Achaians – they must fall back on their black ships. All those who before now were our leading fighters are lying wounded in their ships, shot or stabbed at the hands of the Trojans – and their strength grows all the time. But help me at least and take me to my black ship. Then cut the arrow from my thigh, and wash the dark blood from it with warm water, and spread soothing medicines on the wound, those benign drugs they say you have learnt from Achilleus – and he was taught them by Cheiron, most civilised of the Centaurs. As for our healers, Podaleirios and Machaon, I think that Machaon is lying wounded in his hut, in need himself of an excellent healer, and the other is out on the plain brunting the anger of the Trojans' attack.'

Then the brave son of Menoitios answered him: 'How can all this be done? What are we to do, lord Eurypylos? I am on my way to speak to the warrior Achilleus as Gerenian Nestor, warden of the Achaians, has urged me. But even so I will not desert you in your trouble.'

So he spoke, and held the shepherd of the people round the waist, and helped him to his hut. His lieutenant, when he saw him, spread ox-hides for him to lie on. There Patroklos laid him down, and with a knife cut the sharp piercing arrow-head from his thigh, and washed the dark blood from it with warm water, and applied a bitter root, rubbing it first in his hands, a pain-killer, which stopped all his pain: and the wound dried, and the bleeding ceased.

BOOK 12
THE ASSAULT ON THE WALL

So the brave son of Menoitios was healing the wounded Eurypylos there in his hut. Meanwhile the others fought on, Argives and Trojans in massed battle. And the Danaans' ditch was not going to hold longer, or the broad wall rising above it, which they had made round their ships and driven the ditch along its length, without offering splendid hecatombs to the gods. They had made it to protect their fast ships and the mass of booty it held behind it: but it was built without the immortal gods' sanction, and therefore it did not stand long. For as long as Hektor was alive and Achilleus kept up his anger, and the city of king Priam remained unsacked, the great wall of the Achaians also stood firm. But when all the leading men of the Trojans had been killed, and many of the Argives brought down, while others survived, and the city of Priam was sacked in the tenth year, and the Argives had left in their ships for their dear native land, then Poseidon and Apollo planned the destruction of the wall, turning the power of the rivers against it, all the rivers that flow out to the sea from the mountains of Ida, Rhesos and Heptaporos and Karesos and Rhodios and Grenikos and Aisepos, and holy Skamandros and Simoeis, where many ox-hide shields and helmets and a race of men half-divine had fallen in the dust. Phoibos Apollo turned all these rivers to join at one mouth, and for nine days he hurled their waters at the wall: and Zeus rained without ceasing, to wash the wall the sooner into the sea. The Earth-shaker himself took the foremost part, his trident in his hands, and carried away in his waves all the foundations of logs and stones that the Achaians had laboured to set, and made all smooth beside the strong flow of the Hellespont, and covered the deep shore once more with sand, after vanishing the wall: and he turned the rivers to run in the course where their lovely waters had flowed before.

This then was how Poseidon and Apollo were going to deal with it in later time. But then the clamour of battle was blazing round the well-built wall, and the timbers of the battlements rang with blows. The Argives, beaten down by the lash of Zeus, were kept penned back at their hollow ships in their fear of Hektor, that powerful creator of panic – and Hektor fought as he had before, like a whirlwind. As when a boar or a lion, revelling in his strength, turns and turns about amid a company of dogs and huntsmen: they form themselves into a wall and stand to face him, and let fly volleys of spears from their hands: but his glorious heart feels no fear or fright, and it is his courage that kills him: constantly he rounds in an attempt on the ranks of men, and wherever he charges the ranks give way. So Hektor went turning up and down the mass of his companions, urging them to cross the ditch. But his swift-footed horses would not make the attempt for him, but stopped whinnying loud, at the edge of the lip. They were frightened by the breadth of the ditch, not easy to jump right over or to cross through, as along the whole length both sides rose in overhanging cliffs, and the upper edge was fitted with sharp stakes which the sons of the Achaians had fixed there, long and close-set, as a defence against their enemies. A horse pulling a strong-wheeled chariot could not easily get over there, and they were wondering if they could succeed in crossing on foot. Then Poulydamas came up to brave Hektor and said: 'Hektor, and you other leaders of the Trojans and allies, it is folly for us to drive our fast horses across the ditch. It is very hard to cross – there are sharp stakes set on its edge, and the Achaians' wall is close beyond them. There is no room there for horsemen to dismount and fight – it is a narrow space, where I think we will suffer losses. Now if Zeus the high-thunderer is planning misery for them and their utter destruction, and is eager to give help to the Trojans – then of course I would want that to happen immediately, the Achaians to perish here in oblivion far from Argos. But if they round on us in counter-attack from the ships, and we are fouled in the ditch they have dug, then under the rally of the Achaians I doubt that even one man would get back to the city with the news. No, come, let us all do as I say. The horses should be held by our lieutenants at the ditch's edge, while we cross on foot, dressed in all our armour, all of us massing behind Hektor. The Achaians will not stand our attack, if indeed they are fastened now in the threads of death.'

So Poulydamas spoke, and his saving advice pleased Hektor. He immediately jumped down to the ground from his chariot with all his armour: and the other Trojans did not stay formed in their chariots either, but they all jumped down when they saw Hektor do so. Then each gave instructions to his charioteer to pull in the horses in proper order right by the ditch's edge; and they arranged themselves in separate companies, and marched behind their leaders in five divisions.

Those who went with Hektor and the excellent Poulydamas were the largest and bravest of the companies, and the most determined to break through the wall and carry the battle to the hollow ships: and Kebriones was the third in their number – Hektor had left another man with his chariot, a lesser man than Kebriones. The next company was led by Paris and Alkathoös and Agenor, and the third by Helenos and godlike Deïphobos, two sons of Priam – and their third leader was the hero Asios, Asios son of Hyrtakos, whose great bay horses had carried him from Arisbe, from the river Selleëis. The fourth was led by Anchises' noble son Aineias, and with him two sons of Antenor, Archelochos and Akamas, both skilled in all the ways of battle. Sarpedon led the famous allies, and chose to join him Glaukos and the warrior Asteropaios: they seemed to him preeminently the best men of the others, after himself – he was outstanding among them all. They dressed close to each other, joining their shields of worked ox-hide, and then charged furiously straight for the Danaans: and they thought there would be no holding them now, but they would hurl themselves on the black ships.

Then all the other Trojans and their far-famed allies followed the advice of the excellent Poulydamas. But Hyrtakos' son Asios, chief of his people, would not leave his horses where they were, or his charioteer lieutenant, but came up to the fast ships chariot and all – poor fool, he was not to escape the vile fates of death and make his return back from the ships to windy Ilios in all the glory of his horses and chariot: before that accursed doom enfolded him by the spear of Idomeneus, proud son of Deukalion. Asios went to the left of the ships, the way where the Achaians used to return from the plain with their horses and chariots. Here he drove his horses and chariot across, and found at the gateway that the two doors with their long cross-bar were not shut to – men were holding them open, to allow any of their companions running in from the battle a safe return to the ships. He held his horses right on, aiming straight for it, and his men followed with loud cries, thinking that the Achaians could not hold them now, and would be hurled back on their black ships. Poor fools – in the gateway they came upon two men of the bravest, great-hearted sons of Lapith spearmen, one the son of Peirithoös, strong Polypoites, and the other Leonteus, a man like Ares the curse of men. These two took their stand in front of the tall gates like high-topped oak-trees in the mountains, which stand firm against wind and rain for all their days, fast-fixed by their great roots stretching down. So these two, confident in the strength of their hands, stood firm against the onrush of the huge Asios and would not turn to flight. With a great war-shout, and holding high their shields of dried ox-hide, the Trojans made straight for the strong-built wall, around lord Asios and Iamenos and Orestes, and Asios' son Adamas and Thoön and Oinomaos. For a while the two Lapiths had been inside the wall, urging the well-greaved Achaians to fight in defence of their ships. But when they saw the Trojans storming at the wall, and there was the clamour of panic among the Danaans, they rushed out of the gates and began fighting in front of them, like a pair of wild boars in the mountains which face a rowdy rabble of men and dogs as it moves up on them, and with slanting charges they smash the undergrowth around them and tear it out by the roots, and there comes a gnashing of their tusks, until a man hits them with his cast and takes the life from them. So there came a clatter from the shining bronze on the breasts of these two as they faced the hurl of weapons. They fought on with great power, confident in their own strength and the troops on the wall above, who kept up a barrage of stones flung from the well-built battlements, fighting for their own safety and for their huts and speedy ships. Stones showered to the ground like snowflakes, which a blizzard wind, bowling the shadowy clouds, drives thick over the nourishing earth. So the weapons streamed from their hands, from Achaians and from Trojans: and helmets and bossed shields rang hollow as rocks huge as mill-stones crashed onto them. Then Asios, son of Hyrtakos, groaned aloud, and struck his thighs and cried out in anguish: 'So, father Zeus, even you too are turned utter liar! I never thought that the Achaian heroes would hold against our fury and our invincible hands. But now, like twist-waisted wasps or bees who have made their houses by a rocky path, and will not leave their hollow home, but face the men who come to hunt them and fight to defend their babies, so these men, only two of them, will not give way from the gates before killing or being killed.'

So he spoke, but these words did not turn the mind of Zeus: his heart wished to give the glory to Hektor.

Now other companies were fighting at other gates – a hard task for me to tell of all this, as if I were a god: because all around the stone wall monstrous fire was rising, and the Argives were forced in their misery to fight now for their ships. And all the gods who helped the Danaans in battle were anguished at heart.

But the two Lapiths now joined fierce battle. Then Peirithoös' son, strong Polypoites, struck Damasos with his spear through his bronze-cheeked helmet: the bronze of the helmet could not stop it, but the bronze spear-point went right through and smashed the bone, and all his brains were spattered inside, and the man brought down in his fury. And then he killed Pylon and Ormenos. And Leonteus, branch of Ares, struck Hippomachos with his spear, the son of Antimachos, hitting him through the belt. Next he drew his sharp sword from its scabbard, sprang forward into the mass of men, and at close quarters struck Antiphates first – he crashed to the earth on his back and lay still: then next Menon and Iamenos and Orestes – all these, one after another, he brought down to the nourishing earth.

While these two were stripping the glittering armour from the men they had killed, the young men with Poulydamas and Hektor, who formed the largest and bravest of the companies, and the most determined to break through the wall and fire the ships, were still standing along the edge of the ditch in hesitation. A bird-omen had appeared to them as they stood eager to cross, a soaring eagle which skirted the front of the army from right to left, holding in its talons a monstrous blood-red snake, alive and still struggling: and the snake had not yet lost its will to fight – it twisted back and struck at its captor on the breast beside the neck, and the eagle, stung by the pain, let it fall to the ground, dropping it in the middle of their numbers, then with a yelp it flew on along the breath of the wind. The Trojans shuddered with fright when they saw the wriggling snake lying there among them, a potent sign from Zeus who holds the aegis. Then Poulydamas came up to brave Hektor and said: 'Hektor, you always seem to be hard on me in assemblies when I give good advice, since of course it is not at all right for a commoner to speak his mind against yours, either in debate or on the battle-field – no, we must all uphold your authority. Now however I shall speak out as seems to me best. We should not go on to fight the Danaans for their ships. I tell you what I think will be the result – if indeed this was an omen for the Trojans which appeared to us as we stand eager to cross, the soaring eagle which skirted the front of our army from right to left, holding in its talons a monstrous blood-red snake, alive: but then it dropped the snake before reaching its own home, and did not succeed in bringing it back to give to its children. So it will be with us. Even if we bring our great strength and break through the gates and the Achaians' wall, and the Achaians give way, there will be no orderly return for us along the same ways back from the ships. We shall leave many of the Trojans behind, cut down by the Achaians' bronze as they fight to defend their ships. This is the interpretation a seer would give, one with sure knowledge of signs in his heart, and the confidence of his people.'

Hektor of the glinting helmet scowled at him and said: 'Poulydamas, what you say now is not to my liking. You are capable of conceiving better advice than this. But if this is a serious proposal you are making, then the very gods themselves have destroyed your wits, if you are telling me to ignore the will of loud-thundering Zeus, the promise and solemn assent which he himself gave me, while you would have me put my trust in birds flapping their wings – I have no thought for them, I care nothing for them, whether they fly to the right towards the east and the sunrise, or to the left towards the western darkness. No, let us put our trust in the will of great Zeus, who is king over all mortals and immortals. One omen is best of all – to fight for your country. What have you to be afraid of in battle and fighting? Even if all the rest of us are slaughtered right and left by the Argive ships, you need have no fear of being killed – because you have not the heart that faces the enemy and fights. But if you do hold back from the fighting, or work your persuasion on anyone else to turn him away from battle, then my spear will instantly strike you down and take the life from you.'

So speaking Hektor led on, and the men followed with a tremendous clamour. And with them Zeus who delights in thunder raised a storm of wind from the mountains of Ida, which whirled the dust straight at the ships: he was fooling the minds of the Achaians and granting the glory to Hektor and the Trojans. So they, trusting in the signs from Zeus and their own strength, began the attempt to break through the great wall of the Achaians. They tore at the supports for the battlements and tried to smash down the parapets, they brought levers to the posts which the Achaians had angled in the ground at the face to buttress the fortifications, and tried to root them out, hoping that this would collapse the Achaian wall. But the Danaans would not yet yield to their attack: they fenced the battlements with ox-hides, and from there they kept up a volley against the enemy as they came up under the wall.

The two Aiantes ranged up and down along the battlements, constantly urging the Achaians and spurring their strength for the fight – kind words for some, for others hard words of abuse, whenever they saw a man hanging right back from the fighting: 'Friends, Argives of all ranks – outstanding fighters, middle-rankers, and lesser men – not all men are of equal worth in war, but now there is work for all of you, and you must know that yourselves. No turning back to the ships, now you have heard your commander's orders, but keep on forward and urge each other on, and Zeus the Olympian lord of the lightning may grant that we beat back the attack and send the enemy running to their city.'

So these two, shouting their encouragement, spurred on the Achaians' fighting. Like the flakes of snow which fall thick on a winter's day, when Zeus the counsellor has begun to snow and reveals his weaponry to mankind: he stills the winds and pours down a fall without ceasing, until he has covered the peaks of the high mountains and the sharp headlands and the plains where clover grows and the rich fields of men's farming: and along the grey sea it piles on inlets and capes, though the waves beating in on it can keep it back: all else is enfolded from above, when Zeus' shower falls heavy — so thick flew the stones on both sides, on the Trojans, and on the Achaians from Trojan hands, as they hurled them at each other, and the noise of it rose over the whole length of the wall.

And even then the Trojans and glorious Hektor would not yet have broken through the gate of the wall and its long cross-bar, if Zeus the counsellor had not set his own son Sarpedon at the Argives, like a lion on twist-horned cattle. He held the even circle of his shield in front of him — a fine shield of beaten bronze, which a smith had beaten out for him, then stitched layers of ox-hide inside with stitches of gold thread running all round the rim. Holding this shield in front of him and with two spears in his grip he set out like a mountain lion, who has been long without meat, and his proud heart urges him to break right in to a close-built fold and try for the sheep: even if he finds herdsmen there, watching over their sheep with dogs and spears, he will not run from the steading without an attempt, but either he leaps in and makes his kill, or is himself hit in the first defence by a spear from a quick hand. So then his heart prompted godlike Sarpedon to storm the wall and break through the battlements. And first he spoke to Glaukos, the son of Hippolochos: 'Glaukos, why is it that we two are held in the highest honour in Lycia, with pride of place, the best of the meat, the wine-cup always full, and all look on us like gods, and we have for our own use a great cut of the finest land by the banks of the Xanthos, rich in vineyard and wheat-bearing ploughland? That is why we should now be taking our stand at the front of the Lycian lines and facing the sear of battle, so that among the heavy-armoured Lycians people will say: "These are no worthless men who rule over us in Lycia, these kings we have who eat our fat sheep and drink the choice of our honey-sweet wine. No, they have strength too and courage, since they fight at the front of the Lycian lines." Dear friend, if we were going to live for ever, ageless and immortal, if we survived this war, then I would not be fighting in the front ranks myself or urging you into the battle where men win glory. But as it is, whatever we do the fates of death stand over us in a thousand forms, and no mortal can run from them or escape them – so let us go, and either give his triumph to another man, or he to us.'

So he spoke, and Glaukos did not ignore him or fail to obey. So these two went straight onward taking with them the great company of the Lycians. And Menestheus, the son of Peteos, shuddered at the sight of them – it was his section of the wall they were coming at, bringing disaster. He peered along the Argive wall, looking for one of the leaders who could save his men from destruction. He saw the two Aiantes, gluttons for battle, standing still, and Teukros just now coming up from his hut. They were close by, but he could not carry to them with a shout – so loud was the din, and the clamour that reached to the sky, from the battering on shields and horse-crested helmets and on the gates. The noise of war was besetting every gate, and the Trojans were gathered at them trying to break them down and force their entry. Quickly Menestheus sent off his herald Thoötes to Aias: 'Go, godlike Thoötes, run and call Aias, or rather the two of them if possible: that would be far the best of all, as soon there will be stark destruction done here, so overwhelming is the attack the Lycians' leaders have made – and they have shown before their violence in the fury of battle. But if they have trouble and fighting broken out where they are too, then at least let brave Telamonian Aias come on his own, and Teukros come with him, the skilled archer.'

So he spoke, and the herald did not fail to do as he had heard. He went running along the wall built by the bronze-clad Achaians and came and stood by the two Aiantes, and spoke immediately to them: 'Aiantes, leaders of the bronze-clad Achaians, the dear son of the god-ordained king Peteos asks you to come where he is to face the labour of battle, if only for a little while, the two of you if possible: that would be far the best of all, as soon there will be stark destruction done there, so overwhelming is the attack the Lycians' leaders have made – and they have shown before their violence in the fury of battle. But if warfare and fighting have broken out here too, then at least let brave Telamonian Aias come on his own, and Teukros come with him, the skilled archer.'

So he spoke, and the huge Aias, Telamon's son, did not refuse. Straightaway he spoke winged words to the son of Oïleus: 'Aias, you two, you and strong Lykomedes, keep your stand here and spur the Danaans to fight with all their strength. I shall go over there and face the fighting – I shall be quickly back when I have seen to their defence.'

So speaking Aias son of Telamon set off, and with him went his brother Teukros, his own father's son: and Pandion accompanied them, carrying Teukros' curved bow. Going along inside the wall, they reached great-hearted Menestheus' section, and they came on men hard-pressed in the fighting, as the powerful leaders and lords of the Lycians were mounting the battlements like a black storm-wind. They closed in battle against them, and the clamour rose.

Aias son of Telamon was the first to kill a man, one of Sarpedon's companions, great-hearted Epikles, hitting him with a jagged rock, a huge stone that lay at the top of a pile inside the wall by the parapet. A man could not easily hold that stone with both hands, even a very strong man, of the folk that live now. But Aias lifted it high and flung it down on him, and crushed the four-bossed helmet and shattered all his skull to pieces: he dropped from the height of the wall like a diver, and the life left his bones. And Teukros hit Glaukos, strong son of Hippolochos, shooting him with an arrow as he stormed at the high wall, where he had seen his arm exposed – and he put a stop to his fighting. Glaukos jumped down from the wall, withdrawing quietly so that no Achaian should see that he was hit and raise a shout of triumph over him. Sarpedon was pained that Glaukos was gone, as soon as he realised. But even so he did not lose his will for the fight, but struck at Alkmaon, Thestor's son, with his spear and stabbed him, and pulled the spear out: the man came with it and fell headlong, and the bronze of his crafted armour rang over him. Sarpedon then took the parapet in his powerful hands and heaved, and the whole piece came away all along. The top of the wall was laid bare, and he had opened a passage for many.

Then Aias and Teukros both attacked him at the same time. Teukros hit him with an arrow in the shining baldric across his chest which held his covering shield: but Zeus kept the fates of death away from his son, so he should not be brought down at the sterns of the ships. And Aias leapt on him and speared his shield – the spear did not go right on through, but it slammed him back in his onslaught. He went back a little way from the battlement, but would not withdraw completely, as his heart still hoped to win glory. He turned about and called to the godlike Lycians: 'Lycians, why this slacking of your fighting spirit? It is hard for me, strong though I am, to break through alone and open our path to the ships. Come with me, then – the more the men, the better the work is done.'

So he spoke, and they were abashed at their leader's reprimand, and brought more weight to the attack around their counsellor king. And on the other side the Argives strengthened their ranks inside the wall, and there followed a huge struggle for both sides. The powerful Lycians could not break through the Danaans' wall and open a path to the ships, and the Danaan spearmen could not push the Lycians back from the wall when once they had reached it. But as two men quarrel over the boundary stones in a common field, each holding measuring-rods and wrangling over their fair allotment in a narrow plot of land, so the two armies were kept apart by the battlements between them: and over them they hacked at each other, at the ox-hides held over their chests, great round shields or fluttering targes. Many had their flesh cut into by the pitiless bronze, both when a fighter turned and his back was exposed, and many hit right through the shield itself. All along its length the wall and battlements were spattered with men's blood on either side, from Trojans and Achaians. But even so they could not force the Achaians to flight, but the sides held even like the scales a careful spinning-woman holds, lifting the beam with the weight and the wool on either side, so she can earn a meagre provision for her children. So the battle was strained taut and level between them, until the time when Zeus granted the greater glory to Hektor, son of Priam, who was the first to leap inside the Achaians' wall. He called in a great carrying shout to all the Trojans: 'On now, you horse-taming Trojans, break through the Argives' wall and set their ships alight with monstrous fire.'

So he spoke, urging them on, and every ear heard him; and they charged in a mass at the wall. So they then began climbing on the battlements' supports with sharp-edged spears in their hands, while Hektor had grasped a rock that lay in front of the gate and was carrying it forward. It was broad at the base and the top end was pointed: two men, the best in a township, could not easily lever that stone on to a wagon from the ground, of the folk that live now, but he swung it easily on his own – the son of devious-minded Kronos made it light for him. As when a shepherd easily carries the fleece of a ram, lifting it with one hand, and its weight is little burden to him, so

Hektor lifted the rock and carried it straight for the doors which closed the high double gates, fitting strong and close together – inside two bars held them, crossing over each other, and a single bolt secured them. Hektor went in and stopped close, then taking a firm stance he hurled the rock at the centre of the doors, spreading his legs well apart to give more power to his cast, and he smashed off the hinges on either side – its own weight carried the stone on inside, and the gates groaned loud and the bars could not hold: and the doors were shattered in flying fragments under the impact of the rock. Then glorious Hektor leapt inside, his face like the rush of night. He shone with the fearful bronze that covered his body, and there were two spears in his hands. None but the gods could have faced and stopped him when he leapt through the gates: and his eyes blazed with fire. He swung round and shouted to the mass of Trojans to cross over the wall, and they followed his command. At once some climbed over the wall, and the others poured in through the strong-built gateway itself. The Danaans were sent running in panic among their hollow ships, and the din rose unceasing.

BOOK 13
THE ACHAIANS RALLY

Now when Zeus had brought Hektor and the Trojans through to the ships, he left the men to endure hardship and misery beside them in relentless battle, and he turned his shining eyes away, looking far out over the land of the horse-herding Thracians, and the Mysians, fighters at close quarters, and the proud Hippemolgoi who live on mares' milk, and the Abioi, most civilised of all men. Towards the land of Troy now he did not turn his shining eyes at all – he did not think in his heart that any of the immortals would come to bring help to either Trojans or Danaans.

But the Earthshaker, powerful lord, was not keeping blind watch. He too was gazing at the battle and the fighting, sitting high on the tallest peak of wooded Thracian Samos: from there all of Ida could be seen, and Priam's city and the ships of the Achaians. He had gone up from the sea and seated himself there – and he felt pity for the Achaians being broken by the Trojans, and furious anger at Zeus.

Immediately he came down from the rocky mountain with fast strides, and the high mountains and the forests trembled under the immortal feet of Poseidon in motion. He took three strides and with the fourth reached his goal, Aigai, where his glorious palace was built in the depths of the water in gleaming gold, imperishable for ever. There he went, and harnessed a pair of bronze-hoofed horses to his chariot – wing-swift horses, with flowing manes of gold – and dressed himself in gold, and took up his whip which was finely made of gold, and mounted his chariot and went driving out over the waves. The sea-beasts gathered from their lairs and gambolled at his coming, and they recognised their lord. The sea divided a path for him in joyfulness: and the horses flew lightly on, and the bronze axle below was not wetted. So his bounding horses carried him to the ships of the Achaians.

There is a wide cave, deep down in the water, half-way between Tenedos and rocky Imbros. There Poseidon the earthshaker reined in his horses, unyoked them from the chariot, and tossed immortal fodder down for them to eat. And he put golden hobbles round their feet, which could not be broken or slipped, so they should wait there unmoving for the return of their master. He then went to the Achaian army.

The Trojans were coming on in a mass behind Hektor, son of Priam – like flame or a storm-wind, full of insatiable fury, and joining their shouts in a single roar: their thoughts were of taking the Achaians' ships and killing all the best of their men beside them. But Poseidon, the encircler and shaker of the earth, had come from the deep sea and began to spur on the Argives, taking the form and tireless voice of Kalchas. He spoke to the two Aiantes first, who were already eager for the fight: 'Aiantes, you two must save the Achaian army – fill your minds with courage, and no thoughts of chilling flight. Elsewhere I have no fear of the powerful hands of the Trojans, who have climbed over the great wall in their masses – the well-greaved Achaians will be able to hold them all. But it is here that I have the most terrible dread of a disaster for us, where that madman is leading them on like a flame of fire – Hektor, who could well be a son of almighty Zeus himself. May some god make it your thought to stand strong against him yourselves and urge the others too – then for all his fury you could turn him back from the speedy ships, even if the Olympian himself is driving him on.'

So speaking the encircler and shaker of the earth struck them both with his staff and filled them with strength of spirit, and made their limbs light, their legs and their arms above. Then he left them, as a swift-winged hawk darts into flight, when it hovers off a sheer rock-face, very high, then swoops down over the plain in chase of another bird: so fast and sudden was the leaving of Poseidon the earthshaker. Quick Aias, Oïleus' son, was the first of them to recognise a god's work, and he spoke at once to Aias son of Telamon: 'Aias, this was one of the gods who hold Olympos taking the seer's form and urging us to fight by the ships – it was not Kalchas, our prophet and augur. I could tell it well from the form of his feet and legs from the back as he left us – it is easy to recognise the gods. And my own heart in my breast is keener now for battle and fighting, and there is eagerness in my legs under me and my arms above.'

Then Aias son of Telamon answered him: 'It is the same for me too – my invincible hands now feel eager on my spear, my strength is aroused, both legs beneath me are urging me on. I long to meet Hektor, son of Priam, in all his insatiable fury, and fight him single-handed.'

Such were their words to each other, as they exulted in the fighting urge which the god had put in their hearts. Meanwhile the encircler of the earth roused the other Achaians at the rear. They were back by the fast ships trying to revive their spirits – the strength of their bodies was collapsed in the pain of exhaustion, and at the same time despair came over their hearts at the sight of the Trojans who had climbed over the great wall in their masses. As they looked out at them the tears began to fall from their eyes – they did not think they could escape disaster. But the Earthshaker moved effortlessly among them and spurred their battalions to strength. He came first with his incitement to Teukros, and Leïtos and the hero Peneleos and Thoas and Deïpyros and Meriones and Antilochos, rousers of the battle-cry. He spoke to them in winged words, urging them on: 'Shame, you Argives, mere boys! You are the ones I trust in to save our ships, if you will fight. But if you men hang back from the misery of battle, then the day of our crushing by the Trojans is now here to be seen. Oh, this is a great astonishment for my eyes, a fearful thing that I never thought would come about, the Trojans moving on our ships – men who before now were like timorous deer who make food for jackals and leopards and wolves in the forest as they wander about in utter helplessness, with no fight in them. So the Trojans before now were not prepared to stand and face the fury of the Achaians' hands, even for a little while. But now they have brought the fight far from their city right to our hollow ships, through the fault of our leader and the reluctance of his people, who in their resentment of him are not willing to fight for the speedy ships, but allow themselves to be killed among them. But even if all the blame truly belongs to the hero son of Atreus, wide-ruling Agamemnon, for his slighting of the swift-footed son of Peleus, yet we cannot possibly hold back from fighting. No, we must be quick to set it right – brave men's hearts are easily righted. But this slacking of your fighting spirit does you no credit now – you who are all leading men in the army. I would not quarrel with a man hanging back from battle if he were a poor creature of no account – but for you my heart is filled with anger. Dear friends, soon this reluctance of yours will lead to something much worse than its cause. Put some shame in your hearts, each of you, for yourselves and for the anger of others. A great struggle is on us now. Hektor, master of the war-cry, has broken the gates and their long cross-bar and is fighting now in strength by our ships.'

So, with constant urging, the encircler of the earth roused the

Achaians. And the battalions formed round the two Aiantes in full strength, such that not even Ares, if he had part in it, would make light of them, nor Athene the rouser of armies. There the choice of their leading men stood firm to face godlike Hektor and the Trojans, fencing spear by spear, shield rooted against shield. Shield then pressed on shield, helmet on helmet, man on man. The horse-hair crests in the bright ridges of their helmets touched when they moved their heads, so close to each other were they dressed: and the spears gripped in brave hands made a serried line. Their intent did not waver, and they were eager for the fight.

The Trojans charged forward in a mass, with Hektor at their head pressing furiously on like a boulder broken from a wall of rock, which a river swollen in winter spate has swept over the edge, when the huge flood of rain-water has broken the stubborn rock's hold on it. It bounds in the air and goes flying down, and the undergrowth crashes beneath it: it runs straight on without check until it reaches level ground, and then it can roll no more for all its energy. So Hektor for a time threatened to sweep easily through the huts and ships of the Achaians right to the sea, killing along his path. But when he came against those close-set battalions, he pressed in hard but was brought to a stop. The sons of the Achaians faced him, thrusting at him with swords and double-pointed spears, and pushed him away from them: and he was shaken back in retreat. Hektor called in a great carrying shout to the Trojans: 'Trojans and Lycians and close-fighting Dardanians, stand by me! The Achaians will not hold me for long, even though they have formed themselves into a wall against me – no, I think they will give way under my spear, if it was indeed the greatest of gods that inspired my attack, the loud-thundering husband of Hera.'

So speaking he spurred the strength and heart in each of them. And among them Deïphobos strode out with high thoughts in his mind, one of Priam's sons: he held the even circle of his shield in front of him and stepped lightly forward, advancing under cover of his shield. Meriones took aim at him with his shining spear, and did not miss, hitting in the even circle of his bull's-hide shield. But well before it could drive through it the long spear broke off at the socket: and Deïphobos held his bull's-hide shield well away from him, his heart frightened by the warrior Meriones' spear. But the hero moved back into the mass of his companions, doubly furious, both for the robbing of his victory and for the spear that had broken: and he set off to the huts and ships of the Achaians to bring back a long spear which he had left in his hut.

Meanwhile the others fought on, and the clamour rose ceaseless. Teukros, Telamon's son, was the first to kill his man – the spearman Imbrios, son of Mentor rich in horses. He used to live in Pedaios before the sons of the Achaians came, and was married to a bastard daughter of Priam, Medesikaste. But when the Danaans' balanced ships came, he returned to Ilios, and was a leading man among the Trojans, and lived with Priam, who showed him the same honour as his own children. Telamon's son stabbed him with his long spear under the ear, and pulled the spear out. He dropped like an ash-tree which is felled by the bronze on the peak of a far-seen mountain and brings its soft leaves down to the ground. So he fell, and the bronze of his crafted armour rang over him. Teukros leapt forward, eager to strip his armour: and as he leapt Hektor cast at him with his shining spear. But he had looked ahead, and avoided the bronze spear by a small margin, and Hektor's cast hit Amphimachos, son of Kteatos of Aktor's line, in the chest as he came into battle – he fell with a crash and his armour clattered about him. Hektor leapt forward to pull the helmet from great-hearted Amphimachos' head, where it fitted close round his temples: and as he leapt Aias thrust at Hektor with his shining spear. But no part of his flesh could be seen, and he was covered all over in fearsome bronze – but Aias struck at the boss of his shield, and with his huge strength pushed him back: Hektor pulled back from the two bodies, and the Achaians dragged them away. Stichios and godlike Menestheus, leaders of the Athenians, carried Amphimachos back to the Achaian lines, while the two Aiantes, raging with battle-fury, lifted Imbrios as two lions seize a goat from under the guard of saw-toothed dogs and carry it off through the thick brush, holding it high over the ground in their jaws. So the two warrior Aiantes held Imbrios high and stripped off his armour. And the son of Oïleus hacked the head from his soft neck, in fury at the death of Amphimachos, then swung it round and hurled it like a ball into the mass of men: and it dropped in the dust at Hektor's feet.

And then Poseidon's heart was enraged at the fall of his grandson Amphimachos in the grim combat, and he went along by the huts and ships of the Achaians to urge on the Danaans, and he was preparing trouble for the Trojans. Now Idomeneus met him, the famous spearman, on his way from seeing to one of his company who had just now come out of the fighting, wounded in the ham by a sharp spear. His companions had carried him in, and Idomeneus had instructed the healers and was now going to his own hut, as he was eager still to face more of the fighting. The Earthshaker, powerful lord, spoke to him, taking the voice of Thoas, son of Andraimon, who was king over the Aitolians in all of Pleuron and in steep Kalydon, and honoured by his people like a god: 'Idomeneus, counsellor of the Cretans, where are those threats gone that the sons of the Achaians used to make against the Trojans?'

Then Idomeneus, leader of the Cretans, answered him: 'Thoas, no man is now to blame, as far as I can see it. We all know how to fight. Not one of us has been gripped by fear and had the heart taken from him, no-one is giving way to terror and shirking the misery of battle – no, such it seems must be the pleasure of Zeus the almighty, that the Achaians perish here in oblivion, far from Argos. But, Thoas, you have always been one to face the enemy and spur others on too, whenever you see a man slacking: so do not stop now – keep urging on every man you meet.'

Then Poseidon the earthshaker answered him: 'Idomeneus, may the man who this day deliberately holds back from the fight never make his return from the land of Troy, but stay here to give the dogs their sport. Come then, fetch your armour and come with me. This is business we must dispatch together, if we are to do some good as a pair. Combination brings courage even in the poorest of fighters, and we two are men who could fight with the best.'

So speaking Poseidon went back, a god among the sufferings of men. And when Idomeneus reached his well-built hut, he clothed his body in his fine armour and took up a pair of spears, and set out like the lightning which the son of Kronos takes in his hand and hurls from bright Olympos, to reveal a sign to mankind, and its flash is brilliant in men's eyes: so the bronze flashed bright on his chest as he ran. Now his brave lieutenant Meriones met him, not far yet from his hut. He was on his way to fetch a bronze spear, and the mighty Idomeneus spoke to him: 'Meriones, son of Molos, quick runner, dearest of my friends, why have you left the battle's conflict to come here? Have you perhaps been hit, is the wound from a spear-point paining you? Or have you come for me with some message of summons? I for one have no wish to sit idle in the huts, but I want to be fighting.'

Then Meriones, good man of sense, answered him: 'Idomeneus, counsellor of the bronze-clad Cretans, I am coming to fetch a spear, if there is one left in your hut. I have just broken the one I carried before, when my cast hit the shield of the braggart Deïphobos.'

Then Idomeneus, leader of the Cretans, answered him: 'As for spears, you will find one, or twenty if you wish, standing against the polished wall in my hut – Trojan spears, which I take from the men I kill. It is not my idea to stand at a distance when fighting my enemies. So I have spears there, and bossed shields and helmets and bright-gleaming corselets.'

Then Meriones, good man of sense, answered him: 'I too have Trojan spoils in plenty in my hut and in my black ship, but not close by for the taking. I can claim too not to have lost my spirit for the fight – no, in the battle where men win glory I take my stand with the front-fighters, whenever the conflict of war breaks out. It may be that some other bronze-clad Achaians see little of how I fight, but I think you know it well for yourself.'

Then Idomeneus, leader of the Cretans, answered him: 'I know the measure of your courage – what need for you to recount all this? Because if now all the best of us were to be selected by the ships for an ambush – this is where men's courage is best seen, where the coward and the brave man are revealed: the coward's skin changes from colour to colour, and his heart within him will not keep him sitting quietly, but he keeps shifting his feet and squats now on one leg now on the other: his heart thumps loud in his chest as he imagines the fates of death, and his teeth begin to chatter: but the brave man's colour does not change, and he feels no great fear from the moment he is settled in the men's ambush, but his prayer is to engage in the grim fighting as soon as can be – even there no-one would scorn your fury in battle or the strength of your hands. If you were hit or stabbed in the labour of fighting, the weapon would not land in your neck behind or your back, but would meet you in chest or stomach as you pressed forward to join the dalliance of the champions. But come, we should not stay here bragging on like little boys, or people may resent it strongly. No, you go to my hut and take yourself a heavy spear.'

So he spoke, and Meriones, like the swift war-god himself, quickly took up a bronze spear from the hut and set out after Idomeneus, all his thoughts on battle. Like Ares, curse of men, when he goes out to war, and with him there goes his own son Panic, powerful and fearless, who can turn even a strong-hearted warrior to flight – these two come out from Thrace to arm for battle with the Ephyroi, or with the great-hearted Phlegyes: and they will not listen to both sides' prayers, but grant the glory to one or the other – such were Meriones and Ido-meneus, leaders of men, as they went out to battle helmeted in gleaming bronze. Meriones spoke first, and said to Idomeneus: 'Son of Deukalion, where do you want to enter the fighting? Out on the right of the army, or in the centre, or on the left? That is where I think the long-haired Achaians will be weakest in the battle.'

Then Idomeneus, leader of the Cretans, answered him: 'At the centre of the ships there are others to make the defence, the two Aiantes and Teukros, who is the best of the Achaians with the bow, and a good man too in close fighting – they will exercise Hektor, Priam's son, to the full, however strong he is and urgent for battle. It will be a hard thing for him, with all his fury for the fight, to beat through their strength and their invincible hands and fire the ships, unless the son of Kronos himself were to hurl a blazing brand on our fast ships. But there is no man that huge Aias, son of Telamon, will yield to – no man that is mortal and eats the bread of Demeter, and can be broken by bronze or massive stones. He would not even give way to Achilleus, breaker of men, in a standing fight – but at the run there is no competing with Achilleus. So keep on as we are for the left of the army, so we can know soon whether we shall give his triumph to another man, or he to us.'

So he spoke, and Meriones led on like the swift war-god himself, until they came to the part of the army that Idomeneus had told him.

When the Trojans saw Idomeneus, looking like a flame in his power, him and his lieutenant in their crafted armour, they called across their massed ranks and made for him all together: and the battle was joined thick by the sterns of the ships. As when the gusts swirl strong under the shrilling of the winds, on a day when the dust lies thickest over the paths, and the winds sweep it all into a great standing cloud of dust, so the battle gathered and thickened between them, and their hearts' desire was to kill each other with the sharp bronze in the welter of fighting. The murderous battle shivered with the long spears they held to cut through flesh: their eyes were blinded in the flash of bronze from shining helmets and new-polished corselets and bright shields as the men came on in their masses. It would be a hard-hearted man indeed who could take pleasure in that sight and not be struck with horror.

And the two powerful sons of Kronos, their purposes opposed, caused grim suffering for the human warriors. Zeus willed victory for Hektor and the Trojans, to do glory to Achilleus the swift-footed: he did not wish the Achaian army to be utterly destroyed in front of Ilios, but he was bringing glory to Thetis and her strong-hearted son. And

Poseidon had come up out of the sea, unseen, to go among the Argives and spur them on: he felt pain to see them broken by the Trojans, and furious anger at Zeus. Both these were indeed of the same descent and parentage, but Zeus was the older born and had wider knowledge. So Poseidon avoided giving open help, but went covertly up and down the army in man's shape, constantly rousing them to fight. So those gods crossed and tied the ropes of hard conflict and levelling war over both armies, and stretched them taut, not to be slipped or broken – but they broke the strength of many men.

Then, grizzle-haired though he was, Idomeneus called the Danaans on and leapt at the Trojans, and set them panicking. He killed Othryoneus, a visitor in Troy from Kabesos, who had come lately, drawn by news of the war, and had asked for the most beautiful of Priam's daughters, Kassandra, without payment of bride-price – but instead he had promised a great achievement, to force the Achaians out of the land of Troy. The old man Priam had assented and promised to give her: and Othryoneus was fighting in the confidence of these promises. But Idomeneus aimed at him with his shining spear, and hit him full as he pranced forward: the bronze corselet he wore could not protect him, and the spear fixed in mid-belly. He fell with a crash, and Idomeneus spoke in triumph over him: 'Othryoneus, I congratulate you above all mortal men, if you are really going to accomplish all that you undertook for Dardanian Priam, when he promised you his daughter. Now we could make you the same promise. We could give you the most beautiful of the son of Atreus' daughters, and fetch her from Argos for you to marry, if you help us to sack the well-founded citadel of Ilios. Come with me, then, to our seafaring ships, so we can agree terms for your marriage – you will not find us hard bargainers for the match.'

So speaking the hero Idomeneus took him by the foot and began dragging him through the fury of battle. But Asios came up to protect him, on foot in front of his horses, which his charioteer held close behind him so their breath was always on his shoulders. His heart was intent on hitting Idomeneus: but he, quicker with his cast, struck Asios with his spear in the neck under his chin, and drove the bronze right through. He fell as an oak-tree falls or a poplar, or a tall pine which carpenters cut down in the mountains with fresh-whetted axes to make a ship's timber. So he lay there stretched flat in front of his horses and chariot, bellowing, and clutching at the blood-soaked dust. His charioteer's wits were shocked out of him, so he did not have the sense to wheel the horses round and escape from the enemies' hands, and brave Antilochos caught him with his spear and pinned him through the middle: the bronze corselet he wore could not protect him, and the spear fixed in mid-belly. He fell gasping from the well-made chariot, and the horses were driven off by Antilochos, son of great-hearted Nestor, away from the Trojans and back to the well-greaved Achaians.

Then Deïphobos came up very close to Idomeneus, in anger at Asios' death, and cast at him with a shining spear. But Idomeneus had looked ahead, and avoided the bronze spear. He covered himself behind the even circle of the shield which he always carried, built out of rings of ox-hide and gleaming bronze, and braced with two cross-bars. He crouched his whole body under it, and the spear flew over him – his shield rasped hollow as the spear grazed past it. But it was no wasted shot that Deïphobos let fly with the strength of his arm – he hit Hypsenor son of Hippasos, shepherd of the people, in the liver under the midriff, and instantly collapsed his strength. Deïphobos shouted loud in terrible triumph: 'So now Asios does not lie there unavenged – even on his journey down to Hades the strong Keeper of the Gate, I think he will be happy at heart, now I have given him a guide.'

So he spoke, and the Argives were pained at his boasting, and most of all he moved the warrior Antilochos' heart to anger. Yet for all his pain he did not forget his companion, but ran to bestride him and covered him with his shield. Then two loyal companions bent under him, Mekisteus son of Echios and godlike Alastor, and carried him groaning heavily back to the hollow ships.

But Idomeneus would not slacken his high fury, but his urge was relentless to envelop some Trojan in black night or crash down himself in defending the Achaians from destruction. Then he killed the hero Alkathoös, dear son of the god-ordained king Aisyëtes. He was son-in-law to Anchises, married to the eldest of his daughters, Hippodameia: she was loved with all their hearts by her father and her honoured mother in their house, since she surpassed all girls of her age in beauty and handcraft and sense – and so it was the best man in the broad land of Troy that married her. And now Poseidon brought him down at the hands of Idomeneus: he mazed his shining eyes, and rooted his bright body, so he could not run back or escape, but stood there motionless like a gravestone or a high leafy tree, while the hero Idomeneus stabbed with his spear in the centre of his chest, and broke through the bronze coat that covered it and had kept destruction from his flesh before now – but then it grated loud as the spear tore it. He fell with a crash, the spear fixed in his heart, and the heart's jerking made the spear quiver right to the butt: and then monstrous Ares took away its force. Idomeneus shouted loud in terrible triumph: 'Deïphobos, are we then to reckon it a fair bargain yet, three men killed for one? – since that is the way you like to boast. No, friend, you too – stand and face me yourself, so you can see the make of this offspring of Zeus that has come to your land. It was Zeus in the beginning who fathered Minos to be guardian over Crete, then Minos had as son the excellent Deukalion, and Deukalion fathered me to be king over many people in broad Crete – and now my ships have carried me here as a curse to you and your father and the other Trojans.'

So he spoke, and Deïphobos was torn in thought, whether to draw back and make company with some other great-hearted Trojan, or to attempt him alone as he was. And this seemed the best plan to his thinking, to go in search of Aineias. He found him at the rear of the battle, standing idle – he kept up a constant anger against godlike Priam, because he would show him no honour, for all that he was a leading man among them. Deïphobos came close and spoke winged words to him: 'Aineias, counsellor of the Trojans, you must fight now for your brother-in-law – the need is great – if grief for him touches you at all. Come with me, let us fight for Alkathoös – he is your sister's husband, and long ago raised you in the house when you were small: and Idomeneus the famous spearman has killed him.'

So he spoke, and moved Aineias' heart in his breast to anger: and he went after Idomeneus, all his thoughts on battle. But no panic seized Idomeneus, as if he were a mere boy. He stood his ground, like a boar in the mountains sure of his power, who faces a great rabble of men coming against him in a solitary place, and bristles the ridge of his back: his eyes flash with fire, and he whets his tusks, ready to beat off dogs and men. So Idomeneus the famous spearman stood his ground, and would not retreat, as Aineias came running against him: but he shouted to his companions, looking to Askalaphos and Aphareus and Deïpyros and Meriones and Antilochos, rousers of the battle-cry. He called to them in winged words, urging them to his aid: 'Over here, friends, and help me! I am alone, and terribly afraid of the attack of swift-footed Aineias, who is coming at me now, and he has all the strength to kill in battle – and he is at the flower of youth too, which is the greatest power in a man. If we two were of the same age with this spirit in us, then there would soon be a great victory won, his or mine.'

So he spoke, and they all came with one purpose in their hearts and closed round him, sloping their shields against their shoulders. And Aineias on the other side called to his companions, looking to Deïphobos and Paris and godlike Agenor, fellow-leaders of the Trojans. And then the common troops followed after him, as when sheep follow after the ram to the drinking place from their pasture, and the shepherd is gladdened at heart: so Aineias' heart was glad in his breast, when he saw the company of his troops following him.

So they joined close battle over Alkathoös with long spears, and the bronze on their chests rang fearfully as they cast at each other in the mass of fighting. Two men were fierce for war beyond all others, Aineias and Idomeneus, men like Ares, urgent to tear each other's flesh with the pitiless bronze. Aineias cast first at Idomeneus: but he had looked ahead, and avoided the bronze spear, and Aineias' weapon went quivering into the ground, sped wasted from his massive hand. Then Idomeneus hit Oinomaos in mid-belly, and broke through his corselet's front-piece, and the bronze let his bowels gush out: he crashed in the dust and his hand clawed earth. Idomeneus pulled his long-shadowed spear out of the body, but could not go on to take the fine armour from its shoulders, as the spears were overwhelming him. His legs no longer had the speed for a quick dash, either to charge in after his own spear-cast or avoid another's: so his way to keep off the pitiless hour of death was to fight a standing battle, as his legs could no longer carry him lightly in escape from the fighting. As he slowly backed away, Deïphobos cast at him with a shining spear – he had a settled hatred for him now. But once more he missed, and hit Askalaphos with the spear, the son of Ares Enyalios: the heavy spear kept on through his shoulder, and he crashed in the dust and his hand clawed earth. But monstrous Ares the loud-shouter did not yet know of his son's fall in the fury of battle. He was sitting under the golden clouds on the height of Olympos, confined there by Zeus' command: and there were the other immortal gods also, debarred from the fighting.

But the men joined close battle over Askalaphos. Deïphobos tore the shining helmet from Askalaphos, but Meriones leapt at him like the swift war-god himself and struck him in the arm with his spear, and the masking helmet fell from his hand clanging to the ground. Meriones leapt in again like a vulture, and pulled the heavy spear from the upper arm, then moved back into the mass of his companions. Polites, full brother of Deïphobos, put his arms round his waist and led him away from the grim clash of war as far as his quick horses, which were standing with their driver and the decorated chariot behind the battle and the fighting: they carried him to the city, groaning heavily in his pain, as the blood ran from the fresh wound in his arm.

Meanwhile the others fought on, and the clamour rose ceaseless. Then Aineias leapt at Aphareus, son of Kaletor, and struck him in the throat with his sharp spear when he turned to face him. His head sank to one side, and his shield and helmet folded in on him, and death the breaker of spirits poured round him. Antilochos watched for Thoön to turn, and then sprang forward and stabbed him, cutting right through the vein that runs all the way up the back to reach the neck: he cut right through this, and Thoön collapsed on his back in the dust, holding out both arms to his dear companions. Antilochos leapt in and began to take the armour from his shoulders, looking sharply about him. And the Trojans gathered to surround him, and thrust at his broad glittering shield: but they could not get past it even to graze Antilochos' soft flesh with the pitiless bronze, because Poseidon the earthshaker was protecting Nestor's son even in that welter of weapons – he was never clear of enemies, but turned and twisted among them, and his spear was not still in his hand, but quivered all the time in the poise of his grip: and the aim of his mind was to cast at some enemy or charge in hand to hand.

But Adamas, Asios' son, noticed him looking for his target in the mass of men, and ran in close and stabbed at the centre of his shield with his sharp bronze – but dark-haired Poseidon crippled his spear and denied it a life. Half of it fixed there in Antilochos' shield like a charred stake, and half lay on the ground. Adamas shrank back into the mass of his companions to avoid destruction. But Meriones caught him as he went back and struck him with his spear between genitals and navel, the place where death in war comes most painfully to suffering mortals. There the spear fixed fast in him. He collapsed around it and writhed struggling as an ox does, when herdsmen have forced ropes round him in the mountains and drag him resistant with them. So he struggled under the blow for a short while, for no great time, until the hero Meriones came close and pulled the spear out of his flesh: and darkness covered over his eyes.

Helenos closed on Deïpyros and struck him with his sword on the temple – a great Thracian sword, which smashed the helmet from his head. The helmet fell dislodged to the ground, and some Achaian picked it up where it rolled among the feet of the fighters: and black night covered over the man's eyes.

At this furious grief came over the son of Atreus, Menelaos the master of the war-cry. He made for the hero lord Helenos, shaking his sharp spear in menace: and Helenos drew back against the grip of his bow. The two were ready to let fly at the same moment, one with a sharp spear and the other with an arrow from the string. Then the son of Priam hit Menelaos on the chest with his arrow, on the front-piece of the corselet, but the bitter arrow flew glancing off it. As when on a great threshing-floor the black-skinned beans or chickpeas fly from the broad shovel, sent spinning by the whistle of the wind and the winnower's swing, so the bitter arrow glanced full off glorious Menelaos' corselet and flew on far. And the son of Atreus, Menelaos master of the war-cry, hit Helenos in the hand where he held the polished bow: and the bronze spear was driven right through the hand into the bow. Helenos shrank back into the mass of his companions to avoid destruction, his hand dangling by his side: and the ash spear trailed after him. Then great-hearted Agenor pulled the spear from his hand, and bound the hand up in a length of twisted sheep's wool, the loop of a sling, which his lieutenant held out for the shepherd of the people.

Now Peisandros came straight for glorious Menelaos, but cruel fate was leading him on towards the end of death, to be brought down by you, Menelaos, in grim combat. When they had advanced to close range, the son of Atreus missed with his cast and his spear swerved to the side. Peisandros pierced glorious Menelaos' shield, but could not drive the bronze right through: the broad shield held it, and the spear snapped at the socket: but he felt joy in his heart, and hope of victory. The son of Atreus drew his silver-studded sword and leapt at Peisandros, while he took from under his shield a fine axe with its blade of strong bronze set on a haft of olive-wood, long and smooth-polished. Their blows struck together. Peisandros hit the ridge of the horse-plumed helmet, at the top just below the crest, and as he came on Menelaos struck him on the forehead above the base of the nose – the bones cracked, and his eyes dropped bloody in the dust at his feet. He doubled and fell, and Menelaos, bracing his foot against his chest, pulled off his armour and spoke in triumph over him: 'That, Trojans, is how you will leave the ships of the fast-horsed Danaans – you violent men, gluttons for the hideous noise of war! No shortage already of your shame and outrage – that outrage done to me, you vile dogs, with no fear in your hearts for the punishing anger of Zeus the thunderer, god of host and guest, who in time will destroy your high city. You took the wife of my marriage and much property besides, and sailed away with her heedless, when you were guests in her house. And now your aim is to throw deadly fire on our sea-going ships, and to kill the fighting men of the Achaians. But you will be stopped, I think, for all your lust for war. Father Zeus, they say your wisdom is beyond all others, men and gods – and yet you are the source of all this, the way you favour these men of violence, these Trojans whose fighting fury has no limit, who cannot sate themselves with the clash of levelling war. Men reach their fill of all things, even of sleep and love and sweet music and the delightful dance, things in which a man would rather slake his pleasure than in war: but the Trojans cannot have their fill of battle.'

So speaking the excellent Menelaos handed the blood-stained armour he had stripped from the body to his companions, and he himself went out again to join the front-fighters.

Then the son of Pylaimenes leapt at him, Harpalion, who had come with his dear father to fight at Troy, but did not return again to his native land. He now came close and stabbed with his spear in the centre of the son of Atreus' shield, but could not drive the bronze right through, and shrank back into the mass of his companions to avoid destruction, looking sharply all round him, so that no-one should find his flesh with their bronze. But Meriones sent a bronze-tipped arrow at him as he retreated, and struck him in the right buttock: the arrow passed on through under the bone and into his bladder. He sank down where he was, in the arms of his dear companions, the life breathing from him, and lay there curled on the earth like a worm: and the dark blood ran from him, soaking the ground. The great-hearted Paphlagonians looked to the body, and lifted him into a chariot and carried him in sorrow to sacred Ilios. And with them went his father with his tears falling, but there was to be no recompense for the death of his son.

Now Paris' heart was greatly angered at the killing of Harpalion, as he was his guest-friend among the many men of Paphlagonia: and in anger for him he let fly a bronze-tipped arrow. There was a man called Euchenor, son of the seer Polyïdos, a rich man and a noble, whose home was in Corinth. He had boarded his ship in full knowledge that this was his doom and destruction – many times the old man, the noble Polyïdos, had told him that he would die of a painful sickness in his house, or join the Achaians' fleet and be brought down by the Trojans. So he came, to avoid both the heavy fine the Achaians would take from him and the pain he would suffer at heart in a hateful sickness. Paris hit him under the jaw and ear: the life sped from his body, and the hateful darkness took him.

So they fought on like burning fire. But Hektor, beloved of Zeus, had not heard of this, and did not know that to the left of the ships his people were being cut down by the Argives. And there might soon have been victory for the Achaians – such was the spurring given the Argives by Poseidon the encircler and shaker of the earth, and he was adding his own strength to their defence. But Hektor kept driving on where he had first stormed through the gates and the wall and broken the close-packed ranks of the Danaan shield-bearers, where the ships of Aias and Protesilaos were pulled up to the shore of the grey sea. The wall protecting these had been built very low, and here the Trojans, foot-soldiers and chariots, were at their most ferocious in attack.

Here the Boiotians and long-coated Ionians, the Locrians and Phthians and glittering Epeians could hardly hold godlike Hektor as he rushed for the ships like a flame, and they were unable to beat him back. Here too were the pick of the Athenians: leader among them was Menestheus, son of Peteos, and with him Pheidas and Stichios and brave Bias. The Epeians were led by Meges, son of Phyleus, and Amphion and Drakios, and at the head of the Phthians were Medon and the staunch fighter Podarkes. Medon was a bastard son of godlike Oïleus, and brother of Aias, but he lived in Phylake, away from his native land, as he had killed a man, the brother of his step-mother Eriopis, wife of Oïleus: and Podarkes was son of Iphiklos, the son of Phylakos. These then were under arms at the head of the great-hearted Phthians and fought together with the Boiotians in defence of their ships. But Aias, quick son of Oïleus, would not now take his place anywhere away from the side of Telamonian Aias, not even a little way: but as a pair of wine-red oxen strain at the jointed plough over fallow land, matched in their eagerness for work, and the sweat springs copious at the base of their horns; only the breadth of the polished yoke separates them as they labour down the furrow until the plough cuts into the headland of the field: so these two took their stand close to each other, side by side. Now the son of Telamon was attended by his people, many brave companions to take his shield from him whenever the sweat of exertion tired his body. But the great-hearted son of Oïleus was not joined by his Locrians – their hearts did not have the will for close fighting, as they had no horse-plumed helmets made of bronze, and no rounded shields or ash spears, but they had come to

Ilios with their confidence in bows and slings of twisted sheep's wool, and their dense volleys with these weapons could break the Trojan battalions. So now the others fought in the front, in their crafted armour, against the Trojans and bronze-armoured Hektor, and the Locrians kept shooting from safety behind – and the Trojans began to lose their spirit for battle, as the arrows threw them into disarray.

Then the Trojans would have made a sorry retreat away from the ships and huts to windy Ilios, if Poulydamas had not come up to brave Hektor and said: 'Hektor, you are a difficult man when advice should be taken. Because god has granted you excellence in battle, this makes you want to outdo others in the mind's work too – but you cannot choose of your own will to have all gifts together. God gives one man skill in battle, and to another he gives dancing, and to a third the playing of the lyre and song: and in another man's breast wide-seeing Zeus puts wisdom, which brings benefit to many men and is the saving of many too, as he knows best of all. Now I shall tell you what seems best to me. All around you there is blazing a ring of battle, but the other great-hearted Trojans, now that they have crossed the wall, are either standing by armed but idle, or scattered among the ships in small groups fighting larger numbers. No, you should pull back and summon all the leading men to join you here. Then we can properly consider our plan overall, whether we should fall on their many-benched ships in the hope that god may be willing to grant us victory, or whether we should rather draw back from the ships without loss. For my part I fear that the Achaians may pay us back their debt of yesterday, as there is waiting by their ships a man who is greedy for war, and I do not think he will keep right out of the fighting any longer.'

So Poulydamas spoke, and his saving advice pleased Hektor. He immediately jumped down to the ground from his chariot with all his armour, and spoke winged words to him: 'Poulydamas, you hold all the leading men here, while I go over there and see to the fighting. I shall be quickly back when I have given them full orders.'

So speaking Hektor set off, like a snow-capped mountain, and shouted as he went, speeding fast through the ranks of Trojans and their allies. And they all streamed to join the son of Panthoös, the kindly Poulydamas, when they heard Hektor's call. But Hektor kept ranging among the front-fighters, looking if he could find Deïphobos and the mighty lord Helenos, and Asios' son Adamas, and Asios son of Hyrtakos. And he found that none of them now had completely escaped death or injury, but two were lying by the sterns of the Achaian ships, their lives lost at the hands of the Argives, and the others were inside the city-wall, wounded by shot or stab. But he did soon find godlike Alexandros, husband of lovely-haired Helen, out on the left of the ruinous fighting, urging on his men and spurring them to battle. Hektor came close and spoke to him with insulting words: 'Paris you pest, good for nothing but looks, you woman-crazed seducer, where are Deïphobos and the mighty lord Helenos, and Asios' son Adamas, and Asios son of Hyrtakos? What have you done with them? And where is Othryoneus? Now the whole of high Ilios is utterly ruined – now your own sheer destruction is assured.'

Then godlike Alexandros answered him: 'Hektor, since you are minded to lay blame where no blame lies, I tell you there may be other times I have held back from the fighting, but not now – I too was not born a complete coward. From the moment you roused your men to battle by the ships we have been here engaging the Danaans without pause. The companions you ask after are killed. Only Deïphobos and the mighty lord Helenos have gone back, both wounded by long spears in the arm – but the son of Kronos kept death from them. Now you lead on, wherever your heart and spirit urge you, and we shall follow in all eagerness: and I do not think there will be any lack of courage, as far as the strength is in us. A man cannot fight beyond his strength, however keen.'

So speaking the hero won his brother's heart: and they set off to where the clash of battle was fiercest, around Kebriones and the excellent Poulydamas, Phalkes and Orthaios and godlike Polyphetes, Palmys, and Askanios and Morys, two sons of Hippotion, who had come as reliefs from fertile Askania at dawn the day before – and now Zeus had roused them into battle. The Trojans came on like the cruel winds' blast, which swoops to earth driven by the thunder of father Zeus, and with a tremendous roar cuts into the salt sea water, and the waves boil countless over the sounding sea, curling and cresting white, rank after rank. So the Trojans came on behind their leaders in close order, rank following rank, and glittering in bronze. At their head, like Ares the curse of men, went Hektor, Priam's son: before him he held the even circle of his shield, close-compacted of hides, with bronze beaten thick over it; and his helmet shook bright around his temples. He would stride forward and try the enemy ranks at every point along their line, hoping they would give way before his advance under cover of his shield – but he could not break the resolve in the hearts of the

Achaians. Aias came out first with huge strides and challenged him: 'Poor man, come closer! Why these empty attempts to frighten the Argives? We Achaians are no novices in battle, but it was the vile lash of Zeus that beat us down. I suppose your heart must be hoping to destroy our ships. But we have hands too, ready at a moment to defend them. Much sooner than that our hands will have taken and sacked your well-founded city. And I tell you the time is close for you yourself, when you will run from us and pray to father Zeus and the other immortals to make your lovely-maned horses faster than hawks as they raise the dust over the plain to carry you back to the city.'

As he spoke these words, a bird flew by him on the right, an eagle soaring high: and the Achaian army shouted its joy at the cheer of the omen. And glorious Hektor answered: 'Aias, great blustering oaf, what rant that is! If only for all my days I could be the son of Zeus who holds the aegis, and have queen Hera for my mother, and be honoured with the honour given to Athene and Apollo, as surely as this day now brings doom to the Argives, to every one of them: and you will die with the others, if you dare to stand against my long spear, which will tear your lily-soft skin – and you will glut the dogs and birds of Troy with your fat and your flesh, lying fallen by the ships of the Achaians.'

So speaking Hektor led on, and his men followed with a tremendous clamour, and the whole army behind shouted with them. And the Argives raised a shout on their side, and would not lose their courage for the fight, but stood firm against the advance of the Trojans' leaders. And the clamour from both sides reached up to the sky and Zeus' brightness.

BOOK 14
THE SEDUCTION OF ZEUS

Now Nestor was drinking his wine in his hut, but he still heard the din of battle, and he spoke winged words to the son of Asklepios: 'Think now, godlike Machaon, what we must do. The shouts of young men fighting are louder now by the ships. You sit on here and drink the gleaming wine until lovely-haired Hekamede has warmed you a hot bath and washed away the clotted blood: and I will go quickly to a place where I can see, and find out what is happening.'

So speaking he took up the crafted shield of his son, Thrasymedes tamer of horses, which lay there in the hut shining bright with bronze – Thrasymedes was carrying his father's shield. And he took up a strong spear, sharp-edged with pointed bronze, and stood outside his hut, and immediately saw a terrible sight, the Achaians running in confusion, and behind them the high-hearted Trojans sweeping them on – and the wall of the Achaians had been overthrown. As when a great stretch of open sea heaves with a sullen swell, sensing the shrill winds on their rapid pathways, but cannot set its waves rolling this way or that, until some settled wind blows down from Zeus, so the old man was torn in thought as he pondered two courses, whether to join the mass of the fast-horsed Danaans or to find Atreus' son Agamemnon, shepherd of the people. And this seemed the best plan to his thinking, to go in search of the son of Atreus. Meanwhile the others fought on and kept up the slaughter, and the unwearying bronze rang about their bodies as they thrust at each other with swords and double-pointed spears.

Now Nestor was met by those god-ordained kings who had been wounded by the bronze, as they came on their way up from their ships – the son of Tydeus, and Odysseus, and Agamemnon son of Atreus. Where their ships had been pulled up on the shore of the grey sea was far away from the fighting, as the first ships in had been hauled right inland, and the wall built along their sterns. Wide though it was, the beach had not been able to hold all the ships, and the men had no room: so they had dragged the ships up in rows, and filled the long bay of the whole coastline bounded by the two headlands. So the kings were going up together, leaning on their spears, to see the battle and the clamour: and there was anguish in their hearts. When the old man Nestor met them, this alarmed yet more the hearts in the breasts of the Achaians. Lord Agamemnon spoke to him: 'Nestor, son of Neleus, great glory of the Achaians, why have you come back here and left the fighting which takes men's lives? I am afraid that monstrous Hektor may now fulfil that threat he once made in the assembly of the Trojans, that he would not go back from our ships to Ilios until he had fired the ships and killed the men as well. That is how he spoke then – and now it is all coming about. Oh, it must be that the rest of the well-greaved Achaians are lodging anger in their hearts against me like Achilleus, and refusing to fight by the sterns of the ships.'

Then the Gerenian horseman Nestor answered him: 'Yes, all this is made fact, and even Zeus the high-thunderer himself could not remake it otherwise. The wall is now fallen, the wall we trusted to be an unbreakable defence for our ships and ourselves. And the men face a relentless battle by the fast ships, ceaseless fighting – and now, hard though you look, you could not tell where the pressure is coming, in front or rear, that is breaking the Achaians in confusion, so universal is the slaughter and the clamour rising to the sky. We must think what we should do, if thought can be of any effect – but I do not say that we should enter the battle: a wounded man can do no fighting.'

Then Agamemnon, lord of men, answered him: 'Nestor, since they are fighting now at the sterns of the ships, and the wall we built was no protection to us, nor the ditch that the Danaans suffered much for and hoped would be an unbreakable defence for their ships and them-selves, such it seems must be the pleasure of Zeus the almighty, that the Achaians perish here in oblivion, far from Argos. I knew when Zeus was giving his full aid to the Danaans, and I know it now, when he is exalting the Trojans as high as the blessed gods, and has shackled the strength of our hands. No, come, let us all do as I say. Let us drag down all the ships that are beached in the front closest to the water, and haul them into the holy sea, and moor them at anchor in deep water, until immortal night comes on – if the Trojans will stop their fighting even then. And then we could haul down all the rest of the ships. There is no shame in running from disaster, even by night: better to run and escape disaster than be caught in it.'

But resourceful Odysseus scowled at him and said: 'Son of Atreus, what is this you have let slip the guard of your teeth? You catastrophe, you should have had some sorry army to command, and not have charge over us, men on whom it seems Zeus has imposed the working through of bitter wars from youth right to our old age, until each one of us has perished. Is this now how you wish to abandon the broad streets of Troy, for which we have been suffering much misery? Quiet, man, or some of the other Achaians will hear this proposal of yours – which no man would ever allow through his lips if he had the power of mind to speak good sense, and was a sceptred king, with as large an army under him as the Argives you command. But now I utterly condemn your judgment for what you have said – when the din of battle is joined you tell us to haul our well-benched ships down to the sea, so that the Trojans, already gaining over us, can win a yet greater triumph, and sheer destruction weigh down on us. With the ships being hauled into the sea, the Achaians will not keep up the fight – they will be looking to their escape, and the spirit for battle will leave them. And then your plan, leader of your people, will be their ruin.'

Then Agamemnon, lord of men, answered him: 'Odysseus, those are hard words and you have hit home in my heart. No, I will not order the sons of the Achaians to drag the well-benched ships into the sea if that is not their will. But now we need a man to propose a better plan than mine – either young man or old – and I shall welcome it.'

Then Diomedes, master of the war-cry, spoke out to them: 'The man is here, and we shall not look long – if you are willing to listen to me, and do not all feel angry resentment that I am the youngest in birth among you. But I too am proud to call myself son of a noble father – Tydeus, buried now under the heaped earth in Thebes. Three excellent sons were born to Portheus, and they lived in Pleuron and steep Kalydon – Agrios and Melas, and the third was the horseman Oineus, my father's father, who was the greatest of them in courage. He lived on there, but my father travelled away and settled in Argos – such must have been the will of Zeus and the other gods. And he married one of the daughters of Adrestos, and lived in a house rich in substance, with wheat-bearing ploughlands in plenty, and many planted orchards on all sides, and many flocks of sheep. And he excelled over all the Achaians in skill with the spear. You will have heard of all this, and know its truth. So now no thought that I am of low and cowardly birth should make you reject the proposal I put before you, if what I say is good. I say we must go back into the fighting even though we are wounded – we have no choice. When there we should keep ourselves away from the conflict, out of range, so that none of us adds to his wounds: but we can spur the others on and send them into battle, those who up to now have been indulging their anger and standing by without fighting.'

So he spoke, and they listened well and agreed. And they set off with Agamemnon, lord of men, at their head.

Now the famous Earthshaker was not keeping blind watch, but he went to meet them in the form of an old man, and took Agamemnon son of Atreus by the right hand, and spoke winged words to him: 'Son of Atreus, now the cruel heart of Achilleus must be happy in his breast, as he looks on the defeat and slaughter of the Achaians – there is no feeling in him, not even a little. Well, may that be his destruction, and may god blight him. But with you the blessed gods are not completely angry. No, there will still come the time when the leaders and lords of the Trojans will raise the dust wide across the plain, and you will see them with your own eyes running for their city away from the ships and your huts.'

So speaking he sped away over the plain and gave a great cry, loud as the shout of nine thousand men or ten thousand men on a battlefield, when they join the clash of war. So loud was the voice that the Earthshaker, powerful lord, released from his chest, and in each Achaian's heart he put great strength for warfare and battle without ceasing.

Hera of the golden throne had stepped out from Olympos, and her eyes looked on from the peak where she stood. Immediately she recognised Poseidon, her own brother and her husband's brother, busying along the battle where men win glory, and she was happy at heart – and she saw Zeus sitting on the highest peak of Ida with the many springs, and he was hateful to her heart. So then the ox-eyed queen Hera wondered how she might fuddle the mind of Zeus who holds the aegis. This seemed the best plan to her thinking, to trick herself out and go down to Ida, hoping that he would feel the desire to lie with her body in lovemaking, and she could pour a gentle, soft sleep over his eyelids and the subtlety of his mind. She went then to her room, which her dear son Hephaistos had built for her, and had made the doors close tightly in their posts with a secret bolt which no other god could open. There she went in, and shut the gleaming doors. First she used ambrosia to wash every stain from her lovely body, and then she rubbed herself richly with oil of immortal sweetness, a perfumed oil she had which if only shaken in the bronze-floored house of Zeus would spread its fragrance over heaven and earth. When she had rubbed this over her beautiful skin, she combed her hair and wove it with her hands into glistening plaits to hang ambrosial and lovely round her deathless head. And she dressed herself in an immortal robe, which Athene had made for her in fine-napped cloth and embroidered it with many figures: she pinned it across her breast with golden clasps, and she fastened round her waist a belt hung with a hundred dangles. And she put earrings in the pierced lobes of her ears, pendant clusters of three drops, glittering bright with beauty. The queen among goddesses covered her head with a beautiful shawl, new-made and white as the sunlight, and bound fine sandals under her shining feet. Then when she had clothed her body in all her finery, she set out from her room, and called Aphrodite aside from the other gods, and said to her: 'Now, dear child, will you do something for me that I tell you – or will you refuse out of anger that I side with the Danaans while you help the Trojans?'

Then Aphrodite, daughter of Zeus, answered her: 'Hera, queenly goddess, daughter of great Kronos, say what is in your mind. My heart prompts me to do it, if I can and it is something possible.'

Queen Hera answered with deceitful intent: 'Give me then Love and Desire, the power with which you overcome all the immortals and mortal men alike. I am going to the ends of the nourishing earth, to visit Ocean, the source of the gods' creating, and mother Tethys. They took me from Rhea and brought me up and reared me in kindness in their house, when wide-seeing Zeus banished Kronos under the earth and the harvestless sea. So I am going to visit them and settle their endless quarrelling. It is a long time now that they have kept from sleeping together in love, after anger entered their hearts. If I can win over their hearts with my persuasion, and bring them to return to love's union in their bed, they will call me their honoured friend for ever.'

Then Aphrodite, smiling goddess, answered her: 'I cannot and should not refuse what you ask, since you are the one who sleeps in the arms of Zeus, the greatest of gods.'

So she spoke, and untied from her breasts the band of elaborate embroidery, in which all her magic powers were worked. Here there was love, and desire, and the sweet allurement of whispered talk, which seduces the heart even in those of good sense. She put this in Hera's hands, and said to her: 'Here now, take this embroidered band and put it away in your breast. It has all things worked in it, and I do not think you will come back disappointed in your heart's desire.'

So she spoke, and the ox-eyed queen Hera smiled, and smiling put the band away in her breast.

Aphrodite, daughter of Zeus, went back then to her house, and Hera darted away from the peak of Olympos and alighted in Pieria and lovely Emathia: then she sped to the snowy mountains of the horse-herding Thracians, on to their highest peak, without her feet touching earth: from Athos she crossed over the swelling sea, and came to Lemnos, the city of godlike Thoas. There she met Sleep, the brother of Death, and she took his hand and spoke to him: 'Sleep, lord over all gods and all men, you have listened to my request before, so now do what I ask once more, and I shall be grateful to you all my days. Close Zeus' shining eyes in sleep under his brows, as soon as I have lain in love beside him. Do this for me, and I shall give you presents – a beautiful throne, imperishable for all time, made of gold: my son, the lame god Hephaistos, will craft it for you, and put a footstool below it, where you can rest your shining feet as you enjoy your feasting.'

Then Sleep the soother answered her: 'Hera, queenly goddess, daughter of great Kronos, any other of the ever-living gods I would readily put to sleep, even the river-stream of Ocean, who is the creator of them all. But I would not come near Zeus, the son of Kronos, or put him to sleep, except when he himself tells me. This is a lesson I learnt from another task you set me before, on the day when that proud-hearted son of Zeus, Herakles, was sailing away from Ilios after sacking the Trojans' city. I then laid to rest the mind of Zeus who holds the aegis, pouring my sweetness round him, while you plotted mischief in your heart for Herakles, and raised a storm of cruel winds over the sea, and then carried him away to the well-founded island of Kos, separated from all his friends. Zeus was furious when he woke, hurling gods around his house, and looking for me above all: and he would have thrown me out of the sky to vanish in the sea, if I had not been saved by Night, who overpowers both gods and men. I ran to her for protection, and Zeus gave up, for all his anger – he was reluctant to do anything to displease quick-passing Night. And now here is another impossible thing you ask me to do.'

Then the ox-eyed queen Hera said to him: 'Sleep, why this concern in your mind? Do you really think that wide-seeing Zeus will show the same anger in aid of the Trojans as he did for Herakles, his own son? No, come now, I will give you one of the younger Graces for you to marry and call your wife.'

So she spoke, and Sleep was delighted, and said in reply: 'Well then, swear me now an oath by the inviolable water of Styx, and take hold of the nourishing earth with one hand, and the gleaming sea with the other, so that all the gods below with Kronos may be our witnesses, and swear that you will give me one of the younger Graces – Pasitheë, the one I have longed for all my days.'

So he spoke, and the white-armed goddess Hera did as he asked, and began the oath he demanded, naming all the gods under Tartaros, who are called Titans. When she had sworn and completed her oath, the two set out, clothed round in mist, and left behind the cities of Lemnos and Imbros, moving quickly on their way. And they came to Ida with the many springs, the mother of wild creatures, to Lekton, where they first left the sea: then they went on over dry land, and the very tops of the trees swayed under their feet. And then Sleep stopped before the eyes of Zeus could see him, and climbed up into a towering pine-tree, which was the tallest that grew then on Ida, and reached up through the lower air into the sky above. Here he sat, close-hidden by the pine branches, in the shape of a singing bird of the mountains, which the gods call bronze-bird, but men's name for it is kymindis.

But Hera went quickly on towards Gargaron, the summit of Ida's height: and Zeus the cloud-gatherer saw her. And as he saw her, so desire enveloped the thought of his heart, as strong as when they first used to go to bed together and join in love without telling their dear parents. He came up to her, and called her and said: 'Hera, what mission brings you down here from Olympos? You could ride in your chariot and horses, but they are not here.'

Then queen Hera answered with deceitful intent: 'I am going to the ends of the nourishing earth, to visit Ocean, the source of the gods' creating, and mother Tethys, who brought me up and reared me in kindness in their house. I am going to visit them, and settle their endless quarrelling. It is a long time now that they have kept from sleeping together in love, after anger entered their hearts. My horses are at the foot of Ida with the many springs, waiting there to carry me over dry land and water. But you are the reason why I have come down here from Olympos now, so that you should not be angry with me afterwards, if I went to the house of deep-flowing Ocean without telling you.'

Then Zeus the cloud-gatherer answered her: 'Hera, you can make your journey there later. Come, let us go to bed now and enjoy our lovemaking. Never before has desire for goddess or woman so flooded the heart in my breast and enslaved it – not even when I fell in love with the wife of Ixion, who bore me Peirithoös, the gods' equal in wisdom; or with Danaë the lovely-ankled daughter of Akrisios, who bore me Perseus, outstanding among all men; or with the daughter of far-famed Phoinix, who bore me Minos and godlike Rhadamanthys; or with Semele or Alkmene in Thebes – the son she gave birth to was the mighty-hearted Herakles, and Semele bore Dionysos, the joy of men; or when I fell in love with queen Demeter with the beautiful hair, or with great Leto, or with you yourself – nothing compares with the love I feel for you now, and the sweet desire that has its hold on me.'

Then queen Hera answered with deceitful intent: 'Dread son of Kronos, what is this you are saying? If your desire is to lie down now and make love on the peak of Ida, where all is open to view, how would it be if one of the ever-living gods were to see us sleeping together and go off and point us out to all the gods? I could not go back to your house after rising from this bed – that would bring shame on me. No, if this is your wish and your heart's desire, there is my bedroom, which my dear son Hephaistos built for me, and made the doors close tightly in their posts. We can go and lie down there, seeing that bed is your pleasure.'

Then Zeus the cloud-gatherer answered her: 'Hera, no need to fear that any god or man will see. I shall wrap us in a golden cloud so thick that not even Helios could see us through it, and his light has the sharpest sight of all.'

So he spoke, and the son of Kronos took his wife in his arms. And underneath them the holy earth put forth fresh-springing grass, and dewy clover and saffron, and hyacinth thick and soft, which held them high away from the ground. In this bed they lay down together, and covered themselves in cloud, beautiful and golden: and from it the dew-drops fell glittering round them.

So the father slept unmoving on the height of Gargaron, overcome by sleep and love, holding his wife in his arms. And Sleep the soother went running to the ships of the Achaians to bring the news to the encircler and shaker of the earth. He came close and spoke winged words to him: 'Help the Danaans now, Poseidon, as much as you will, and grant them the glory – for a little while, for as long as Zeus still sleeps, as I have wrapped him in a soft deep sleep, after Hera seduced him into lying down to make love with her.'

So speaking Sleep went away to visit the famous tribes of humankind, and left Poseidon yet more eager to give help to the Danaans. Immediately he leapt forward among the front-fighters and called loud to them: 'Argives, are we once more to yield the victory to Hektor, son of Priam, so he can take our ships and win glory for himself? That is what he thinks and prays, because Achilleus is staying back by the hollow ships in his heart's anger. But we will not feel his loss too strongly, if the rest of us stir ourselves to support each other. No, come, let us all do as I say. Let us take the best and largest shields in the camp to cover ourselves, and put blazing helmets over our heads, and take up the longest spears in our hands, and go forward. I shall take the lead, and I think that Hektor, Priam's son, will not resist us any longer, however great his fury. Any strong fighter who has a small shield slung from his shoulder should give it to a lesser man, and put on a larger shield himself.'

So he spoke, and they listened well and obeyed him. And the kings themselves supervised the men, although they were wounded – the son of Tydeus, and Odysseus, and Agamemnon son of Atreus. They visited all the troops and directed the change of armour: the good man put on the good armour, and the lesser was given the worse. Then when they had clothed their bodies in gleaming bronze, they set forward. And Poseidon the earthshaker led them on, holding a fearful long-edged sword in his massive hand, a sword like the lightning-flash – men may not come near it in the misery of battle, but fear holds them back.

On the other side glorious Hektor ranged the Trojans. And then dark-haired Poseidon and glorious Hektor racked the clash of battle to its grimmest, one fighting for the Trojans and the other for the Argives. And the sea surged up to the huts and the ships of the Argives, as the two sides joined with a huge clamour. Louder than the waves of the sea crashing against dry land, driven in from the deep by the cruel blast of the north wind; louder than the roar of fire blazing in the hollows of a mountain, when it has caught the forest in its burning; louder than the wind's scream in the high branches of oak-trees, and the wind in its anger roars loudest of all things – so huge was the sound of the fearful shouts of the Trojans and Achaians as they stormed at each other.

Glorious Hektor first cast at Aias with his spear, when Aias was turned to face him straight, and he did not miss, hitting where the two straps lay across his chest, one holding his shield, the other his silver-studded sword: and these saved his soft flesh from the weapon. Hektor was angered that his swift spear had flown wasted from his hand, and he moved back into the mass of his companions to avoid destruction. Then as Hektor stepped back the huge Aias, Telamon's son, took up one of the many stones, used as chocks for the fast ships, which rolled at the feet of the fighters, and with it hit him on the chest above the rim of his shield, close by the neck, and the blow sent him spinning like a top, so he reeled round and round. As when an oak crashes down, uprooted, at a strike from father Zeus, and a terrible smell of sulphur comes from it, and any man who watches from close by is robbed of his courage, as the thunderbolt of mighty Zeus is a fearsome thing – so Hektor's strength suddenly collapsed to the ground in the dust: his spear fell from his hand, and his shield and helmet folded in on him, and the bronze of his crafted armour rang over him. The sons of the Achaians rushed forward with a great shout, hoping to drag him away, and they kept up a dense volley of spears. But none of them could stab or hit the shepherd of the people: before that the leading fighters had stood over him, Poulydamas and Aineias and godlike Agenor, and Sarpedon, leader of the Lycians, and the excellent Glaukos. And none of the others neglected him, but they held the even circles of their shields in front of him. And his companions lifted him in their arms and carried him out of the turmoil, as far as his quick horses, which were standing with their driver and the decorated chariot behind the battle and the fighting: they then carried him towards the city groaning heavily.

But when they came to the fording-place of the lovely stream of the swirling river Xanthos, whose father is immortal Zeus, they brought him down to the ground from the chariot, and splashed water over him. He revived and opened his eyes, and sat up on his heels vomiting dark blood. And then he sank backwards to the earth again, and black night covered over his eyes, his spirit still overcome by the blow.

Now when the Argives saw Hektor leaving the field, they leapt at the Trojans with a new will, and their spirits filled for battle. Then far the first of all quick Aias, Oïleus' son, lunged with his sharp spear and stabbed Satnios, son of Enops, whom the excellent nymph of the water had borne to Enops as he tended his cattle by the banks of the Satnioeis. Aias the famous spearman came close and stabbed him in the side: he collapsed on his back, and over him the Trojans and Danaans joined furious fighting. Poulydamas the spearman, Panthoös' son, came up to defend him, and hit Prothoënor, son of Areïlykos, in the right shoulder: the heavy spear kept on through his shoulder, and he crashed in the dust and his hand clawed earth. Poulydamas shouted loud in terrible triumph: 'Another spear from Panthoös' great-hearted son, which I do not think has leapt from his mighty hand in vain! No, some Argive has taken it in his flesh, and I would say he can use it as a crutch on his way down to the house of Hades.'

So he spoke, and the Argives were pained at his boasting, and most of all he moved the warrior Aias' heart to anger – Telamonian Aias, as he was closest to the man when he fell. As Poulydamas moved back Aias cast at him with a shining spear. Poulydamas himself escaped black doom by jumping sideways, and the spear was taken by Antenor's son Archelochos, as the gods had decreed his destruction. He hit him at the join of head and neck, on the topmost vertebra, and sheared through both the tendons. And his head and mouth and nose reached the ground well before his legs and knees as the man fell. Then Aias shouted to the excellent Poulydamas: 'Think on it, Poulydamas, and tell me truly – is not this man's death a fair exchange for Prothoënor's? He does not seem to me an inferior, or of inferior stock, but he could be the brother of Antenor the horse-tamer, or his son – he has the look of a close relation.'

He spoke knowing full well whom he had killed, and pain seized the Trojans' hearts. Then Akamas, standing over his brother's body, stabbed Promachos the Boiotian with his spear, as he tried to drag the body away by the feet. Akamas shouted loud in terrible triumph over him: 'You bletherskate Argives, always full of threats, we are not the only ones who will suffer hardship and misery, but you too will be killed sooner or later like this man. Think on how Promachos sleeps among you now, brought down by my spear, so that the price for my brother should not go long without payment. That is why a man prays to have a brother left behind in his house, to avenge his death.'

So he spoke, and the Argives were pained at his boasting, and most of all he moved the warrior Peneleos' heart to anger. He charged at Akamas, but he did not stand his ground before lord Peneleos' attack. But Peneleos stabbed Ilioneus, the son of Phorbas, a man rich in flocks: Hermes loved this man most of all the Trojans, and had given him wealth: but Ilioneus was the only child his mother had borne for him. Peneleos struck him under the brow at the base of the eye, and knocked out the eyeball. The spear passed right through the eye-socket and came out through the muscle of the neck, and Ilioneus sank down stretching out both his arms. Peneleos then drew his sharp sword and struck at the middle of his neck, and sliced the head to the ground, helmet and all. The heavy spear was still in the eye-socket, and he lifted up the head like a poppy-head on its stalk, and displayed it to the Trojans and spoke in triumph over it: 'Take my message, Trojans, to proud Ilioneus' dear father and mother, that they should weep for him in their house – because the wife of Promachos, son of Alegenor, she too will not have the joy of her dear husband's return, when we sons of the Achaians leave Troy and go home in our ships.'

So he spoke, and trembling took hold of all their bodies, and every man looked to see where he might escape sheer destruction.

Tell me now, you Muses who have your homes on Olympos, who was the first of the Achaians to win the bloody spoils from a man killed, when the famous Earthshaker swayed the battle. First was Aias, Telamon's son, who stabbed Hyrtios, the son of Gyrtias, leader of the strong-hearted Mysians. And Antilochos killed Phalkes and Mermeros; Meriones cut down Morys and Hippotion; and Teukros slaughtered Prothoön and Periphetes. And then the son of Atreus stabbed Hyperenor, shepherd of his people, in the side. The bronze cut through and let his bowels gush out: his life came rushing through the opened wound, and darkness covered over his eyes. But the most were killed by Aias the quick son of Oïleus: no man was his equal in running to catch men in flight, when Zeus had sent the panic on them.

BOOK 15
FIGHTING AT THE SHIPS

But when the Trojans had crossed back over the ditch and its stakes in their flight, and many had been brought down at the hands of the Danaans, they came to a halt and rallied by their chariots, panic-stricken and pale with fear. And Zeus woke from the side of Hera of the golden throne on the heights of Ida, and leapt to his feet, and saw the Trojans and Achaians, the Trojans running in confusion and behind them the Argives sweeping them on, with the lord Poseidon among them. And he saw Hektor lying there in the plain, and his companions sitting round him, and Hektor gripped by painful gasping, dazed in mind and vomiting blood, as it was not the feeblest of the Achaians that had hit him. When he saw him, the father of men and gods felt pity for him, and scowling fearfully he said to Hera: 'Impossible creature, it is surely your vile scheming, Hera, that has put godlike Hektor out of the battle and panicked his army. I am not sure you may not soon be the first to feel the benefit of your troublesome mischief, when I flog you with blows of the whip. Or do you not remember when you were strung up on high, and I hung two anvils from your feet and fastened a golden rope round your hands that could not be broken? You hung there in the sky and the clouds, and the gods throughout high Olympos were distraught. They stood round quite unable to help you – any one I caught I would seize and hurl from the threshold, till they fell to earth with little strength in them. Even so the constant pain for godlike Herakles would not leave my heart. You together with Boreas the north wind prevailed on the stormwinds and sent him over the harvestless sea, plotting mischief for him, and then carried him away to the well-founded island of Kos. I rescued him from there, and brought him back again to the horse-pasture of Argos after he had suffered much hardship. I shall bring this back to your mind, so you can stop your deceitful ways, and see if your making love in bed will be any help to you, the way you came to sleep with me away from the gods, and tricked me.'

So he spoke, and the ox-eyed queen Hera shuddered in fear, and spoke winged words to him: 'May Earth now be my witness, and the wide Heaven above, and the flowing water of Styx, which is the greatest and the most awesome oath for the blessed gods, and witness too your sacred head and the bed of our own marriage, something I would never swear by falsely – it is not of my doing that Poseidon the earthshaker is afflicting Hektor and the Trojans, and helping the Achaians, but it must be his own heart that prompts him: he must have seen the Achaians suffering by their ships and felt pity for them. But certainly I shall advise him to follow wherever you lead the way, lord of the dark clouds.'

So she spoke, and the father of men and gods smiled, and spoke winged words in answer: 'Well, if from now on, ox-eyed queen Hera, you take your seat among the immortals with your thoughts the same as mine, then Poseidon, however contrary his wish, would quickly bend his purpose to follow your mind and my mind. If what you say is truly so, go now to the company of the gods and call Iris to come here, and Apollo the archer, so that she can go to the army of the bronze-clad Achaians and tell the lord Poseidon to leave the fighting and return to his own house, and Phoibos Apollo can spur Hektor into battle, breathing strength into him again and making him forget the pains which are now wearing his heart: and he can raise a cowardly panic in the Achaians and turn them back again, so they are driven back on the many-benched ships of Achilleus, son of Peleus. And Achilleus will send out his companion, Patroklos: glorious Hektor will kill him with his spear in front of Ilios, after Patroklos has slaughtered many of the other young warriors, and among them my own son, godlike Sarpedon. In anger for his friend godlike Achilleus will kill Hektor. And from that time on I shall make a turn in the battle, driving it constantly back from the ships, until the Achaians capture steep Ilios through the designs of Athene. But I shall not cease my anger or allow any other of the immortals to give help here to the Danaans, until the son of Peleus' desire has been fulfilled, as I promised him at the beginning and nodded agreement with my head, on that day when the goddess Thetis took hold of my knees, begging me to show honour to Achilleus, sacker of cities.'

So he spoke, and the white-armed goddess Hera did not fail to obey, and went up from the mountains of Ida to high Olympos. As when the thought darts in the mind of a man who has travelled over many lands, and in his subtle imagination he calls up many memories, thinking to himself 'Let me be there – or there': so thought-swift was queen Hera's flight in her eagerness. She reached steep Olympos, and came on the immortal gods gathered together in Zeus' house. When they saw her they all rose to their feet and offered their cups in greeting. She ignored the others and accepted a cup from the beautiful Themis, as she came running first to meet her and spoke winged words to her: 'Hera, what has brought you here? You look distraught – it must be the son of Kronos, your husband, who has alarmed you.'

Then the white-armed goddess Hera answered her: 'Do not ask me about it, divine Themis. You know yourself how overbearing and cruel his nature is. No, you start the gods in their shared feasting in the palace, and you will hear together with all the immortals what vile events Zeus is proposing – and even though some may now still be in good humour for the feast, I do not think there will be joy for the hearts of all alike, either gods or men.'

So speaking queen Hera sat down, and there was uproar among the gods in Zeus' house. She smiled with her lips, but on the forehead above her dark brows there was no softening. And she said to them all in vexation: 'Fools we are, thoughtless idiots, to storm against Zeus! We are still intent on facing him, and trying to stop him with argument or force. But he sits there by himself without thought or regard for us, saying that he is preeminently the best of the immortal gods in power and strength. So you must take whatever trouble he sends each of you. And already I think a grief has come for Ares – his son has been killed in the battle, the dearest of men to him, Askalaphos, a man whom monstrous Ares acknowledges as his own.'

So she spoke, and Ares struck his strong thighs with the flat of his hand, and said to them in his sorrow: 'Do not blame me now, you gods who have your homes on Olympos, for going to the ships of the Achaians and avenging the killing of my son, even if it is my fate to be struck by Zeus' lightning and lie among the dead men in the blood and dust.'

So he spoke, and he called Terror and Panic to yoke his horses, while he himself put on his gleaming armour. And now there would have been caused yet greater and more dangerous anger and fury in Zeus against the immortals, if Athene, in fear for all the gods, had not left the seat where she was sitting and gone out after him through the gateway, and taken the helmet from his head and the shield from his shoulders, and seized the bronze spear out of his massive hand and put it away. Then she assailed raging Ares with these words: 'Madman, you brain-crazed fool, you are out of your mind! You might as well have no ears to hear with, and you have lost all sense and judgment. Did you not hear what the white-armed goddess Hera said – and she has come to us straight from Olympian Zeus? Or do you want to have your fill of suffering and then be forced back to Olympos however reluctant, and at the same time sow the seeds of great trouble for all the rest of us? Because Zeus will immediately leave the proud Trojans and the Achaians, and come back to Olympos to beat us about, and he will lay hands on each of us in turn, guilty and innocent alike. So I tell you now to leave your anger for your son. Better men than he in the strength of their hands have already been killed, and will be killed yet. It is impossible for us to save everyone's family and children.'

So speaking she sat raging Ares down on his chair. And Hera called Apollo outside the house, and Iris, the messenger for the immortal gods, and spoke winged words to them: 'Zeus orders you both to go to Ida as quickly as you can. When you are there and have come into Zeus' presence, you must do whatever orders he urges on you.'

So speaking queen Hera went back and sat down on her chair: and the two of them darted off in flight. They came to Ida with the many springs, the mother of wild creatures, and found wide-seeing Zeus sitting on the height of Gargaron, surrounded by a crown of sweet-scented cloud. They went forward and stood before Zeus the cloud-gatherer: and when he saw them his heart was not displeased with them, as they had promptly obeyed his dear wife's instructions. He spoke winged words to Iris first: 'Away with you, swift Iris, take this message to the lord Poseidon, and do not fail to give all of it true. Tell him to leave the battle and the fighting, and go to join the company of gods, or into the holy sea. And if he will not obey my orders but intends to ignore them, let him then consider well in his mind and his heart that for all his power he may not be able to stand my attack, since I say that I am far his superior in strength and his senior by birth. And yet his heart thinks nothing of claiming equality with me, when others fear me.'

So he spoke, and swift Iris with feet quick as the wind did not fail to obey, and she went down from the heights of Ida to sacred Ilios. As when snow or hail is sent flying cold from the clouds under the blast of the north wind, child of the clear air, so swift was quick Iris' flight in her eagerness. She came close to the famous Earthshaker and spoke to him: 'Encircler of the earth, dark-haired god, I have come here bringing a message to you from Zeus who holds the aegis. He has ordered you to leave the battle and the fighting, and go to join the company of gods, or into the holy sea. And if you will not obey his orders but intend to ignore them, he threatens to come here himself to fight you face to face. And he warns you to keep away from his hands, since he says he is far your superior in strength and your senior by birth. And yet your heart thinks nothing of claiming equality with him, when others fear him.'

The famous Earthshaker answered her in fury: 'Oh, this is presumption, great god though he is, to talk of curbing me by force against my will, when I hold equal honour with him. There are three of us brothers borne to Kronos by Rhea, Zeus and I, and the third is Hades, lord over the dead. All the world was divided into three parts, and each of us received his portion. When the lots were cast, I drew the grey sea as my domain for ever, and Hades drew the murky darkness below, and Zeus drew the broad sky among the clouds and the upper air: but the earth and high Olympos were left common to us all. So I shall not live at the will of Zeus. No, for all his strength let him stay content in his own third share. And let him stop trying to frighten me with the violence of his hands, as if I were some weak coward – better to use his fearful threats on his sons and daughters, those he fathered himself, who will be obliged to listen to his orders.'

Then swift Iris with feet quick as the wind answered him: 'Encircler of the earth, dark-haired god, is this then what I am to carry back to Zeus, this harsh and unbending message, or will you change at all? There can be change in the minds of the great. You know how the Furies always go with the elder.'

Then Poseidon the earthshaker said to her: 'Divine Iris, what you have said is quite right and true: and it is an excellent thing when a messenger is possessed of good sense. But this is a grievous thing that touches my heart and spirit with pain, when he is ready to abuse with angry words one who has an equal share with him and is destined with the same endowment. Well, for this time I shall hold myself back and give in to him. But I tell you something else, a threat I make in my heart. If in spite of me and Athene, goddess of spoil, and Hera and Hermes and lord Hephaistos, Zeus spares steep Ilios, and will not sack it and grant a great victory to the Argives, let him be sure of this, that there will be anger without healing between us.'

So speaking the Earthshaker left the Achaian army and went and sank down into the sea: and the Achaian fighters felt his loss. Then Zeus the cloud-gatherer spoke to Apollo: 'Now, dear Phoibos, you go to bronze-armoured Hektor. The encircler and shaker of the earth has left now and gone into the holy sea, to avoid the stark fury I would have shown – that is a battle whose sound would have reached even the gods below with Kronos. No, what has happened is far better both for me and for him too, that before it came to that he held himself back and retreated from my hands – because there would have been sweat enough before we finished. Now you take the tasselled aegis in your hands and shake it hard to put panic in the Achaian fighters. And then, far-shooter, take special care of glorious Hektor: rouse the spirit strong in him until the Achaians' flight reaches their ships and the Hellespont. From that time on I myself shall consider what is to be said and done to give the Achaians relief once more from their hardship.'

So he spoke, and Apollo did not fail to listen to his father, and he went down from the heights of Ida like a swift hawk, the dove-killer, the fastest of all flying creatures. He found the son of wise Priam, godlike Hektor, sitting up now and no longer lying on the ground. He was gathering consciousness again, and beginning to recognise the companions round him: and the gasping and the sweating began to stop, as the will of Zeus who holds the aegis revived him. Apollo the far-worker came close and spoke to him: 'Hektor, son of Priam, why are you sitting here with little strength in you, away from the others? Has some misfortune come over you?'

Then with the strength low in him Hektor of the glinting helmet answered: 'Which of the gods are you, my lord, asking me this face to face? Have you not heard how when I was cutting down his companions by the sterns of the Achaian ships Aias, master of the war-cry, hit me on the chest with a stone, and put a stop to my fighting fury? And indeed I thought that I would breathe out my life and go down to the dead and the house of Hades this very day.'

Then lord Apollo, the far-worker, said to him: 'Take courage now. Such is the ally that the son of Kronos has sent down from Ida to stand by you and protect you – Phoibos Apollo, god of the golden sword: and it is I who have preserved you before, both you yourself and your steep city. But come now, urge your horsemen in all their numbers to drive their quick horses for the hollow ships. And I shall go ahead and make the whole way smooth for the horses, and turn back the Achaian fighters.'

So speaking he breathed great strength into the shepherd of the people. As when some stalled horse who has fed full at the manger breaks his halter and gallops thudding across the plain, eager for his usual bathe in the lovely flow of a river, and glorying as he runs. He holds his head high, and the mane streams back along his shoulders:

sure of his own magnificence, his legs carry him lightly to the haunts where the mares are at pasture. So Hektor set his legs and knees running fast as he urged on the horsemen, after hearing the voice of the god. As when country farmers and their dogs have started a horned stag or a wild goat: the prey finds safety in sheer rock-face or shadowing forest, and the men realise they were not destined to catch him: but roused by their clamour a great bearded lion appears in their path, and sends them all running straight back despite their eagerness. So up till then the Danaans had kept up a massed pursuit, thrusting with their swords and double-pointed spears: but when they saw Hektor ranging his attack on the ranks of men, they were all afraid, and their courage dropped to their feet.

Now Thoas spoke to the Danaans, the son of Andraimon, and far the best of the Aitolians, a man skilled at throwing the spear and also a brave man in the close fighting: and few of the Achaians were his superiors in speaking in the assembly, when the young men competed in debate. In all good will he spoke and addressed the Danaans: 'Oh, this is a great astonishment for my eyes, how Hektor has escaped the fates of death and is back on his feet once more! The heart in every one of us was convinced that he had died at the hands of Aias, son of Telamon. But now some god has rescued and preserved Hektor. He has already collapsed the strength of many of the Danaans, and I think it will be the same now too, as he could not be out there at their head and full of this fury without the help of Zeus the thunderer. No, come, let us all do as I say. Let us order the bulk of the troops to return towards the ships, while all of us who claim to be the best fighters in the army make a stand, with spears held out at the ready, to see if we can meet him first and hold him off – for all his fury I think his heart will shrink from pressing through into the ranks of the Danaans.'

So he spoke, and they listened well and agreed. So then those with Aias and lord Idomeneus and Teukros and Meriones and Meges, a man like Ares, called together the leading fighters and formed a battlefront to face Hektor and the Trojans. And the bulk of the troops behind them set off back towards the ships of the Achaians.

The Trojans charged forward in a mass, and Hektor at their head, taking huge strides. And in front of him went Phoibos Apollo, with mist wrapped round his shoulders, and holding the mighty aegis, a fearful thing, shaggy-fringed and brightly seen, which the smith Hephaistos had given to Zeus to wear for the panicking of men: with this in his hands Apollo led the Trojan army on.

But the Argives stood their ground all together, and the clamour rose shrill on both sides – arrows leapt from the string: many spears were thrown by brave hands, and some sank into the bodies of quick young warriors, and many, eager to taste flesh, stuck in the earth between before they could reach white skin. As long as Phoibos Apollo held the aegis still in his hands, the weapons thrown by both sides reached their mark, and men kept falling. But when he looked straight into the faces of the fast-horsed Danaans and shook the aegis, and uttered a huge great shout himself, then he bewildered the hearts in their breasts, and they forgot their fighting spirit. As when two wild beasts stampede a herd of cattle or a great flock of sheep, coming suddenly at the dead of black night when the herdsman is away, so the Achaians were panicked to cowardice. It was Apollo who sent the panic on them, and gave glory to Hektor and the Trojans.

Then man killed man as the battle-front broke. Hektor killed Stichios and Arkesilaos, one the leader of the bronze-clad Boiotians, the other a trusted companion of great-hearted Menestheus. Aineias cut down Medon and Iasos. Medon was a bastard son of godlike Oïleus, and brother of Aias: but he lived in Phylake, away from his native land, as he had killed a man, the brother of his step-mother Eriopis, wife of Oïleus. And Iasos was a captain of the Athenians, known as the son of Sphelos, son of Boukolos. Poulydamas killed Mekisteus, and Polites Echios in the first rush: and godlike Agenor took Klonios. Paris struck Deïochos at the base of the shoulder from behind as he fled with the front-fighters, and drove the bronze right through.

While the Trojans stripped the armour from these bodies, the Achaians were running in panic this way and that, fouled in the ditch they had dug and its stakes, and they were forced behind their wall. Hektor called with a great shout to the Trojans: 'Go fast for the ships, and leave the blood-stained spoils. Any man I find elsewhere, away from the ships, I shall see him killed on the spot, and the men and women of his family will not give him in death the due rite of burning, but the dogs will tear him in front of our city.'

So speaking, Hektor swung his whip full from the shoulder and lashed his horses on, calling to the Trojans across the ranks. And they all shouted in response, and drove the horses that pulled their chariots to follow him, raising a tremendous clamour. And in front of them Phoibos Apollo kicked down the banks of the deep ditch with ease, and piled them in the space between, bridging a long broad path across, as wide as the distance that a spear carries when a man throws it to test his strength. The Trojans poured across this in their massed squadrons, and Apollo went before them holding the precious aegis. And he threw down the Achaians' wall with utter ease, as when a little boy knocks over sand-castles on the sea-shore – he builds them to play with in his childish way, and then amuses himself by flattening them again with hands and feet. So you, lord Apollo, smashed all the work the Argives had laboured at with much pain, and started a panic among them.

So they were brought up alongside the ships and stood there, calling to each other: and every man held up his hands to all the gods and prayed aloud. And Nestor prayed most of all, the Gerenian, the warden of the Achaians, holding out his hands to the sky where the stars are: 'Father Zeus, if ever any of us burned for you the fat-wrapped thigh-bones of ox or sheep in the wheatlands of Argos and prayed for his return, and you assented and promised it, remember that now, Olympian, and keep the pitiless hour of death from us. Do not allow the Achaians to be crushed in this way by the Trojans.'

So he spoke in prayer, and Zeus the counsellor thundered loud, hearing the prayers of the old man, the son of Neleus.

When the Trojans heard the thunder of Zeus who holds the aegis, they leapt at the Argives with a new will, and their spirits filled for battle. As a huge wave sweeps down over the sides of a ship in the broad paths of the sea, driven on by the wind's violence, which raises the waves to their greatest height: so the Trojans swept over the wall with a tremendous clamour, and drove their chariots through. And close fighting began by the sterns of the ships: the Trojans fought from their chariots with double-edged spears, and the Achaians climbed high on to their black ships and used from there the long jointed pikes which they had lying on deck for sea-fighting, with their tips shod in bronze.

Now Patroklos, as long as the Achaians and Trojans were fighting for the wall, away from the ships, was sitting in the hut of the kindly Eurypylos and entertaining him with talk, while he applied medicines to the grievous wound, which soothed the black pains. But when he saw the Trojans storming at the wall, and there was the clamour of panic among the Danaans, then he groaned aloud and struck his thighs with the flat of his hands, and said to Eurypylos in distress: 'Eurypylos, I cannot stay any longer with you here, even though you need me – a great battle is on us now. No, your lieutenant must look after you, while I hurry to Achilleus, to urge him into the fight. Who knows if, with god's help, I might move his heart with my persuasion? There is power in a friend's persuasion.'

This said, his legs carried him away. Meanwhile the Achaians stood firm against the Trojan attack, but could not push them back from the ships even though their numbers were less: and the Trojans too could never break through the Danaan ranks to get among the huts and ships. But as the carpenter's line keeps straight the cut of a ship's timber in the hands of a skilful shipwright, a man who is knowledgeable in all the ways of his craft through the inspiration of Athene, so the battle was strained taut and level between them. There was fighting joined at ship after ship, but Hektor went straight for glorious Aias. These two then struggled over a single ship: Hektor could not drive Aias away and set fire to the ship, and Aias could not push Hektor back, now that god had brought him that far. Then glorious Aias killed Kaletor, son of Klytios, as he brought fire to the ship, hitting him in the chest with his spear: he fell with a crash, and the firebrand dropped from his hand. When Hektor's eyes saw his cousin fall in the dust in front of the black ship, he called to the Trojans and Lycians with a great shout: 'Trojans and Lycians and close-fighting Dardanians, do not now give ground in your fighting in this pass we are in, but rescue the son of Klytios, so the Achaians do not strip his armour where he has fallen among the assembly of ships.'

So speaking he cast at Aias with a shining spear. He missed his aim, but hit Lykophron, son of Mastor, a lieutenant of Aias from Kythera, who had lived with Aias after killing a man in holy Kythera. Hektor hit him with his sharp spear on the head above the ear, where he stood close to Aias: he dropped to the ground from the stern of the ship and fell on his back in the dust, and his body went slack. Aias shuddered, and called to his brother: 'Teukros, dear friend, now our trusted companion has been killed, the son of Mastor, who came to our household from Kythera and we honoured him as much as our own dear parents. Where then are your arrows of quick death and the bow that Phoibos Apollo gave you?'

So he spoke, and Teukros heard and came running to stand beside him, holding his curved bow and the quiver that kept his arrows: and quickly he began shooting arrows at the Trojans. And he hit Kleitos, Peisenor's splendid son and a companion of Poulydamas, proud son of Panthoös. He had the reins in his hands and was busy with his horses, as he was driving them in to where the fighting ranks swarmed thickest, thinking this would please Hektor and the Trojans. But disaster came quickly on him, and none could keep it from him however much they wanted to. The fatal arrow fixed in his neck from behind: he crashed from the chariot, and his horses shied at his loss, rattling an empty chariot behind them. Their master Poulydamas was quick to see it, and the first to intercept the horses. He handed them then to Astynoös, son of Protiaön, with strict instructions to watch carefully and to hold the horses close: and he himself went back to join the front-fighters.

But Teukros took out another arrow, for bronze-armoured Hektor, and would have stopped his fighting by the ships of the Achaians, if he had hit him in the time of his glory and taken the life from him. But Zeus was guarding Hektor, and his subtle mind did not fail to notice. He robbed Telamonian Teukros of his triumph, breaking the twisted string on his excellent bow as he drew it against Hektor: the bronze-weighted arrow was sent veering off course, and the bow fell from his hand. Teukros shuddered, and said to his brother: 'Look – some divine power is wholly frustrating the skill of all our fighting. He has knocked the bow out of my hands, and broken the new-twisted string which I tied on this morning to stand the number of arrows that would leap from it.'

Then huge Aias, Telamon's son, answered him: 'Well, my friend, put down your bow and cluster of arrows and let them be, since some god with a grudge against the Danaans has made them useless. Rather take a long spear in your hands and a shield on your shoulder, and fight with the Trojans like that, rousing on the rest of your people. Even though they have beaten us, let us make sure they do not take our well-benched ships without a struggle: no, let our spirits fill for battle!'

So he spoke, and Teukros put the bow back in his hut, and slung round his shoulders a shield of fourfold hide, and on his mighty head he placed a well-made helmet with a plume of horse-hair, and the crest nodded fearfully from its top. He took up a strong spear, sharp-edged with pointed bronze, and set out, running quickly to stand at Aias' side.

When Hektor saw that Teukros' weapons were blighted, he called to the Trojans and Lycians with a great shout: 'Trojans and Lycians and close-fighting Dardanians, be men, my friends, and fill your minds with spirit for the fight among the hollow ships. I have just now seen with my own eyes one of their leading men's weapons blighted by Zeus' power. Men can easily tell the strength that comes from Zeus, both those to whom he grants the glory of victory, and those he belittles and refuses to protect – as he is now belittling the strength of the Argives, and giving help to us. Fight, then, by the ships all together! And whichever of you meets his death and doom through shot or stab, let him die. It is no shame for a man to die in defence of his country – his wife and children will be safe thereafter, and his home and property untouched, if the Achaians are sent back with their ships to their own native land.'

So speaking he spurred the strength and heart in each of them. And Aias on the other side called to his companions: 'Shame, you Argives! Now it is certain – either we die, or we save ourselves and beat back disaster from the ships. Or do you think, if Hektor of the glinting helmet takes our ships, each of us will be able to walk back to his native land? Do you not hear Hektor urging on his whole army? His aim now is to fire the ships. It is not a dance he is inviting them to join, but a battle. For us, there can be no better thought or plan than to take them on in close fighting, hand to hand and strength to strength. Better to settle it once and for all – to die or to live – than to be slowly strangled like this in grim combat by our ships, by men who are worse than we.'

So speaking he spurred the strength and heart in each of them. Then Hektor killed Schedios, son of Perimedes, a leader of the Phocians, and Aias killed Laodamas, captain of the foot-soldiers, the splendid son of Antenor. Poulydamas slaughtered Otos from Kyllene, a companion of Meges son of Phyleus, and leader of the great-hearted Epeians. Meges leapt at Poulydamas when he saw this, but he ducked under the attack so that Meges missed him – Apollo would not allow the son of Panthoös to be brought down in the front of the fight – but he caught Kroismos with his spear in mid-chest. He fell with a crash, and Meges began to strip the armour from his shoulders. But as he did so, Dolops leapt at him, a skilled spearman, the son of Lampos: he was the best of the sons that Lampos, son of Laomedon, had fathered, and a man well versed in fighting. He then ran in close to the son of Phyleus and stabbed at the centre of his shield with his spear: but the thick corselet he wore, with its fitted plates, protected him. Phyleus had brought this corselet from Ephyre, from beside the river Selleëis – his guest-friend Euphetes, lord of men, had given it to him to wear into battle as a defence against his enemies: and now it protected his son's body too from destruction. Meges stabbed at Dolops with his sharp spear, hitting the very crown of his bronze horse-plumed helmet, and shearing away its crest of horse-hair – it dropped entire to the dust on the ground, bright with its fresh purple. Dolops stood his ground and fought on, still hoping for victory, but meanwhile the warrior Menelaos had come to help Meges. He came up from the side with his spear, unnoticed by Dolops, and struck him in the shoulder from behind. The spear-point, pressing eagerly forward, came out through his chest, and he sank to the ground headlong. Menelaos and Meges moved in to strip the bronze armour from his shoulders. But Hektor called out to his kinsmen, to all of them, and the first to feel his anger was the son of Hiketaon, the mighty Melanippos. In earlier times he had grazed his shambling cattle in Perkote, while the enemy were still far away: but when the Danaans' balanced ships came, he returned to Ilios, and was a leading man among the Trojans, and lived with Priam, who showed him the same honour as his own children. Hektor called him and spoke angrily to him: 'Are we going to hold back like this, then, Melanippos? Is it no concern to your heart that your cousin is killed? Do you not see how they are busy with the stripping of Dolops' armour? Come with me, then. We cannot keep our distance any longer from the Argives, but must join battle until either we kill them or they take utter hold of steep Ilios and slaughter its people.'

So speaking he led the way, and the godlike man went with him. And the huge Aias, Telamon's son, spurred on the Argives: 'Be men, my friends, and put pride in your hearts. In the battle's fury think proudly of your honour in each other's eyes. When men have pride, more are saved than killed; but when they turn to flight, there can be no glory there or courage to resist.'

So he spoke, and they were ready for defence even without his urging. They took his words to their hearts, and fenced the ships with a wall of bronze: and Zeus drove the Trojans against them. Then Menelaos, master of the war-cry, spurred on Antilochos: 'Antilochos, none of the younger Achaians is faster than you on his feet, or as brave in the fight – perhaps you could dash out and strike down one of the Trojans.'

So speaking he ran back, but his words roused Antilochos. He leapt forward from the front-fighters, looked sharply all around him, and cast with his shining spear. The Trojans gave ground, faced by a man's spear-cast: and his shot was not wasted, but hit the son of Hiketaon, high-hearted Melanippos, in the chest by the nipple as he came into battle. He fell with a crash, and darkness covered over his eyes. Antilochos sprang at him as a dog pounces on a fawn shot by a hunter, who hits him with his shot as he runs from his lair, and collapses his strength. So brave Antilochos leapt at you, Melanippos, to strip your armour. But godlike Hektor did not fail to notice, and he came running through the fighting to face him. Antilochos, quick fighter though he was, would not stand his ground, but ran like a wild beast that has done some bad thing, killing a dog or a cowherd in attack on the cattle, and runs away before a group of men is gathered against him. So Nestor's son went running, and Hektor and the Trojans, raising a tremendous clamour, hurled showers of pain-fraught weapons after him. Then he turned and stood firm when he had reached the mass of his companions.

Now the Trojans swept on at the ships like lions who eat raw flesh. They were effecting the will of Zeus, who constantly roused the spirit strong in them, and bewildered the hearts of the Argives and denied them glory, while spurring on the Trojans. His heart wished to give the glory to Hektor, son of Priam, so he could throw the untiring power of monstrous fire on the beaked ships, and thus the disastrous prayer of Thetis could be granted in full. Zeus the counsellor was waiting for his eyes to see the blaze of a ship alight: from that moment he intended to turn the battle, pushing the Trojans back from the ships and giving the glory to the Danaans. So with these thoughts he was spurring Hektor, son of Priam, against the hollow ships, though Hektor was full already of his own fury. And he raged now like Ares with spear in hand, or as destroying fire rages on the mountains, in the thick wood of a deep forest. Foam gathered at his mouth, his eyes flashed under his grim brows, and the helmet shook fearfully round his temples as he fought – because his ally was Zeus himself in the sky above, who was giving honour and glory to this one man among the multitude of others, as he would live only a short time: already Pallas Athene was advancing the day of his fate, at the hands of the strong son of Peleus. And now his aim was to break through the ranks, pushing at them where he could see the largest number of men and the finest armour. But even so, for all his fury, he could not break through. They closed wall-like against him and stood their ground, like a huge sheer cliff at the edge of the grey sea, which stands against the shrill winds on their rapid pathways and the waves that swell large and burst on it. So the Danaans stood firm before the Trojans and did not break in flight. But Hektor, blazing with fire all round, leapt into the mass of men and fell on them as when a wave, wind-fed to high fury under the clouds, falls on a fast ship and shrouds it wholly in foam: the fearful blast of the wind roars in the sail, and the sailors' hearts tremble with fear, as they are carried only just out of the grip of death – so the Achaians' spirits were troubled in their breasts. And Hektor fell on them like a vicious lion attacking cattle, as they graze in the grassy flat of a great water-meadow, a huge herd, and a herdsman among them without full knowledge of how to fight a wild beast away from killing a twist-horned cow – he is always walking with the first or the hindmost, but the lion springs at the middle of the herd and eats a cow as all the others stampede. So then all the Achaians were sent running in unspeakable terror by Hektor and father Zeus, but he killed one man only, Periphetes of Mykene, the dear son of Kopreus, who had often been the runner bringing orders from king Eurystheus to the mighty Herakles. From this inferior father came a son much his better in every fine quality, good at running and fighting, and among the foremost in Mykene for intelligence. He now gave Hektor yet higher glory. He had turned round to run back, and tripped on the rim of the ankle-length shield he always carried to protect him from spears: tangled in this, he fell over on his back, and his helmet rang fearfully around his temples as he hit the ground. Hektor quickly saw it, and came running to stand beside him, and fixed his spear in his chest, killing him right by his dear companions – but they could not help him, for all their grief for their friend: they themselves were terrified of godlike Hektor.

And now they were in among the ships, surrounded by the upper line of ships, those that had been hauled first on shore. But the Trojans poured after them, and the Argives were forced to give back from the first line of ships. When they reached the huts, they stood their ground there all together, and did not scatter throughout the camp. Pride and fear stopped them, as they called constant encouragement to each other. And Nestor appealed to them most of all, the Gerenian, the warden of the Achaians, entreating each one of them for their parents' sake: 'Be men, my friends, and put pride in your hearts for the regard of others. And think, every one of you, of your children and your wives, your property and your parents, whether they are living or dead – they are not here, but I beg you now for their sakes to stand firm and not be turned to flight.'

So speaking he spurred the strength and heart in each of them. And Athene drove away the strange mist of darkness that had fogged their eyes, and they had bright light on both sides, both back towards the ships and out over the joining of battle. And now Hektor, master of the war-cry, and his men were clearly seen, those who had fallen back and were standing idle out of the fight as well as those who were fighting the battle by the fast ships.

But now great-hearted Aias was not content to take position where the other sons of the Achaians had fallen back: but he went up and down the decks of the ships with huge strides, wielding in his hands a great sea-fighting pike, fitted together with clamps to a length of twenty-two cubits. As when a man skilled in riding horses has tied together four horses, choosing these four out of many, then sets them at the gallop and rides them in from the plain to a large city along the main highway: many men and women look on admiring, as he constantly switches from one mount to another, leaping across sure-footed and without fail, while the horses fly onwards. So Aias kept crossing from deck to deck over many fast ships, taking huge strides, and his voice reached up to the sky, as with constant fearful shouting he urged the Danaans to defend their ships and huts. And Hektor too would not stay among the throng of the heavy-armoured Trojans: but as a russet eagle swoops on a flock of winged birds feeding by a river – geese or cranes, or long-necked swans – so Hektor dashed out straight for a dark-prowed ship to face Aias. And Zeus was pushing him on from behind with his mighty hand, and urging his men along with him.

And now once more there was bitter fighting by the ships. They fought so furiously you would say that this was a battle joined by fresh troops, men unwearied by war. These were the thoughts on each side as they fought on: the Achaians did not think they could escape disaster, but expected to die, and the heart in the breast of every Trojan hoped to fire the ships and slaughter the Achaian fighting men. These then were their feelings as they closed with each other. And Hektor took hold of the stern of a sea-going ship, a fine vessel, fast on the water, which had brought Protesilaos to Troy, but did not take him back again to his native land. Round this ship now the Achaians and Trojans cut at each other hand to hand. It was not a battle now of keeping distance and facing arrows and spears flying in volleys, but they stood at close quarters, equal fury on both sides, and fought with sharp axes and hatchets, long swords and double-pointed spears: and many fine swords with black-bound hilts fell to the ground, some dropping from their hands as the men fought, others cut from their shoulders: and the black earth ran with blood. Hektor would not let go of the ship where he had grasped it at the stern, gripping the poop-end in his hands, and he called out to the Trojans: 'Bring fire, and raise the war-cry all together. Now Zeus has given us a day that repays us for all – the capture of the ships, which came here against the gods' will and have brought much pain on us: this was through the cowardice of the elders – I wanted to fight right by the sterns of the ships, but they stopped me and held back the army. Well, if wide-seeing Zeus was crazing our wits then, now he is giving his direct command and urging us on.'

So he spoke, and they leapt at the Argives with a new will. And Aias, beset by flying spears, could no longer hold his ground, but left the poop-deck of the balanced ship, thinking he would be killed, and gave back a little way to the seven-foot bridge. There he took his stand, watching for them. And whenever any Trojan brought up untiring fire, he beat them back from the ships with his pike. And all the time he kept shouting fearfully, calling to the Danaans: 'Friends, Danaan heroes, Ares' men-at-arms – be men, my friends, and fill your minds with fighting spirit. Or do we think there are men behind us to come to our aid, or some stronger wall which could save men from disaster? We have no city near us ringed with battlements, where we could defend ourselves and raise more troops to turn the battle. No, we find ourselves here in the plain held by the heavy-armoured Trojans, pressed back against the sea, and far from our native land. So salvation is in the strength of our hands, not courtesy in battle.'

So he spoke, and laid about him furiously with his sharp pike. When any Trojan came up against the hollow ships with blazing fire, hoping to serve Hektor's command, Aias was watching for him and stabbed him with the long pike: and there were twelve that he wounded in front of the ships with a stab straight from his hand.

BOOK 16

THE DEATH OF PATROKLOS

So they fought on round the well-benched ship. And Patroklos came up to Achilleus, shepherd of the people, letting his warm tears fall like a spring of black water, which trickles its dark stream down a sheer rock's face. Swift-footed godlike Achilleus felt pity when he saw him, and spoke winged words to him: 'Why are you all in tears, Patroklos, like a little girl running along by her mother and demanding to be carried, pulling at her dress and holding her back as she tries to hurry on, and looking up at her tearfully until she picks her up? That is what you look like, Patroklos, with these soft tears falling. Have you some news for the Myrmidons, or for me myself? Have you had some message from Phthia that no-one else has heard? Menoitios, Aktor's son, is said to be living still, and Peleus, son of Aiakos, is alive among his Myrmidons – these are the two whose deaths would grieve us most. Or is it that you are distressed for the Argives, as they die by the hollow ships through their own folly? Tell me, do not hide it inside you, so that both of us can know.'

Then, horseman Patroklos, you answered with heavy groans: 'Achilleus, son of Peleus, far the greatest of the Achaians, do not be angry with me – the misery that has overcome the Achaians is indeed that great. All those who were our leading men before now are lying wounded in their ships, shot or stabbed. Tydeus' son, strong Diomedes, has been hit: Odysseus, the famous spearman, and Agamemnon have been stabbed: Eurypylos too has been hit by an arrow in the thigh. The doctors with their many medicines are busy with them now, healing their wounds. But you, Achilleus, are impossible to deal with. May I never be taken by an anger like yours, this anger you are feeding! Your pride is ruinous – what good will you do for any other man in time to come, if you do not save the Argives from shameful destruction? Cruel man! So your father was not Peleus the horseman, or Thetis your mother – it was the grey sea that spawned you, or the stark cliffs, such is the hardness of your heart. But if there is some prophecy known in your heart which prevents you, or some word from

Zeus told you by your honoured mother, then at least send me out without delay, and let me have with me all the rest of the Myrmidon army, and I could bring saving light to the Danaans. And give me your own armour to wear on my shoulders, so the Trojans might take me for you and hold off their fighting, and the warrior sons of the Achaians gain relief in their weariness – there is little respite in war. We are fresh, and the Trojans exhausted in the clamour of battle – we could easily drive them back on their city away from our ships and huts.'

So he spoke in entreaty, the poor fool – what he was begging would be a wretched death for himself and his own destruction. Swift-footed Achilleus answered him in vexation: 'Oh, my lord Patroklos, what is this you are saying? I am not influenced by any prophecy known to me, and there is no word from Zeus told me by my honoured mother. But this is a grievous thing that touches my heart and spirit with pain, when a man is ready to do down his equal and take back a prize of honour, because his power is the greater – this is a grievous pain to me, after all I have suffered in the war. The girl that the sons of the Achaians chose out as my prize, and I won with my own spear when I sacked her strong-walled city – lord Agamemnon, son of Atreus, has taken her back from my hands as if I were some migrant without rights. But all this is past and we should let it be. It seems I cannot after all be angry in my heart for ever – and yet I thought I would put aside my anger only when the clamour of battle reached my own ships, no sooner. But you now put my glorious armour over your shoulders, and lead the war-loving Myrmidons into battle, now that a black cloud of Trojans has settled round the ships in force, and the Argives are pressed back on the break of the sea, holding only a small stretch of ground. The whole city of Troy has come against them in high heart, as they do not see the face of my helmet blazing near them – they would soon run in flight and fill the gullies with their dead, if lord Agamemnon would treat me kindly: but now as it is they are fighting all round the encampment. The spear of Diomedes, son of Tydeus, is not raging in his hands to keep destruction from the Danaans, and I have not heard the voice of the son of Atreus calling from his hateful head: but the sound of murderous Hektor urging on his Trojans breaks round me – they have beaten the Achaians in battle, and cover the entire plain with their war-cry. But even so, Patroklos, fall on them with all your strength to keep destruction from the ships, so they do not put blazing fire to our ships and take away our longed-for return.

But follow exactly the aim of the instruction I now put in your mind, so that you can win great honour and glory for me from all the Danaans, and they bring me back the beautiful girl and offer splendid gifts besides. When you have driven them from the ships, come back. And if the loud-thundering husband of Hera grants you the chance to win glory, do not press on without me to fight the war-loving Trojans – that will reduce my worth. And do not lead your men on towards Ilios, slaughtering Trojans, in the delight of battle with the enemy, or one of the ever-living gods from Olympos might come against you – Apollo the far-worker has much love for the Trojans. No, turn back again once you have brought saving light to the ships, and let the others fight on over the plain. Oh, father Zeus and Athene and Apollo, if only none of all the Trojans would escape death, and none of the Argives, but only you and I could survive destruction, so that we alone could break Troy's holy crown of towers!'

Such were their words to each other. But Aias, beset by flying spears, could no longer hold his ground. He was being beaten down by the will of Zeus and the proud Trojans hitting all the time: the bright helmet round his temples kept up a fearful clatter under the constant hitting, and there was hit after hit on the well-made cheek-pieces. His left shoulder was tiring from the continuous holding of his glittering shield: but for all the pressure of their spears they could not dislodge it from him. All the time he was gripped by painful gasping, and the sweat ran in streams from all over his body, and he had no chance to recover his breath – all around him danger was piled on danger.

Tell me now, you Muses who have your homes on Olympos, how it was that fire was first thrown on the ships of the Achaians.

Hektor came close and struck at Aias' ash spear with his great sword, hitting by the socket behind the spear-head, and sheared it clean off. So Aias, son of Telamon, was left with just a docked spear quivering in his hand, and the bronze head spun far away and thudded to the ground. Aias' noble heart shuddered to recognise the hand of the gods, how Zeus the high-thunderer was wholly frustrating the skill of his fighting, and willing victory for the Trojans: and he fell back out of range of the weapons. Then the Trojans threw untiring fire on the fast ship, and immediately unquenchable flame poured over it. So the fire worked on the stern of the ship: and Achilleus struck his thighs and spoke to Patroklos: 'Up now, lord Patroklos, driver of horses! I can see the rush of destroying fire by the ships. They must not take our ships and then there be no more chance of escape. Put your armour on quickly, while I gather our men.'

So he spoke, and Patroklos began to arm himself in gleaming bronze. First he placed greaves on his legs, a fine pair, fitted with silver ankle-pieces. Next he put round his chest the crafted star-bright corselet of the fast runner Achilleus, of Aiakos' stock. Over his shoulders he slung a bronze sword, the hilt nailed with silver, and then a great massive shield. On his mighty head he placed a well-made helmet with a plume of horse-hair, and the crest nodded fearfully from its top. And he took up a pair of strong spears, well fitted to the grip of his hands. Only the spear of the excellent Achilleus he did not take, the huge, heavy, massive spear which no other Achaian could wield, but Achilleus alone had the skill to handle it, the spear of Pelian ash from the height of Pelion, which Cheiron had given to his dear father to be the death of fighting men. Patroklos told Automedon to harness the horses quickly – he was the man he held in highest honour after Achilleus the breaker of men, and could trust most to follow his call in battle. So Automedon brought the fast horses under the yoke for him, Xanthos and Balios, horses that flew swift as the blowing of the winds: they were borne to the west wind Zephyros by Podarge the Storm-mare, as she grazed in a meadow beside the stream of Ocean. In the side-traces he put the excellent Pedasos, a horse that Achilleus had brought back when he took Eëtion's city: mortal though he was, he could run with the immortal horses.

Meanwhile Achilleus went along the huts and brought all the Myrmidons under arms. They gathered like wolves, eaters of raw flesh, their hearts full of boundless fury, who have pulled down a great horned stag in the mountains, and then tear him, so that all have their jaws running with blood. Then they go in a pack to drink from a spring of black water, lapping with their slim tongues at the dark surface of the stream, and belching clots of blood: their bellies are strained full, and their hearts fearless in their breasts. Such were the leaders and lords of the Myrmidons as they swarmed round the brave lieutenant of the fast runner Achilleus, of Aiakos' stock. And Achilleus the warrior stood there among them, urging on the horses and the fighters with their shields.

There were fifty fast ships which Achilleus, loved of Zeus, led to Troy: and in each ship there were fifty of his companions manning the benches. He had made five leaders, men he trusted to command, while he himself ruled over all in his great power. The first contingent was led by Menesthios of the glittering corselet, the son of Spercheios, the river rain-fed from Zeus: he was borne by a daughter of Peleus, lovely Polydore, to Spercheios the untiring, when woman had lain with god, but in name he was the son of Boros, son of Perieres, who made her his wife in open marriage, and gave an immense bride-price for her. The second was led by the warrior Eudoros, the child of an unmarried mother, born to a girl who was lovely in the dance, Polymele, daughter of Phylas. Strong Hermes, slayer of Argos, fell in love with her when his eyes saw her among the chorus of girls dancing for Artemis of the golden distaff, goddess of the loud hunt. Immediately Hermes the kindly god went up to her room and lay with her secretly, and gave her a splendid son, Eudoros, an outstanding runner and a fighter. And then when Eileithyia, goddess of birth-pains, brought the child out to the light and it saw the brightness of the sun, the powerful lord Echekles, son of Aktor, gave a countless bride-price for her and took her to his house as wife: and the old man Phylas brought the child up and reared him in kindness, wrapping him in love as if he were his own son. The third was led by the warrior Peisandros, son of Maimalos, who was the best of all the Myrmidons at fighting with the spear, after Achilleus' friend Patroklos. The old horseman Phoinix led the fourth contingent, and Alkimedon the fifth, the excellent son of Laerkes. Then when Achilleus had them all stationed beside their leaders in proper order, he gave them stern instructions: 'Myrmidons, let me have none of you forgetting those threats you kept making by the fast ships throughout all the time of my anger – what you would do to the Trojans. And you all used to blame me, saying: "Cruel son of Peleus, it was gall then that your mother nursed you on, pitiless man, keeping your companions here by the ships against their will! Let us go back home again in our seafaring ships, now that this wretched anger has lodged in your heart." That is what you were always saying about me in your gatherings. Well now you have a great task before you, the battle you have been yearning for. So let us have men with courage in their hearts to fight the Trojans.'

So speaking he spurred the strength and heart in each of them. And the ranks dressed closer together as they heard their king. As when a man builds a wall for a high house with the stones fitting closely, to keep out the force of the winds, so their helmets and bossed shields locked close. Shield then pressed on shield, helmet on helmet, man on man: the horse-hair crests in the bright ridges of their helmets touched when they moved their heads, so close to each other were they dressed.

And two men stood armed in front of them all, Patroklos and Automedon, with a single desire in their hearts, to fight at the head of the Myrmidons. But Achilleus went to his hut and opened the lid of the beautiful finely-worked chest which silver-footed Thetis had stowed in the ship for him to take with him, lovingly packing it with tunics and cloaks to keep the wind out and woolly blankets. There he kept a tooled goblet, from which no other man would ever drink the gleaming wine, and he would pour libations from it to none of the gods except father Zeus. He now took this goblet from the chest, and first purified it with sulphur, then washed it in a clear stream of water, and washed his own hands, and drew some gleaming wine. Then he stood in the middle of the yard to make his prayer, and poured out the wine looking up into the sky, and Zeus who delights in thunder looked on. 'Zeus, king, lord of Dodona, Pelasgian, you who live far away and rule over wintry Dodona: and your prophets live round you, the Helloi, whose feet are not washed and whose beds are the ground. As you heard my former prayer, and brought honour to me and great harm to the Achaian people, so now grant this my further desire. Myself, I shall stay in the assembly of ships, but I am sending my companion to fight, and the Myrmidons with him in their numbers. Send glory with him, wide-seeing Zeus, strengthen the heart within him, so that Hektor can see whether my lieutenant proves his skill to fight on his own, or if his hands are only invincible in battle when I join the fray of war. But when he has driven the fighting and the clamour away from the ships, then let me see him come back to the fast ships unharmed, with all his armour and his close-fighting companions.'

So he spoke in prayer, and Zeus the counsellor heard him. Half of the prayer the father granted him, and half he refused. He granted that Patroklos should push the battle back from the ships, but refused his safe return from the fighting. Achilleus then went back into his hut after his libation and prayer to father Zeus, and put the goblet away in the chest. He came out then and stood in front of the hut, his heart eager still to watch the grim combat of Trojans and Achaians.

Now great-hearted Patroklos' men marched out with him under arms, until they charged in high fury on the Trojans. They swarmed out all at once like wasps by the side of a road, constantly irritated by boys who make a habit of teasing them in their nest by the roadside – the little fools, they create a public nuisance for many others. If a man passing along the road disturbs them accidentally, they all fly out to the attack with hearts full of courage to fight for their babies. Such was the furious heart in the Myrmidons as they streamed out from the ships, and the clamour rose ceaseless. Patroklos called with a great shout to his companions: 'Myrmidons, companions of Achilleus son of Peleus, be men, my friends, and fill your minds with fighting spirit, so we can bring honour to the son of Peleus, who is far the best of the Argives by the ships and has the best close-fighters serving him – and so even the son of Atreus, wide-ruling Agamemnon, may come to recognise his folly in paying no honour to the best of the Achaians.'

So speaking he spurred the strength and heart in each of them, and they fell on the Trojans in a mass: and round them the ships echoed fearfully to the shouts of the Achaians.

When the Trojans saw the brave son of Menoitios, him and his lieutenant, glittering in their armour, all their hearts were shaken and their ranks wavered, thinking that the swift-footed son of Peleus had abandoned his anger by the ships and chosen unity with his friends: and every man looked to see where he might escape sheer destruction.

Patroklos first cast with his shining spear straight into the eye of battle, where the fighters swarmed thickest, by the stern of great-hearted Protesilaos' ship: and he hit Pyraichmes, who had led the Paionian charioteers from Amydon, from the broad river Axios. He hit him in the right shoulder. He screamed and fell on his back in the dust, and the Paionian companions with him scattered in flight – Patroklos put panic in all of them when he killed their leader, the best of them in battle. He drove them away from the ships, and extinguished the fire that was blazing there. So the ship was left half-burnt where it was, and the Trojans scattered with a tremendous clamour. The Danaans poured after them between the hollow ships, and the din rose unceasing. As when Zeus the lightning-gatherer moves the dense cloud from the high peak of a great mountain, and all the hill-tops and sharp headlands and mountain glens spring into sight, and brightness bursts infinite down from the sky – so the Danaans drove the enemy fire back from the ships, and won a brief respite, but there was no cease in the fighting. The Trojans were not yet in headlong flight from the black ships: they were forced by the Achaian warriors to give way from the ships, but they still stood to face them.

Then man killed man among the leaders when the battle-front broke. First the brave son of Menoitios struck Areïlykos at the moment when he turned, hitting in the thigh with his sharp spear, and drove the bronze right through: the spear shattered the bone, and he fell face-forward on the earth. The warrior Menelaos stabbed Thoas where his chest was exposed by the shield, and collapsed his strength. Meges, son of Phyleus, watched for Amphiklos to charge, then took him first with a thrust at the top of his leg, where a man's muscle is thickest: the spear-point sliced through the tendons, and darkness covered over his eyes. Then the two sons of Nestor killed their men. Antilochos stabbed Atymnios with his sharp spear, and drove the bronze spear through his side, and he crashed forwards. But Maris in fury for his brother stood in front of the body and lunged at Antilochos from close to with his spear. But before he could make his stab godlike Thrasymedes caught him first with a quick thrust at the shoulder, and did not miss: the spear-point tore the arm away from the muscles at its base, and sheared the bone right through. He fell with a crash, and darkness covered over his eyes. So the two of them were brought low by the two brothers and went down to Erebos: they were brave companions of Sarpedon, spearmen sons of Amisodaros, who had reared the Chimaira, the ruin of many men. Aias, son of Oïleus, sprang forward and caught Kleoboulos alive, where he was blocked in the confusion: but he collapsed his strength there and then, striking him on the neck with his hilted sword. The whole blade warmed with his blood: over his eyes came the surge of death, and strong fate took him. Now Peneleos and Lykon closed. They had missed each other with their spears, both making wasted casts: so now they closed on each other with swords. Then Lykon hit at the ridge of Peneleos' horse-crested helmet, but the sword shattered at the hilt. And Peneleos struck him on the neck below the ear, so the whole blade sank in, and only the skin held: his head fell hanging at the side, and his strength collapsed under him. Meriones on his quick legs came up with Akamas and stabbed him in the right shoulder as he tried to mount behind his horses: he crashed from the chariot, and mist spread down over his eyes. Idomeneus stabbed Erymas in his mouth with the pitiless bronze. The bronze spear passed right through and up under the brain, smashing the white bones. His teeth were knocked out and both his eyes flooded with blood: wide-mouthed he spurted a well of blood through nostrils and mouth: and the black cloud of death covered him over.

These then were the leaders of the Danaans who each killed their man. As marauding wolves attack lambs or kids in the mountains, snatching them from under their mothers, when the shepherd's carelessness has let them separate from the flock: they have no fight in them, and the wolves quickly tear them apart when they see them – such was the Danaans' attack on the Trojans. The Trojans' minds filled with the clamour of panic, and they forgot their fighting spirit.

The great Aias was eager all the time to cast at bronze-armoured Hektor. But he, in his experience of battle, kept his broad shoulders covered behind his bull's-hide shield, and was watching for the whistle of arrows and the thud of spears. He knew well now the battle was turning to victory against him, but even so he held his ground and tried to save his loyal companions.

As when a cloud comes from the bright air above and spreads over the sky from Olympos, when Zeus is setting a storm, so the Trojans spread in clamorous flight away from the ships, and crossed back to the plain in disorder. Hektor's swift-footed horses carried him and his armour away, and he left the Trojan army snarled and blocked by the ditch the Achaians had dug. Many pairs of fast chariot-horses left their masters' chariots in the ditch, broken off at the end of the pole, while Patroklos pressed on his pursuit, shouting loud to the Danaans, and with murder in his heart for the Trojans. Scattered now, they filled all the paths with the clamour of their flight: and a storm of dust spread high under the clouds as their strong-footed horses galloped back towards the city away from the ships and the huts. With a great shout Patroklos held his course for where he saw the greatest seethe of troops running in confusion. Men fell headlong from their chariots under his wheels, and their cars crashed over. Straight over the ditch leapt the swift immortal horses that the gods had given as a splendid gift to Peleus, urging their way on as Patroklos' heart called him against Hektor, eager to strike him down – but his fast horses had carried him away. As all the dark earth is burdened under a storm on an autumn day, when Zeus pours down the most violent rain, in anger at men who have raised his fury by forcing corrupt judgments in the assembly and driving out justice, with no regard for punishment from the gods: then the flow of all their rivers is swollen in spate, and many slopes are cut away by torrents rushing with a loud roar headlong from the mountains into the heaving sea, and the work of men's cultivation is ruined – such was the sound raised loud by the Trojan horses as they ran.

Now when Patroklos had cut through the leading Trojan battalions, he penned them back again towards the ships, and would not allow them their desire to reach their city, but in the space between ships and river and high city-wall he kept charging in and killing, and he took payment for many Achaian deaths. There he struck Pronoös first with his shining spear, hitting where his chest was exposed by the shield, and collapsed his strength: he fell with a crash. He next sprang at Thestor, son of Enops – he was sitting huddled in his polished chariot, his wits crazed and the reins slipped from his hands. Patroklos came up and stabbed him with his spear in the right side of his jaw, piercing on through the teeth, then gripped the spear and with it swung him over the chariot-rail, as when a man sitting on a rocky point hauls a monster fish out of the sea with his line and bright bronze hook. So Patroklos hauled him out of the chariot, his mouth gaping round the shining spear, and thrust him down on his face: the life left him where he fell. Then as Erylaos rushed to attack he struck him with a rock full on the head. The head was smashed completely in two inside the heavy helmet: he dropped face-forward on the ground, and death the breaker of spirits poured round him. Then next Erymas and Amphoteros and Epaltes, Tlepolemos son of Damastor, and Echios and Pyris, Ipheus and Euippos and Polymelos son of Argeas – all these, one after another, he brought down to the nourishing earth.

Now when Sarpedon saw his bare-tunicked companions cut down at the hands of Patroklos son of Menoitios, he called angrily to the godlike Lycians: 'Shame, you Lycians! Where are you running? Now is the time to fight bravely. I shall go to face this man, to find out who this is who is holding the field and has already done much harm to the Trojans, collapsing the strength of many brave men.'

So he spoke, and jumped to the ground from his chariot with all his armour. And seeing him Patroklos on his side jumped down from his chariot. Then as two vultures with hooked talons and curved beaks fight on a high rock-face, screaming loud, so, with loud cries, these two rushed at each other. And seeing them the son of devious-minded Kronos was moved with pity, and spoke to Hera his sister and wife: 'Alas, that it is fate for Sarpedon, dearest of men to me, to be brought down by Patroklos son of Menoitios. As I think on it, there are two ways my heart pulls – should I snatch him out of the ruinous fighting and set him alive in the rich land of Lycia, or should I bring him down now at the hands of the son of Menoitios?'

Then the ox-eyed queen Hera answered him: 'Dread son of Kronos, what is this you are saying? Do you intend to take a man who is mortal and long ago destined by fate, and release him from grim death? Do it then – but we other gods will not all approve you. I tell you another thing, and you mark it well in your mind. If you bring Sarpedon alive to his home, think how after this some other god too may wish to rescue his own dear son from the fury of battle. Many men fighting round the great city of Priam are sons of immortals, and you will cause these gods bitter anger. No, if he is dear to you, and your heart feels pity for him, let him be brought down in the battle's fury at the hands of Patroklos son of Menoitios – but then when the life and spirit have left him, send Death and soothing Sleep to carry him away, until they come to the land of broad Lycia, where his brothers and kinsmen will give him full burial with mound and gravestone: such is the right of the dead.'

So she spoke, and the father of men and gods did as she wished. But he let drops of blood rain to the ground, to do honour to his dear son, whom he was now to see killed by Patroklos, in fertile Troy, far from his native land.

When they had advanced to close range, Patroklos cast and hit famous Thrasymelos, the brave lieutenant of lord Sarpedon, in the lower belly, and collapsed his strength. Sarpedon then made his attack. He missed the man with his shining spear, but the spear struck Pedasos the horse in the right shoulder: he shrieked as the life breathed from him, and fell screaming in the dust, and his spirit flitted away. The other two horses shied apart, so the yoke creaked and their reins tangled together, now the trace-horse was lying in the dust. Automedon the famous spearman found the remedy for this: he drew the long sharp sword from beside his thick thigh, and with a quick dash cut away the trace-horse without delay. The others then straightened, and pulled in the harness. And the two men joined again in heart-consuming battle.

Once more Sarpedon missed with his shining spear: the point of the spear passed over Patroklos' left shoulder and did not hit him. Then after him Patroklos rose to his cast, and the weapon did not fly wasted from his hand, but struck him where the midriff is close to the beating heart. He fell as an oak-tree falls or a poplar, or a tall pine which carpenters cut down in the mountains with fresh-whetted axes to make a ship's timber. So he lay there stretched flat in front of his horses and chariot, bellowing, and clutching at the blood-soaked dust. Like a bull that a lion kills in attack on the herd, gleaming and proud among the shambling cattle, and it dies roaring under the jaws of the lion, so the leader of the Lycian shield-fighters struggled as he died at Patroklos' hands, and called out to his dear companion: 'Glaukos, dear friend, warrior among men, now is the time above all to show yourself a spearman and a brave fighter. Now grim war must be all your desire, if you have courage in you. First you must go round all the leaders of the Lycians and urge them to fight for Sarpedon – and then fight for me yourself with your own spear. After this I shall be a shame and disgrace to you all your days without end, if the Achaians strip me of my armour where I have fallen, here by the assembly of ships. No, hold firm, and spur on all our people.'

As he spoke, the end of death covered over his eyes and nostrils. Patroklos braced his foot against his chest and pulled the spear out of his flesh, and the midriff came with it: it was both life and spear-point that he drew from Sarpedon's body. And the Myrmidons held close by his snorting horses, trying to bolt now they had left their master's chariot.

Bitter pain came over Glaukos when he heard Sarpedon's voice, and his heart was distressed that he could not go to his aid. He gripped his arm in his hand and pressed it: he was pained by the wound that Teukros, fighting to keep disaster from his companions, had given him with an arrow as he stormed at the high wall. Then he spoke in prayer to Apollo the far-shooter: 'Hear me, lord. You may be in the rich land of Lycia or perhaps in Troy. But from anywhere you can listen to a man in distress, as now distress has come upon me. I have this wound that is mastering me. My arm is shot through with sharp pains, my blood will not staunch, and my shoulder is heavy with it. I cannot hold my spear steadily, or go into battle with the enemy. And the best of men is killed, Sarpedon, Zeus' son – Zeus does not protect even his own child. But you, lord, please heal this wound that masters me, quell the pains, and give me strength, so that I can call on our companions from Lycia and urge them into battle, and fight myself for the dead man's body.'

So he spoke in prayer, and Phoibos Apollo heard him. Instantly he stopped the pains, and staunched the dark blood running from the cruel wound, and put strength in his heart. And Glaukos was joyfully aware in his heart that the great god had heard his prayer. First he went round all the leaders of the Lycians and urged them to fight for Sarpedon: and then he went with huge strides to find Trojans, meeting Poulydamas son of Panthoös and godlike Agenor, and on to Aineias and bronze-armoured Hektor. Coming close he spoke winged words to them: 'Hektor, now you have wholly forgotten your allies. For your sake they are losing their lives here far from their own family and country – and you are not willing to help them. Sarpedon lies dead, the leader of the Lycian shield-fighters, who was the guardian of Lycia with his judgments and his strength – and now brazen Ares has brought him down under Patroklos' spear. Come then, friends, stand by him, with shame and anger in your hearts to stop the Myrmidons stripping his armour and dishonouring his body in fury for all the Danaans that have died, killed by our spears beside the fast ships.'

So he spoke, and intolerable, unrelenting sorrow overwhelmed the Trojans – he had been the buttress of their city, even though he came from another land: many men had come with him, and he was the bravest of them all in battle. They went straight for the Danaans, furiously, and Hektor led them on in anger for Sarpedon. Meanwhile the Achaians were roused by the strong heart of Patroklos son of Menoitios. He spoke to the two Aiantes first, who were already eager for the fight: 'Aiantes, now let your one thought, both of you, be to beat back the enemy – the way men have seen you before, or even better. The man who was first to break through the Achaian wall lies dead – Sarpedon. If only we could capture his body and dishonour it, and strip the armour from his shoulders, and bring down some of his companions with the pitiless bronze as they fight to defend him!'

So he spoke, and they were ready for defence even without his urging. When both sides had strengthened their ranks, Trojans and Lycians and Myrmidons and Achaians, they clashed together over the dead man's body, shouting terribly, and the men's armour rang loud. And Zeus spread a deadly darkness over the furious battle, so there should be dire work in the fighting for his dear son.

At first the Trojans pushed back the bright-eyed Achaians, because by no means the worst man among the Myrmidons had been hit, the son of great-hearted Agakles, godlike Epeigeus. He had lived in well-founded Boudeion at first, but then, after killing a noble cousin, he had come as a suppliant to Peleus and silver-footed Thetis: and they had sent him with Achilleus, breaker of men, to go with him to Ilios, the city rich in horses, and fight against the Trojans. Now as he was putting his hand to the corpse glorious Hektor struck him with a stone on the head: his head was smashed completely in two inside the heavy helmet, and he fell face-forward over the dead body, and death the breaker of spirits poured round him. Anguish for his fallen companion came over Patroklos, and he darted through the front-fighters like a swift hawk who scatters the jackdaws and starlings. So fast, horseman Patroklos, did you charge straight for the Lycians and the Trojans, angered at heart for your companion. And he hit Sthenelaos, dear son of Ithaimenes, in the neck with a stone, and broke through both its tendons. The Trojan front-fighters and glorious Hektor gave back, as far as the cast of a slim javelin reaches, when a man lets it fly at the limit of his strength either in a contest or indeed in war, when the enemy are on him to break his life. Such was the distance the Trojans gave way, pushed back by the Achaians. The first to turn was Glaukos, leader of the Lycian shield-fighters. He killed great-hearted Bathykles, dear son of Chalkon, who was noted for his wealth and substance among the Myrmidons, where he had his home in Hellas. Glaukos stabbed him full in the chest with his spear, turning suddenly as Bathykles came up with him in pursuit. He fell with a crash, and heavy sorrow came over the Achaians, that a brave man had fallen: but the Trojans were overjoyed, and came in a mass to stand over his body. The Achaians lost none of their fighting spirit, and carried their fury straight for them. Then Meriones killed a Trojan warrior, Laogonos, brave son of Onetor, who was the priest of Idaian Zeus, and honoured like a god by his people. Meriones hit him under the jaw and ear: the life sped from his body, and the hateful darkness took him. Aineias cast his bronze spear at Meriones, hoping to hit him as he advanced under cover of his shield. But he had looked ahead, and avoided the bronze spear – he stooped forward, and the long spear was driven into the ground behind him, so that the butt of the spear quivered on: and then monstrous Ares took away its force. Aineias was angry at heart and called out: 'Meriones, you may be a good dancer but my spear would have stopped you quickly enough once and for all, if I had hit you.'

Then Meriones the famous spearman answered him: 'Aineias, you may be a strong man but it will be hard for you to quell the force of every man that comes against you and fights – you were made a mortal like other men. If I were to cast and hit you in the middle with the sharp bronze, then for all your strength and confidence in your hands' power you would quickly give me my triumph, and a life to Hades the horseman.'

So he spoke, but the brave son of Menoitios spoke angrily to him: 'Meriones, what need for this talk in a brave fighter? My dear friend, insulting words will not move the Trojans from the body – before that the earth will cover many a dead man. It is actions that win wars – words are for debate. So it is not long speeches that we need, but fighting.'

So speaking he led on, and Meriones, a godlike man, went with him. Then like the crashing that arises in the glens of a mountain when woodcutters are at work, and the noise can be heard from far away, so from the wide-wayed earth rose up the thud and clash of the men's bronze and leather and well-made ox-hide shields, as they thrust at each other with swords and double-pointed spears. Now even a knowledgeable man could not have recognised godlike Sarpedon, as he was covered over from his head right to the tips of his feet with weapons and blood and dust. And they kept swarming round the body, as when flies in a sheepfold buzz round the brimming pails in the spring season, when milk is flooding the buckets. So they swarmed round the body: and Zeus never turned his shining eyes away from the battle's fury, but looked constantly down on them and pondered in his heart, thinking long about the killing of Patroklos, whether he too should die there over godlike Sarpedon, and glorious Hektor cut him down now with the bronze in the fury of this battle and strip the armour from his shoulders, or whether he should heap higher the stark misery for yet more men. And this seemed the best plan to his thinking, that the brave lieutenant of Achilleus son of Peleus should once more drive the Trojans and bronze-armoured Hektor back towards their city, and take the life from many men. Then Zeus put a heart without courage in Hektor first of all. He mounted his chariot and turned it for flight, and called to the rest of the Trojans to run, as he could tell the swing of Zeus' sacred scales. Then not even the strong Lycians stood firm, but they all fled in fear when they had seen their king struck in the heart and lying in a pile of corpses, as many others had been brought down over him when Zeus strained the battle hard and furious. Then the Achaians took the gleaming bronze armour from Sarpedon's shoulders, and the brave son of Menoitios gave it to his companions to carry back to the hollow ships. And then Zeus the cloud-gatherer spoke to Apollo: 'Come, dear Phoibos, go now and clean the dark blood from Sarpedon away from the weapons' range, and then carry him far away and wash him in the running stream of a river, and anoint him with ambrosia, and dress him in immortal clothing: and give him into the hands of the swift messengers, Sleep and Death, twin brothers, to carry him with them, and they will quickly set him down in the rich land of broad Lycia, where his brothers and kinsmen will give him full burial with mound and gravestone – such is the right of the dead.'

So he spoke, and Apollo did not fail to listen to his father, and he went down from the heights of Ida into the grim battle, and immediately lifted godlike Sarpedon away from the weapons' range, and carried him far away and washed him in the running stream of a river, and anointed him with ambrosia, and dressed him in immortal clothing:

and he gave him into the hands of the swift messengers, Sleep and Death, twin brothers, to carry him with them, and they quickly set him down in the rich land of broad Lycia.

But Patroklos called to his horses and Automedon and went in pursuit of the Trojans and Lycians, and this was a fatal error, poor fool – if he had kept to the instruction of the son of Peleus, he would have escaped the vile doom of black death. But Zeus' mind is always stronger than the mind of men – he can bring terror on even the brave man and easily rob him of victory: and then again he himself will spur a man to fight. And it was Zeus then who put the urge in Patroklos' heart.

Then who was the first, and who the last that you killed, Patroklos, when the gods now called you to your death? Adrestos first, and Autonoös and Echeklos and Perimos son of Megas, and Epistor and Melanippos, and then Elasos and Moulios and Pylartes. These he killed: and every one of the others had his thoughts on flight.

And now the sons of the Achaians would have taken high-gated Troy at the hands of Patroklos, as he was raging with his spear beyond all measure, if Phoibos Apollo had not taken his stand on the well-built battlement, with his mind on death for Patroklos and defence of the Trojans. Three times Patroklos went to climb the angle of the high wall, and three times Apollo knocked him back, pushing at his bright shield with his immortal hands. But when for the fourth time Patroklos flung himself on like a god, then with a fearful shout Apollo called to him in winged words: 'Back, lord Patroklos! It is not fate for the proud Trojans' city to be sacked by your spear, nor even by Achilleus, a far greater man than you.'

So he spoke, and Patroklos gave back a long way, avoiding the anger of Apollo the far-shooter.

But Hektor held in his strong-footed horses at the Skaian gates. He was uncertain whether to drive back into the rout and fight on, or to shout to his people to gather inside the wall. As he was thinking on this, Phoibos Apollo came up to him, taking the form of a man of strength and power, Asios, who was uncle to Hektor the tamer of horses, being full brother of Hekabe and son of Dymas: he had his home in Phrygia by the stream of Sangarios. Taking his form, then, Apollo the son of Zeus spoke to Hektor: 'Hektor, why have you stopped fighting? It is wrong of you. If only I were as much your superior as I am now below you, then you would soon learn the cost of shirking battle. No, come, hold your strong-footed horses against Patroklos – it may be that you can kill him, and Apollo grants you your triumph.'

So speaking Apollo went back, a god among the sufferings of men: and glorious Hektor ordered the warrior Kebriones to whip his horses into battle. But Apollo went into the press of fighting, and set a dire confusion among the Argives, and gave the glory to Hektor and the Trojans. Hektor ignored the rest of the Danaans and killed none of them, but held his strong-footed horses at Patroklos. On the other side Patroklos jumped to the ground from his chariot holding his spear in his left hand. With the other hand he picked up a glinting jagged stone which the grasp of his hand could cover, took a firm stance, and hurled it. The stone was not long in reaching a man, and his throw was not wasted, but he hit Hektor's charioteer Kebriones, a bastard son of famous Priam, who was holding the reins of the horses. The sharp stone hit him in the space between the eyes, smashing the two brows together: the bone could not hold, and his eyes dropped to the ground in the dust right there in front of his feet. He fell like a diver from the well-made chariot, and the life left his bones. Then, horseman Patroklos, you spoke in mockery of him: 'Oh, this is a really agile man, a ready acrobat! I should think he would be good too if he was out on the fish-filled sea – this man could feed a large number with the oysters he could find, diving off a ship, even in rough weather, to judge by his easy tumble to the plain from his chariot. Oh yes, the Trojans have their acrobats too!'

So speaking he went for the hero Kebriones with the spring of a lion, who has been hit in the chest as he ravages the sheepfolds, and his own courage brings his death – such, Patroklos, was the way you leapt at Kebriones in your fury. Hektor too on the other side jumped to the ground from his chariot. Then these two fought over Kebriones like two lions, who are both hungry and fight in high fury on the peak of a mountain over a deer that is killed. So over Kebriones these two rousers of the battle-cry, Patroklos son of Menoitios and glorious Hektor, were urgent to tear each other's flesh with the pitiless bronze. Hektor had caught hold of Kebriones' head, and would not let go: and on the other side Patroklos had hold on a foot. And now the rest of the Trojans and Danaans joined a furious battle.

As the east wind and the south wind contend with each other in the glens of a mountain to toss the deep woods of oak and ash and slim-barked cornel, and the trees clash together their tapered branches with a tremendous noise, and there is the clatter of breaking timber, so the Trojans and Achaians leapt at each other and cut men down, and neither side had any mind for cruel flight. Many sharp spears had driven in around Kebriones, and feathered arrows leaping from the string, and many great stones battered their shields as they fought on over him: and he lay there in a swirl of dust, huge and hugely fallen, forgotten now his horsemanship.

As long as the sun straddled the centre of the sky, the weapons thrown by both sides reached their mark, and men kept falling. But when the sun moved over to the time when oxen are unyoked, then beyond all destiny the Achaians were the stronger. They dragged the hero Kebriones out of the weapons' range and away from the Trojans' clamour, and took the armour from his shoulders. And Patroklos charged at the Trojans with murder in his heart. Three times then he charged like the swift war-god himself, shouting fearfully, and three times he killed nine men. But when for the fourth time he flung himself on like a god, then, Patroklos, the ending of your life was revealed. Phoibos met you in the battle's fury, terrible god. Patroklos did not see him moving through the rout. Apollo came against him hidden in thick mist, and stood behind him, and struck his back and broad shoulders with the flat of his hand, so that his eyes spun round. Then Phoibos Apollo knocked the helmet from his head, and the great masking helmet rolled clattering under the horses' feet, and the hair of its crest was sullied with blood and dust. Before now it was not permitted for this horse-crested helmet to be sullied in the dust, but it guarded the head and fine brow of a godlike man, Achilleus: and now Zeus allowed Hektor to wear it on his head, as his death was close upon him. And all the length of his long-shadowed spear, huge, heavy, massive, and tipped with bronze, was shattered in his hands: and from his shoulders his fringed shield dropped with its strap to the ground. And lord Apollo, son of Zeus, broke the corselet off him. Bewilderment took his mind, and the strength collapsed from his bright body, and he stood there dazed. Then from behind a Dardanian man came close and struck him with his sharp spear in the back, between the shoulders. This was Euphorbos, son of Panthoös, the best man of his age in spear-throwing and horsemanship and the speed of his legs: it was the first time he had entered battle with his chariot, his apprenticeship in war, and on this day he had brought twenty men down from their chariots. It was he who first cast his spear at you, horseman Patroklos, but he did not break you: he snatched his ash spear out of your body, and ran back to join the crowd of men – he would not face Patroklos in open battle, unarmed though he was. And Patroklos, overcome by the blow from the god and the man's spear, began to move back into the mass of his companions to avoid destruction.

But when Hektor saw great-hearted Patroklos moving back, and wounded by the sharp spear, he came up close to him through the ranks and stabbed him with his spear in the base of his belly, and drove the bronze right through. He fell with a crash, and brought anguish to the Achaian army. As when a lion masters an untiring boar in battle, when they fight in high fury on the peak of a mountain over a little spring of water where both want to drink, and the boar, panting hard, is brought down under the lion's power – so Hektor, son of Priam, with a close spear-thrust took the life from the brave son of Menoitios when he had killed many men, and spoke winged words in triumph over him: 'Patroklos, you must have thought that you would sack our city, and take the day of freedom from the women of Troy and carry them off in your ships to your own native land – poor fool! In their defence Hektor's swift horses speed into battle, and I am renowned for my spear among all the war-loving Trojans, for keeping the day of compulsion from them – but you, the vultures will eat you here. Poor wretch, not even Achilleus, for all his greatness, could help you. He must have given you firm instructions when he stayed behind and sent you out, saying, "Let me not see you back at the hollow ships, horseman Patroklos, until you have ripped and bloodied murderous Hektor's tunic on his chest." That is what he will have said, and swayed your foolish heart.'

Then with the strength low in you, horseman Patroklos, you said to him: 'Yes, make your great boasts now, Hektor. You were given the victory by Zeus the son of Kronos and Apollo – it was they who overpowered me with ease: they took the armour from my shoulders. But if twenty such men as you had come against me, they would all have died where they stood, brought down under my spear. No, it is cruel fate and Leto's son that have killed me, and of men Euphorbos – you are the third in my killing. I tell you another thing, and you mark it well in your mind. You yourself, you too will not live long, but already now death and strong fate are standing close beside you, to bring you down at the hands of Achilleus, great son of Aiakos' stock.'

As he spoke the end of death enfolded him: and his spirit flitted from his body and went on the way to Hades, weeping for its fate, and the youth and manhood it must leave. Then glorious Hektor spoke to him, dead though he was: 'Patroklos, why make me this prophecy of grim death? Who knows if Achilleus, son of lovely-haired Thetis, might be struck by my spear first, and lose his life before me?'

So speaking he braced his foot against him and pulled the bronze spear out of the wound, then kicked him over on his back free of the spear. Then immediately he went after Automedon with his spear, the godlike lieutenant of swift-footed Achilleus, eager to hit him: but he was carried clear by the swift immortal horses that the gods had given as a splendid gift to Peleus.

BOOK 17
THE BATTLE OVER PATROKLOS

Now Atreus' son, the warrior Menelaos, had not failed to see Patroklos brought down in battle by the Trojans. He strode through the front ranks, helmeted in gleaming bronze, and took his stand over Patroklos as a mother cow stands lowing over her first-born calf, untried before in childbirth. So fair-haired Menelaos stood over Patroklos, holding out over him his spear and the even circle of his shield, intent on killing any man who came against him. And Panthoös' son too, Euphorbos of the ash spear, did not let be the fallen body of excellent Patroklos. He came and stood close by it, and said to the warrior Menelaos: 'Back, lord Menelaos, son of Atreus, leader of your people – away from the body, leave its blood-stained armour, the spoils of war. I was the first of all the Trojans and their famous allies to strike Patroklos with my spear in the battle's fury. Let me then win the honour and glory among the Trojans – or else with a cast of my spear I shall take away the sweetness of your life.'

Fair-haired Menelaos answered him in great anger: 'Father Zeus, how vile it is to brag beyond all bounds! The leopard takes pride in its power, and the lion, and the vicious wild boar, whose chest holds the proudest heart of all, revelling in its own strength – but greater still is the pride of the sons of Panthoös with their ash spears. But not even the mighty Hyperenor the horse-tamer, not even he lived to enjoy his manhood, when he faced me and taunted me, calling me the most contemptible fighter among the Danaans. It was not his own feet, I think, which carried him back to gladden his dear wife and his loved parents. Your strength too I shall break as I did his, if you stand against me. No, go back, I tell you, back into the crowd, and do not oppose me, before you come to harm: it is only the fool who learns too late.'

So he spoke, but he did not turn Euphorbos' purpose. He answered: 'Now, lord Menelaos, you will surely pay for my brother. You killed him, and speak in triumph over his death. You widowed his wife deep in her new marriage-home, and on his parents you brought the curse of grief and lamentation. I could put an end to the misery of their sorrow if I bring your head and your armour and put them in the hands of Panthoös and godlike Phrontis. But it will not be long now for our struggle to come to the test of battle, the trial of courage or cowardice.'

So speaking he stabbed at the even circle of Menelaos' shield. The bronze of his spear did not break through, but the point was turned in the stout shield. Then Atreus' son Menelaos rose to his attack, making a prayer to father Zeus. As Euphorbos was moving back Menelaos stabbed him at the base of the throat, and pressed on the spear with all his weight, trusting in the strength of his hand. The point went right through the soft neck: he fell with a crash, and his armour clattered around him. Blood soaked his hair, lovely as the Graces' hair, and his plaits tight-bound with gold and silver. As when a man nurtures a flourishing olive-shoot in a solitary place, where plenty of water wells up – a fine, healthy shoot it is, shaken by the breath of every wind that blows, and it blossoms thick with white flowers: but suddenly there comes a wind in a great storm, and uproots it from its trench and lays out its length on the earth. Such was the son of Panthoös, Euphorbos of the ash spear, as Menelaos son of Atreus killed him, and set to stripping his armour.

As when a mountain lion, sure of his own power, takes the finest heifer from a grazing herd: first he breaks her neck in the grasp of his strong jaws, then tears her, gulping her blood and all her inwards: around him dogs and herdsmen set up a great din, but at a distance, unwilling to come close, as fear has its pale grip on them. So it was that no Trojan's heart within him had the courage to come against glorious Menelaos. Then the son of Atreus could easily have taken the glory of his armour from Panthoös' son, if Phoibos Apollo had not grudged it him, and set Hektor against him like the swift war-god himself. Apollo took human form, that of Mentes, the leader of the Kikones, and called to Hektor with winged words: 'Hektor, all this time you have been running after fierce Achilleus' horses, chasing what can never be caught. Those horses are hard for any mortal man to control or drive, except for Achilleus, and he is the son of an immortal mother. Meanwhile Menelaos, Atreus' warrior son, has stood over Patroklos' body and killed the best of the Trojans, Euphorbos son of Panthoös, and put a stop to his fighting fury.'

So speaking Apollo went back, a god among the sufferings of men. Sharp pain clouded Hektor's dark heart. He looked then through the ranks of men and quickly saw the two of them, one stripping off the glorious armour, and the other lying there on the ground, blood streaming from his open wound. He strode through the front ranks helmeted in gleaming bronze, like an undying flame of fire, and bellowing loud. The son of Atreus did not fail to hear Hektor's loud shout, and said in dismay to his own great heart: 'What am I to do? If I leave this fine armour and the body of Patroklos who lies here killed for my avenging, then I fear that any Danaan who sees it will think the worse of me. But if shame for that makes me fight single-handed against Hektor and the Trojans, then they will have me surrounded and outnumbered many to one – Hektor of the glinting helmet is bringing all the Trojans over here. But what need for this debate in my heart? Whenever a man is prepared to go against divine will and fight a man who is honoured by a god, then disaster rolls fast on him. So no Danaan will think the worse of me if he sees me backing away from Hektor, as Hektor is fighting with a god's support. But if I could somewhere get word of Aias, master of the war-cry, then the two of us could go back and recall our fighting spirit, even against god's will, and try to rescue the body for Achilleus son of Peleus – that would be the best in this trouble.'

While he was pondering this in his mind and his heart, the Trojan ranks came on, and Hektor at their head. Menelaos began to back away and leave the dead body, rounding on them as he retreated like a great bearded lion driven from a farmstead by dogs and herdsmen with spears and shouting: his bold heart within him is chilled with fury, forced against his will to leave the cattleyard. So it was that fair-haired Menelaos moved back from Patroklos. He turned and stood firm when he had reached the mass of his companions, looking for the huge Aias, Telamon's son. He quickly caught sight of him far on the left of the fighting, urging on his men and spurring them to battle, as Phoibos Apollo had put a monstrous panic into them. Menelaos set off running, and said to him as soon as he reached his side: 'Aias, come, dear friend, Patroklos is killed and we must run to fight for him, and try to bring his body back for Achilleus, though it is naked now – Hektor of the glinting helmet has his armour.'

So he spoke, and moved the warrior Aias' heart to anger. He strode through the front ranks, and fair-haired Menelaos with him. Hektor had taken the glory of Patroklos' armour, and was pulling him away, to cut the head from his shoulders with the sharp bronze and drag off the body to give it to the dogs of Troy. Aias came close, carrying his shield like a tower. Hektor drew back again into the mass of his companions, and jumped into his chariot, giving the fine armour to the Trojans to carry back to the city, to be a great glory for him. Aias covered the son of Menoitios with his broad shield, and took his stand over him as a lion stands over his young, when huntsmen have met him in the forest as he leads his babies along: he stands glorying in his power, and draws down all his brow in a frown that hoods his eyes. So Aias stood in defence of the hero Patroklos: and on the other side the son of Atreus, the warrior Menelaos, took his stand, the grief swelling strong in his heart.

But Glaukos, son of Hippolochos, leader of the men from Lycia, scowled at Hektor and attacked him with hard words: 'Hektor, it seems, then, you are good for nothing but looks, and fall far short as a fighter. The great fame you enjoy is for nothing – you are a coward. So you must think now how to save your city and settlement by yourself, with the people whose homeland is Ilios. No Lycian now will go out to fight the Danaans for your city, since it appears there is no thanks if a man fights the enemy relentlessly on and on. How will you ever bring a lesser man safe back to your own people, you cruel man, when you have left Sarpedon, your guest-friend and companion, to become a spoil and prize for the Argives – a man who was a great help to you and your city, when he was alive: and now you have not the heart to keep the dogs from him. So now if any of the Lycians will listen to me, we shall go home, and Troy's sheer destruction will be seen. Because if there was now in the Trojans that unshakeable strength of courage that enters men who have joined the hard struggle with their enemies in defence of their own country – then we could quickly have Patroklos dragged inside Ilios. And if that man's body were pulled out of the fighting and brought to lord Priam's great city, then the Argives would immediately release Sarpedon's fine armour, and we would have his body itself to carry back to Ilios. Such is the importance of the man whose lieutenant has been killed – far the best of the Argives by the ships and with the best close-fighters serving him. But you did not have the courage to face great-hearted Aias amid the clamour of the enemy and look him in the eyes, or fight it out straight with him – since he is a better man than you.'

Then Hektor of the glinting helmet scowled at him and said: 'Glaukos, why this insulting talk? It surprises me in a man like you. I had thought you the most intelligent man of all those who live in fertile Lycia. But now I utterly condemn your judgment for what you have said, claiming that I would not stand up to the enormous Aias. I tell you I am not frightened of battle or the clatter of chariots. But Zeus' mind is always stronger than the mind of men – he can bring terror on even the brave man and easily rob him of victory: and then again he himself will spur a man to fight. But come here, my friend, stand by me and see what happens, whether I am a coward all day long, as you say, or whether I shall stop some Danaans, for all their fury, from fighting in defence of Patroklos' dead body.'

So speaking, Hektor called with a great shout to the Trojans: 'Trojans and Lycians and close-fighting Dardanians, be men, my friends, and fill your minds with fighting spirit, while I put on great Achilleus' beautiful armour, which I stripped from mighty Patroklos when I killed him.'

So speaking, Hektor of the glinting helmet left the battlefield, and ran at full speed to catch up his companions who were carrying the glorious armour of the son of Peleus back to the city: his legs were quick, and he caught them when they had not gone far. Then, standing at a distance from the battle's misery, he exchanged armour. He gave his own to the war-loving Trojans to take back to sacred Ilios, and put on the immortal armour of Achilleus son of Peleus, which the heavenly gods had given to Achilleus' dear father: and when he was old he gave it to his son – but the son was not to grow old in his father's armour.

Now when Zeus the cloud-gatherer saw Hektor away from the battle arming himself in the armour of the godlike son of Peleus, he shook his head and said to his own heart: 'Poor wretch, death is not in your thought at all, and it is now coming close to you. You are dressing in the immortal armour of the best of men, a man all others fear. And you have now killed this man's friend, who was kind and strong, and you have taken the armour from his head and shoulders, wrongly. But for the moment I shall grant you great power, in recompense for what will happen – you will never return home from the fighting, for Andromache to take from you the famous armour of the son of Peleus.'

So the son of Kronos spoke, and nodded his dark brows. And the armour fitted close to Hektor's body, and the fearful war-god Ares entered into him, and inside him his body was filled with courage and strength. With a great shout he went to join the famous allies, and was revealed to the eyes of all glittering in the armour of great-hearted Achilleus, son of Peleus. He went up and down with words of encouragement to each of them, to Mesthles and Glaukos and Medon and Thersilochos, Asteropaios and Deisenor and Hippothoös, Phorkys and Chromios and Ennomos the bird-diviner. He spoke to them all in winged words, urging them on: 'Listen to me, you countless tribes of our allies and neighbours. It was not mere numbers I was looking for or needing when I summoned each of you here from your cities – but men who would give me whole-hearted help in protecting the Trojans' wives and their little children from the war-loving Achaians. That is my purpose in wearing out my people with the need for gifts and food, to strengthen the heart in each of you. So let me now have men turning straight for the enemy, to die or survive – that is the dalliance of war. And whichever of you drags Patroklos, corpse though he is, back among the horse-taming Trojans, and makes Aias give way, I shall assign him half of the spoils, and keep half for myself: and his fame will be equal to mine.'

So he spoke, and they charged in their full strength straight for the Danaans, with spears held out at the ready. Their hearts were full of hope that they would pull the body away from Aias son of Telamon – the fools: he took the life from many of them over it where it lay. Then Aias called to Menelaos, master of the war-cry: 'Lord Menelaos, dear friend, I am not sure now that we two will get back from the battle ourselves. I am afraid not so much for the corpse of Patroklos, which will soon be glutting the dogs and birds of Troy, as for the harm that may come to my own head and yours, since Hektor is a cloud of war darkening all around us, and we are faced with sheer destruction. So come, call out to the leading men of the Danaans, if any can hear.'

So he spoke, and Menelaos, master of the war-cry, did as he asked. He called in a great carrying shout to all the Danaans: 'Friends, leaders and lords of the Argives, you who drink your wine at public expense with the sons of Atreus, Agamemnon and Menelaos, and have command over your own people, with the honour and glory that is given by Zeus – it is hard for me to pick out each one of you leaders, such is the blaze of battle that has broken out: but come, every one of you of his own accord, with shame and anger in your hearts that Patroklos should become the sport of the Trojan dogs.'

So he spoke, and quick Aias son of Oïleus immediately heard him. He was the first to run through the fighting and join him, then after him came Idomeneus and Idomeneus' follower Meriones, the equal of the murdering war-god. But what man's mind could tell the names of all the others who came after this and roused the Achaian fight?

The Trojans charged forwards in a mass, and Hektor at their head. As when the huge sea waves roar against the current at the mouth of a river rain-fed from Zeus, and on either side the jutting headlands boom as the salt water spews in, such was the roar of the Trojans' attack. But the Achaians took their stand over the son of Menoitios with united purpose, fenced behind their bronze-faced shields. And the son of Kronos spread a thick mist over their bright helmets, as he had had no enmity for the son of Menoitios before, while he was alive and lieutenant to Achilleus, and he hated now that he should become a prey to the enemy dogs of Troy: and so he spurred his companions to defend him.

At first the Trojans pushed back the bright-eyed Achaians, and they abandoned the body and ran back in fear. The high-hearted Trojans did not kill any of them with their spears, for all their efforts, but they began to drag the corpse away. But the Achaians were to desert the body only for a short while: very quickly they were turned and rallied by Aias, who was the greatest of all the Danaans in looks and action, after the excellent son of Peleus. He charged through the front ranks with the fighting spirit of a wild boar, which easily scatters dogs and strong young huntsmen in the mountains, when it turns at bay and charges through the glens. So the son of proud Telamon, glorious Aias, easily scattered the ranks of the Trojans when he came on them, where they stood round Patroklos fully intending to drag him back to their own city and win the glory.

In fact the glorious son of Pelasgian Lethos, Hippothoös, was beginning to drag Patroklos away by the foot through the battle's fury, with his shield-strap tied round the tendons at the ankle, thinking he would please Hektor and the Trojans. But disaster came quickly on him, and none could keep it from him however much they wanted to. The son of Telamon sprang forward into the mass of men and at close quarters struck him through the bronze cheek-piece of his helmet. The horse-crested helmet was torn open round the spear-point, smashed by the huge spear and the power of the hand behind it. His brains spurted from the wound and ran all bloody along the socket of the spear. His strength collapsed where he stood, and his hands let the foot of great-hearted Patroklos fall back to lie on the ground. And he fell on his face right there over the dead body, far from fertile Larisa: and he could not repay his dear parents for the care of his rearing, but his life was cut short, brought down by the spear at great-hearted Aias' hands.

Hektor then cast at Aias with a shining spear. But he had looked ahead, and avoided the bronze spear by a small margin, and Hektor's cast hit Schedios, son of great-hearted Iphitos, far the best of the men of Phokis, who had his home in famous Panopeus and ruled over many people. He hit him below the centre of the collar-bone: the point of the bronze spear went right through and stuck out by the base of his shoulder. He fell with a crash, and his armour clattered about him.

Then Aias struck Phorkys, the warrior son of Phainops, in mid-belly as he stood over Hippothoös' body, and broke through his corselet's front-piece, and the bronze let his bowels gush out: he crashed in the dust and his hand clawed earth. Then the front-fighters and glorious Hektor fell back: and the Argives gave a great shout and dragged away the dead bodies, Phorkys and Hippothoös, and removed the armour from their shoulders.

Then soon the Trojans would have fled back into Ilios, driven broken and spiritless before the Achaian warriors, and the Argives through their own force and strength would have taken glory even beyond what Zeus had destined. But Apollo himself urged on Aineias, in the form of the herald Periphas, son of Epytos, who had grown old as herald to Aineias' old father, and was a man of wise and loyal heart: taking his form, then, Apollo son of Zeus spoke to Aineias: 'Aineias, how could you and your companions ever save steep Ilios if god were against you? – as before now I have seen other men do, putting their trust in their own force and strength and manhood and their own numbers, even though their people were full of fear. But in our case Zeus wills victory much more for us than for the Danaans: and yet you are all running in complete panic and refusing to fight.'

So he spoke, and Aineias recognised Apollo the far-shooter when he looked in his face, and called in a great shout to Hektor: 'Hektor, and you other leaders of the Trojans and our allies, this is a shameful thing now, to run back into Ilios before the Achaian warriors, broken and spiritless! No, one of the gods has come up beside me and says that Zeus, the counsellor most high, is still our helper in battle. So let us go straight for the Danaans, and not let them bring the dead Patroklos back to their ships unopposed.'

So he spoke, and leapt out and took his stand far ahead of the front-fighters: and the Trojans rallied and turned to face the Achaians. Then Aineias stabbed Leiokritos with his spear, the son of Arisbas and brave companion of Lykomedes. When he fell the warrior Lykomedes felt pity for him: going in close he took his stand and cast with his shining spear, and hit Apisaon, Hippasos' son, shepherd of the people, in the liver under the midriff, and instantly collapsed his strength – he had come from fertile Paionia, and was the best of their fighters after Asteropaios.

When he fell, the warrior Asteropaios felt pity for him, and he too charged forward ready to fight the Danaans, but now he could not get at them. They had gathered round Patroklos and were fenced in on all sides behind their shields, with spears held out at the ready. Aias had gone round them all with repeated firm instructions: his orders were that no-one should drop back behind the body, and no-one should fight out in front of the other Achaians, but they should all take their stand close round the corpse, and fight at short range. Such were the orders of the huge Aias: and the earth was soaked with their red blood, and dead bodies fell piled on each other, Trojans and their strong allies and Danaans alike – the Danaans too did not fight without losses, but many fewer of them were killed, as they always had their minds on protecting each other from stark death in the mass of fighting.

So they fought on like fire, and you would have said that sun and moon were no longer fixed in the sky, since a fog covered over all that part of the battle where the leading men had made their stand over the dead son of Menoitios. But the rest of the Trojans and well-greaved Achaians fought in the ease of a bright sky, with the sunlight spreading clear and sharp, and no cloud to be seen over all the earth or the mountains: and they fought a desultory battle, keeping at great distance and avoiding each other's casts of pain-fraught weapons. But those in the centre were suffering cruelly in the fog and the fighting, worn down by the pitiless bronze. Here were all the leading fighters, except that two men of renown, Thrasymedes and Antilochos, had not yet learnt that the excellent Patroklos was dead, and they thought he was still alive and fighting the Trojans in the clash of the front lines. These two were fighting away from the centre, keeping a careful watch for death or desertion of the field among their men, as these were Nestor's instructions when he urged them into battle from the black ships.

But for the others the great struggle stretched on all day long in painful battle. All the time the sweat of their effort ran relentlessly over every man's knees and shins and feet below, over their hands and eyes as they fought on over the brave lieutenant of swift-footed Achilleus. As when a man gives the skin of a great bull to his people to stretch, when it has first been drenched with fat: they take it and pull at it, standing all round it in a circle, and quickly its moisture comes out and the fat sinks in, with many hands pulling so that the whole skin is thoroughly stretched. So it was that both sides pulled at the body this way and that in the narrow space: and their hearts were full of hope that they could drag him away, the Trojans into Ilios and the Achaians back to the hollow ships. And the struggle that arose over him grew fierce – not even Ares, the rouser of armies, nor Athene if they looked on would have made light of it, even in their deepest anger: such was the misery of war's work that Zeus strained hard for men and horses over Patroklos on that day. But godlike Achilleus did not yet know that Patroklos was dead. They were fighting far away from the fast ships, close under the wall of Troy: so he never supposed that he was dead, but that he would press right up to the gates and then return alive, as he could not think either that Patroklos would sack the city without him – or indeed with him: he had heard that many times in secret from his mother, who would always tell him of great Zeus' will. But this time his mother had not told him of the disaster that had now happened, the death of his most loved companion.

But over the body the two sides kept up relentless pressure with their sharp spears and cut each other down. And this is what one of the bronze-clad Achaians would say: 'Friends, it can be no glory for us to return to the hollow ships, but rather may the black earth gape for us all here. That would be the best for us without doubt, if we abandon this body for the horse-taming Trojans to drag back to their city and win the glory.' And on their side one of the great-hearted Trojans would say: 'Friends, even if it is fated for all of us together to be brought down here beside this man, let us have no-one giving back from the fighting.'

That is what they said, and spurred the courage in every man. So they fought on, and the din rose iron-hard through the barren air to reach into the brazen sky. But the horses of Achilleus, standing away from the battle, were weeping, ever since they first learnt that their charioteer had fallen in the dust at the hands of murderous Hektor. Automedon, brave son of Diores, tried hard with many strokes of his flailing whip, and he tried with many coaxing words, and then with threats: but the two horses would not move, either back to the ships by the broad Hellespont or to join the Achaians in the battle, but as a grave-stone stands unmoving, set on the mound of a man or a woman who has died, so they stood there holding the beautiful chariot motionless, hanging their heads to the ground. Warm tears ran down from their eyes to the earth as they mourned for the loss of their charioteer: and their thick manes were dirtied where they spilled down from under the yoke-pad on either side of the yoke.

Seeing them mourn the son of Kronos felt pity for them, and he shook his head and said to his own heart: 'Poor wretches, why did we give you to lord Peleus, a mortal man, when you are ageless and immortal? Was it for you to share the pain of unhappy mankind? Since there is nothing more miserable than man among all the creatures that breathe and move on earth. But at least Hektor son of Priam will not be carried by you and your crafted chariot: I shall not allow it. Is it not enough that he has the armour, and glories in that? But I shall put strength in your knees and your hearts, so that you can bring Automedon safe out of the fighting back to the hollow ships – because I shall still give the Trojans glory, to keep on killing until they reach the well-benched ships and the sun sets and the holy darkness comes on.'

So speaking he breathed strength and courage into the horses. They shook the dust from their manes onto the ground, and quickly carried the fast-running chariot among the Trojans and Achaians. Automedon fought from the chariot, in anger for his companion, charging in with his horses like a vulture among geese – he could easily get clear from the Trojans' clamour, and easily charge in again bearing down on a great mass of men. But he could not kill his men when he sped in pursuit of them: being alone in the chariot he could not both attack with his spear and control the fast horses. But at length one of his companions caught sight of him, Alkimedon, the son of Laerkes son of Haimon. He came up behind the chariot and said to Automedon: 'Automedon, which of the gods now has put this useless idea in your heart, and taken away your good sense – the way you are fighting the Trojans in the clash of the front lines with no-one to help you? Your fighting-companion is killed, and Hektor is glorying in Achilleus' armour on his own shoulders.'

Then Automedon, son of Diores, replied: 'Alkimedon, which other Achaian could equal you in controlling and taming the spirit of these immortal horses, except Patroklos, the gods' equal in wisdom, when he was alive? But now death and fate have overtaken him. So you take the whip and the shining reins, while I dismount from the chariot to fight.'

So he spoke, and Alkimedon jumped into the fast chariot and quickly took the whip and the reins in his hands, and Automedon jumped down. Glorious Hektor saw this, and spoke quickly to Aineias, who was close by: 'Aineias, counsellor of the bronze-clad Trojans, I can see here the horses of swift-footed Achilleus coming into battle with poor charioteers. I think I might capture them, if your heart is ready to help, since those two will not have the courage to face an attack from the two of us and stand to fight us.'

So he spoke, and Anchises' noble son did not fail to obey. So the two of them went straight forward, covering their shoulders behind shields made of ox-hide, tanned and tough, with bronze beaten thick over them. And with them went Chromios and godlike Aretos both together, their hearts full of the hope of killing the men and driving off the strong-necked horses – poor fools, they were not going to come back away from Automedon without blood spilt. He prayed to father Zeus, and his dark heart filled full with courage and strength: he spoke quickly to Alkimedon, his trusted companion: 'Alkimedon, do not hold the horses too far from me, but keep them breathing right on my back. I do not think that Hektor son of Priam will be stopped in his fury, before he has killed the two of us and mounted behind Achilleus' lovely-maned horses and spread panic among the Argive ranks – or is killed himself among the front-fighters.'

So speaking he called to the two Aiantes and Menelaos: 'Aiantes, leaders of the Argives, and Menelaos, leave the dead body now for the bravest of the others to stand over it and beat back the enemy ranks. We are alive, and need you to keep the pitiless hour of death from us – because Hektor and Aineias, the best of the Trojans, have come through the ruinous battle and brought the weight of their attack on us here. But these things lie in the lap of the gods: I shall make a cast too, and Zeus will decide the outcome.'

So he spoke, and steadying his long-shadowed spear he let it fly, and hit the even circle of Aretos' shield: and the shield could not stop the spear, but the bronze went on right through, and drove through the belt into the base of his belly. As when a strong young man with a sharp axe in his hands strikes a field ox behind the horns and cuts through the whole sinew, and the ox jerks forward and collapses – so Aretos jerked forward and fell on his back: and the spear quivering sharp in his bowels collapsed his strength. Then Hektor cast at Automedon with a shining spear. But he had looked ahead, and avoided the bronze spear – he stooped forward, and the long spear was driven into the ground behind him, so that the butt of the spear quivered on: and then monstrous Ares took away its force. And now they would

have charged in to close battle with their swords, if the two Aiantes
had not parted them in their fury, coming through the mass of fighting
at the call of their companion. Frightened by them, Hektor and Aineias
and godlike Chromios gave back again, and left Aretos lying there
where he was with the life cut from him. Then Automedon, like the
swift war-god himself, stripped him of his armour and spoke in triumph over him: 'Now my heart is relieved of a little of the pain for
Patroklos' death, though the man I have killed is less than his equal.'

So speaking he lifted the bloody spoils and put them in his chariot,
and mounted himself, with his feet and hands above covered in blood,
like a lion that has eaten a bull.

Now once more the misery of battle was strained fierce and hard
over Patroklos, the fighting urged on by Athene who had come down
from heaven – wide-seeing Zeus had sent her to spur the Danaans, as
now his purpose was changed. As when Zeus spreads a lurid rainbow
in the sky for mortals to see, as a sign of war, or of a chilling storm
which stops men's work on the earth and troubles their sheep – so
Athene, wrapping a lurid cloud close round her, went in among the
mass of the Achaians and urged on every man. The first she spoke
encouragement to was the son of Atreus, powerful Menelaos, as he
was close by her. Taking the form and tireless voice of Phoinix, she
said: 'You, Menelaos, will have the shame and disgrace, if the trusted
friend of proud Achilleus is to be torn by the quick dogs under the
walls of Troy. No, hold firm, and spur on all our people.'

Then Menelaos, master of the war-cry, answered her: 'Phoinix, old
and honoured father, if only Athene would give me the strength, and
keep away the flying weapons – then I would gladly stand by Patroklos
and defend him, since his death has touched right to my heart. But
Hektor has the frightening rage of fire, and will not stop cutting men
down with the bronze, as Zeus is giving him glory.'

So he spoke, and the bright-eyed goddess Athene was pleased that
she was the god he prayed to before all the others. She put strength in
his shoulders and knees, and set in his heart the daring of a mosquito,
which, though constantly brushed away from a man's skin, still insists
on biting him for the pleasure of human blood. That was the daring
with which Athene filled his dark heart full, and he went to stand over
Patroklos, and cast with his shining spear. There was a Trojan called
Podes, the son of Eëtion, a rich man and a brave one: Hektor held him
in particular honour in the land, as he was his good friend in the
feasting. Fair-haired Menelaos hit him in the belt as he ran off in

flight, and drove the bronze right through. He fell with a crash: and Menelaos, son of Atreus, dragged his body away from the Trojans back to the mass of his companions.

But Apollo came close to Hektor and urged him on, in the likeness of Phainops, son of Asios, who was the dearest of all his guest-friends and had his home in Abydos. Taking his form, then, Apollo the far-worker spoke to Hektor: 'Hektor, what Achaian will ever be frightened of you now? – the way you shrank from Menelaos, who before now has always been a feeble spearman. And now he has single-handedly carried a body out from the Trojan lines and got away – it was your trusted companion he killed, and a brave man among the front-fighters, Podes, son of Eëtion.'

So he spoke, and the black cloud of sorrow enveloped Hektor, and he set off through the front ranks helmeted in gleaming bronze. And then it was that the son of Kronos took up the glittering tasselled aegis, and covered Ida in clouds. He sent a flash of lightning and thundered loud, and shook the aegis, giving victory to the Trojans and putting panic in the Achaians.

The first to begin the flight was Peneleos the Boiotian. He had been constantly facing the enemy, and was hit on the edge of his shoulder – a surface wound, but the spear of Poulydamas, who had come close to throw it, scraped right to the bone. Then Hektor closed with Leïtos, the son of great-hearted Alektryon, and stabbed his hand in the wrist, putting a stop to his fighting. He glanced about him and then ran, as he thought he could no longer hold a spear in his hand to fight the Trojans. As Hektor charged after Leïtos, Idomeneus struck him on the corselet on his breast by the nipple: but the long spear broke off at the socket, and the Trojans shouted. Hektor then cast at Idomeneus, son of Deukalion, where he had mounted a chariot. He missed him by a little, but struck the follower and charioteer of Meriones, Koiranos, who had come with his master from well-founded Lyktos. When Idomeneus left the balanced ships that day he had come on foot, and he would have presented a great triumph to the Trojans, if Koiranos had not quickly driven up his swift horses. So he came as a saving light to Idomeneus and kept the pitiless hour of death from him, but lost his own life at the hands of murderous Hektor. Hektor struck him under jaw and ear, and the thick of the spear-point knocked out his teeth and split his tongue down the middle. He crashed from the chariot, and the reins streamed to the ground. Meriones bent down and picked them from the plain with his own hands, and called to Idomeneus:

'Whip them on now, until you get back to the fast ships – you can see for yourself that there is no victory for the Achaians now.'

So he spoke, and Idomeneus lashed the lovely-maned horses back towards the hollow ships: fear had now entered his heart.

Now great-hearted Aias too and Menelaos did not fail to see how Zeus was turning the battle to victory for the Trojans. Huge Aias, son of Telamon, was the first to speak: 'Oh, now even a complete fool could see that father Zeus himself is helping the Trojans. All their weapons find their mark, whoever lets them fly, brave man or coward – Zeus guides them all equally straight: whereas all ours just fall wasted to the ground. No, we are on our own and must think of the best plan, how to rescue this body, and how to get back ourselves and bring joy to our dear companions – who must be looking this way in anguish, and thinking that there can be no holding the fury of Hektor's invincible hands now, but he will soon hurl himself on our black ships. If only one of our companions could take the message quickly to the son of Peleus, since I do not think he has even heard the terrible news that his loved companion is dead. But I cannot see anywhere an Achaian who could do this – they are all covered in fog, men and horses alike. Father Zeus, save the sons of the Achaians from this fog, make the sky clear, and give us light for our eyes – kill us in daylight, if you will, since this is your pleasure.'

So he spoke, and the Father pitied his tears. Immediately he scattered the fog and dispelled the darkness, and the sun shone out over them, and the whole battle was clearly seen. Then Aias said to Menelaos, master of the war-cry: 'Look now, lord Menelaos, if you can see Antilochos still alive, the son of great-hearted Nestor, and urge him to run quickly to the warrior Achilleus and tell him that the most loved of his companions is dead.'

So he spoke, and Menelaos, master of the war-cry, did not fail to obey. He set off like a lion leaving a cattle-yard when he is worn out with his attacks on dogs and men: they keep night-long watch and will not let him tear the fat from their cows: in his hunger for meat he charges in, but gains nothing – spears fly thick against him from brave hands, and burning faggots, which frighten him back for all his eagerness: and at early morning he goes away in distress of heart. So Menelaos, master of the war-cry, went away from Patroklos with great reluctance. He was very afraid that the Achaians might be forced into painful flight and leave Patroklos there as a spoil for the enemy, and there were firm instructions he impressed on Meriones and the Aiantes:

'Aiantes, leaders of the Argives, and Meriones, think now of poor Patroklos and remember his kindness. His way was to be gentle to all men, when he was alive: but now death and fate have overtaken him.'

So speaking fair-haired Menelaos left them, looking all around him like an eagle, which they say has the sharpest sight of all flying things under the heavens, and, though he is high above, the quick-running hare does not escape his eye where it crouches cowering under a leafy bush, but the eagle swoops down on it, quickly seizes it, and takes the life from it. So then, lord Menelaos, your bright eyes circled all round the mass of your many companions, looking to see Nestor's son some-where still alive. He quickly caught sight of him far on the left of the fighting, urging on his men and spurring them to battle. Fair-haired Menelaos came close and spoke to him: 'Antilochos, come here, my lord, to hear terrible news which I wish had never happened. You will already know, I think, from your own eyes that god is rolling disaster on the Danaans, and the Trojans have the victory. And the best of the Achaians has been killed, Patroklos, bringing a great loss on the Danaans. So will you run straightaway to the ships of the Achaians and tell Achilleus, and ask him – he must be quick – to bring the body safe back to his ship. It is naked now – Hektor of the glinting helmet has his armour.'

So he spoke, and Antilochos sickened on hearing his words. For a long time he was gripped speechless, and his eyes filled with tears, and his strong voice was blocked. But even so he did not ignore Menelaos' instruction, and set off at the run, giving his armour to his excellent companion Laodokos, who had been guiding the strong-footed horses to keep close by him.

So his quick legs carried him out of the battle, weeping, to bring the vile news to Achilleus son of Peleus. And your heart, lord Menelaos, did not wish to stay to defend the hard-pressed company of Pylians from which Antilochos was gone, making a loss they felt sorely. But Menelaos sent godlike Thrasymedes to lead them, while he himself went back to the hero Patroklos, and came running to stand by the Aiantes, and said to them: 'I have sent the man you wanted back to the fast ships, to go to swift-footed Achilleus. But I do not think he will come out right now, however great his anger at godlike Hektor – there is no way he could fight the Trojans without armour. So we must think of the best plan on our own, how to rescue this body, and how to get free ourselves from the Trojan clamour and escape death and destruction.'

Then huge Aias, Telamon's son, answered him: 'All that you have said is right, glorious Menelaos. So now you and Meriones bend down and lift the body as quickly as you can, and carry it out of the fighting. And the two of us will fight off the Trojans and godlike Hektor to cover you – we share both name and courage, and have stood by each other before now to face the battle's anger.'

So he spoke, and they took the body in their arms and lifted it high off the earth in a massive heave: and behind them the Trojan army gave a shout when they saw the Achaians lifting the corpse. They charged in like dogs that rush after a wounded boar ahead of the young huntsmen: for a while they race on, intent on tearing him apart, but when at last he turns on them in the confidence of his strength, they give back and run scattering in terror. So for a while the Trojans kept up a massed pursuit, thrusting with their swords and double-pointed spears. But whenever the Aiantes turned round and stood to face them, their colour changed, and none had the courage to spring forward and fight for the body.

So they laboured on, carrying the body out of the fighting towards the hollow ships. And the battle was strained round them violent as a fire which suddenly breaks out and falls on a city to set it alight, and the houses go down in the huge blaze, as the force of the wind blows it roaring. So, as they moved on back, the ceaseless din of horses and spearmen beat close on them. Like mules that put out all their great strength to haul a beam or a huge ship's timber down from the mountain along a rocky path, and their hearts are wearied with the exertion and the sweat as they press on – so they laboured to carry the body away. And behind them the Aiantes kept the Trojans back, as a wooded ridge that stands right across a plain keeps back the water, and holds off even the persistent stream of the powerful rivers, turning all their flow straight out over the plain, and the strength of their current cannot break it. So all the time the Aiantes held off the Trojans' attack behind the Achaians: but the Trojans kept up the pursuit, and two of them most of all, Aineias, son of Anchises, and glorious Hektor. As a cloud of starlings or jackdaws goes screaming in panic when they see a hawk coming at them, the bringer of death to little birds, so the young Achaians went screaming in panic before Aineias and Hektor, and forgot their fighting spirit. And many pieces of fine armour were dropped all around the ditch as the Danaans ran: and there was no cease in the fighting.

BOOK 18
THETIS, ACHILLEUS,
AND NEW ARMOUR

So they fought on like burning fire, and Antilochos came quick-footed with the news for Achilleus. He found him in front of the horned ships. His mind was foreboding what had indeed come to pass, and in dismay he spoke to his own great heart: 'Oh, why are the long-haired Achaians once more being driven in terror across the plain back to the ships? May it not be that the gods have brought that hateful sorrow on my heart that my mother once revealed to me, saying that while I still lived the best of the Myrmidons would leave the light of the sun under the hands of the Trojans. It must surely be that the brave son of Menoitios is now dead – obstinate man! I told him to come back to the ships once he had driven away the enemy fire, and not face Hektor in full fight.'

While he was pondering this in his mind and his heart, the son of proud Nestor came up close to him with his warm tears falling, and gave his painful message: 'Oh, son of warrior Peleus, there is terrible news for you to hear, which I wish had never happened. Patroklos lies dead, and they are fighting over his body. It is naked now – Hektor of the glinting helmet has his armour.'

So he spoke, and the black cloud of sorrow enveloped Achilleus. He took up the sooty dust in both his hands and poured it down over his head, soiling his handsome face: and the black ashes settled all over his sweet-smelling tunic. And he lay there with his whole body sprawling in the dust, huge and hugely fallen, tearing at his hair and defiling it with his own hands. And the serving-women that Achilleus and Patroklos had won in war shrieked loud in their hearts' grief, and ran out to flock round the warrior Achilleus: all of them beat their breasts with their hands, and the strength collapsed from their bodies. And to one side Antilochos mourned with his tears falling, and he held the hands of Achilleus as his glorious heart groaned: he was afraid that Achilleus might take a knife and cut his own throat. Achilleus gave out a terrible cry, and his honoured mother heard him, where she sat by the side of her old father in the depths of the sea, and she wailed loud in response. And the goddesses gathered round her, all the daughters of Nereus who were there in the deep of the sea. There were Glauke and Thaleia and Kymodoke, Nesaia, Speio, Thoë, and ox-eyed Halië, Kymothoë and Aktaia and Limnoreia, Melite, Iaira, Amphithoë, and Agaue, Doto and Proto and Pherousa and Dynamene, Dexamene and Amphinome and Kallianeira, Doris and Panope and famous Galateia, Nemertes and Apseudes and Kallianassa: and Klymene was there and Ianeira and Ianassa, Maira and Oreithyia and lovely-haired Amatheia, and all the other daughters of Nereus who were there in the deep of the sea. The silvery cave filled with them; and they all beat their breasts together, while Thetis led the lamentation: 'Listen, Nereids, my sisters, so you can all hear and know the sorrows in my heart. Oh, my misery! Oh, the pain of being mother to the best of men! I bore a son who was to be noble and strong, the greatest of heroes, and he shot up like a young sapling. I tended him like a plant in the crown of a garden, and sent him out with the beaked ships to Ilios, to fight the Trojans. But now I shall never welcome him back to Peleus' house – there will be no homecoming. And yet all the time I have him alive and looking on the light of the sun, he is suffering, and I can give no help when I go to him. But even so I shall go, to see my dear child and hear what it is that has come to grieve him now he is withdrawn from the fighting.'

So speaking she left the cave, and the others went with her full of tears, and the swell of the sea parted round them. When they reached the fertile land of Troy, one after another they came up on to the shore, where the Myrmidons' ships were beached close-crowded around swift Achilleus. His honoured mother came and stood by him as he groaned heavily, and with a high wail she took her son's head in her arms, and spoke winged words in sadness for him: 'Child, why are you crying? What pain has touched your heart? Tell me, do not hide it. Look, all that you asked has been brought about by Zeus, when you held out your hands and prayed that all the sons of the Achaians should be penned back by the sterns of their ships through want of you, and be put to terrible suffering.'

With a heavy groan swift-footed Achilleus said to her: 'Mother, yes, the Olympian has done all this for me. But what pleasure can I take in it, when my dear friend is killed, Patroklos, a man I honoured above all my companions, as much as my own life. I have lost him, and Hektor who killed him has stripped the huge armour from him, that lovely armour, wonderful to see, which the gods gave as a splendid gift to Peleus on the day when they brought you to a mortal man's bed. If only you had stayed in your home with the immortal goddesses of the sea, and Peleus had married a mortal wife! But as it is there must now be countless sorrow for your heart too, for the death of a son you will never welcome back to his home – since my heart has no wish for me to live or continue among men, unless first Hektor is struck down by my spear and loses his life, and pays me the price for taking Patroklos son of Menoitios.'

Then Thetis said to him with her tears falling: 'Then, child, I must lose you to an early death, for what you are saying: since directly after Hektor dies your own doom is certain.'

Swift-footed Achilleus answered her in great passion: 'Then let me die directly, since I was not to help my friend at his killing – he has died far away from his native land, and did not have me there to protect him from destruction. So now, since I shall not return to my dear native land, since I have not been a saving light to Patroklos or my many other companions who have been brought down by godlike Hektor, but sit here by the ships, a useless burden on the earth – I, a man without equal among the bronze-clad Achaians in war, though there are others better skilled at speaking – oh, that quarrels should vanish from gods and men, and resentment, which drives even a man of good sense to anger! It is far sweeter to men than trickling honey, and swells to fill their hearts like smoke – such is the anger that Agamemnon, lord of men, has caused me now. But all this is past and we should let it be, for all our pain, forcing down the passion in our hearts. And now I shall go, to find the destroyer of that dear life, Hektor – and I shall take my own death at whatever time Zeus and the other immortal gods wish to bring it on me. Even the mighty Herakles could not escape death, and he was the dearest of men to lord Zeus, son of Kronos: but fate conquered him, and the cruel enmity of Hera. So I too, if the same fate is there for me, will lie finished when I die. But now my wish is to win great glory, to make some of the deep-breasted Trojan and Dardanian women wipe the tears with both hands from their soft cheeks and set them wailing loud, and have them learn that I have stayed too long now out of the fighting. And do not try to keep me from battle, though you love me – you will not persuade me.'

Then the silver-footed goddess Thetis answered him: 'Yes, child, this is true – it is a good thing to save your stricken companions from stark destruction. But think, your fine armour of gleaming bronze is in the Trojans' possession: and Hektor of the glinting helmet is glorying to wear it on his own shoulders – but I do not think that he will have his pride in it for long, as his own death is close on him. No, you must not enter the fray of war until you see me returned to you here – in the morning, at the sun's rising, I shall come bringing you beautiful armour from lord Hephaistos.'

So speaking she turned away from her son, and facing her sisters of the sea she said to them: 'You now go back into the broad lap of the ocean, to visit our father's house and the old man of the sea, and tell him everything. I shall go to high Olympos, to Hephaistos the famous craftsman, to see if he will give a glorious set of gleaming armour for my son.'

So she spoke, and her sisters quickly slipped down through the swell of the sea. And then Thetis, the silver-footed goddess, went on to Olympos, to bring back glorious armour for her son.

So her feet took her on her way to Olympos. And meanwhile the Achaians were running with tremendous clamour under murderous Hektor's attack, and reached their ships and the Hellespont. And the well-greaved Achaians would not now have been able to drag back the body of Patroklos, Achilleus' lieutenant, out of the weapons' range: because once more the Trojan army and their horses caught up with it, and among them Hektor, son of Priam, like a flame in his fury. Three times glorious Hektor caught it by the feet from behind, intent on dragging it away, and shouted loud to the Trojans: and three times the two Aiantes, clothed in fighting spirit, battered him away from the corpse. But he stayed firm, sure of his power, sometimes charging into the crowd, sometimes standing his ground and shouting loud, and he would not give back at all. As country shepherds cannot chase a tawny lion away from a carcass when his hunger is great, so the two warrior Aiantes could not scare Hektor son of Priam back from the corpse. And now he would have dragged it away and won boundless glory, if swift Iris with feet quick as the wind had not come running from Olympos to tell the son of Peleus to arm himself – Hera had sent her, unknown to Zeus and the other gods. She came close and spoke winged words to him: 'Up, son of Peleus, most formidable of all men, and go to defend Patroklos. There is a terrible battle joined over him in front of the ships, and they are killing each other, the Achaians fighting in defence of the dead body, and the Trojans charging in to pull it away to windy Ilios. And above all glorious Hektor is urgent to drag the body off – his fury presses him to cut the head away from its soft neck and fix it on the stakes of the palisade. Up, then, no more staying here inactive. Shame should touch your heart, that Patroklos could become the sport of the Trojan dogs: it will be your disgrace if he goes down to the dead mutilated.'

Then swift-footed godlike Achilleus answered her: 'Iris, goddess, which of the gods was it that sent you with this message for me?'

Then swift Iris with feet quick as the wind said to him: 'It was Hera that sent me, the glorious wife of Zeus. But the son of Kronos who sits on high knows nothing of this, nor any other of the immortals who live on snowy Olympos.'

Then swift-footed Achilleus answered her: 'How then am I to enter the fighting? The enemy have my armour: and my dear mother has told me not to arm myself until I see her returned to me here – she promised to bring me beautiful armour from Hephaistos. And I do not know any other whose glorious armour I could wear – except perhaps the shield of Aias son of Telamon. But he is there himself, I am sure, keeping company with the front ranks and fighting with his spear over the body of Patroklos.'

Then swift Iris with feet quick as the wind said to him: 'Yes, we know too that your glorious armour is in enemy hands. But go to the ditch as you are and show yourself to the Trojans, so they might be terrified at the sight of you and hold off their fighting, and the warrior sons of the Achaians gain relief in their weariness – there is little respite in war.'

So speaking swift-footed Iris left him, and Achilleus, loved of Zeus, rose up. And Athene wrapped the tasselled aegis about his powerful shoulders, and close round his head the queen among goddesses set a golden cloud, and made a flame burn from it gleaming bright. As when the smoke rises up from a city to reach the sky, from an island in the distance, where enemies are attacking and the inhabitants run the trial of hateful Ares all day long, fighting from their city: and then with the setting of the sun the light from the line of beacons blazes out, and the glare shoots up high for the neighbouring islanders to see, in the hope that they will come across in their ships to protect them from disaster – such was the light that blazed from Achilleus' head up into the sky. He went out from the wall and stood at the ditch, but did not go further to join the Achaians, respecting his mother's firm command. There he stood, and shouted, and away to one side Pallas Athene raised her cry: and his shout started a mighty terror in the Trojans. As when the voice of a trumpet cries out sharp and clear, when murderous enemies are surrounding a city, so then

Achilleus' voice carried clear and loud. And when the Trojans heard the brazen shout of Achilleus, all their hearts were shaken in fear – even the lovely-maned horses sensed danger in their hearts and began to pull their chariots round: and the charioteers were terrified when they saw the tireless fire that burned fearfully over the head of the great-hearted son of Peleus, kindled there by the bright-eyed goddess Athene. Three times godlike Achilleus gave his great shout across the ditch, and three times the Trojans and their famous allies were thrown into turmoil. There and then twelve of their best men were killed by their own chariots or their own spears. And then the Achaians gladly took their chance to drag Patroklos out of the weapons' range, and placed him on a litter. His dear companions gathered round in mourning for him, and swift-footed Achilleus went with them, his warm tears falling when he saw his trusted friend lying there on the bier, torn by the sharp bronze, a friend he had sent out to war with his horses and chariot, and could not welcome back on his return.

Now the ox-eyed queen Hera sent the tireless sun hurrying down against his will to the stream of Ocean. So the sun set, and the godlike Achaians could stop the furious struggle of levelling war.

And the Trojans too on their side withdrew from the fury of battle and unyoked their fast horses from the chariots, then gathered in assembly before seeing to their supper. But they kept standing for the assembly, and none had the courage to sit down: all of them were gripped by terror, now that Achilleus had appeared, after long absence from the cruel fighting. The first to speak was Poulydamas in his wisdom, the son of Panthoös, the only man among them with eyes for both past and future. He was a companion of Hektor, the two of them born in the same night, but Poulydamas was far the better with words, as Hektor was better with the spear. In all good will he spoke and addressed the assembly: 'Think very carefully, friends. I advise you to return to the city now, and not wait for the holy dawn out here in the plain by the ships, this far from our city-wall. As long as this man kept up his anger against godlike Agamemnon, the Achaians were easier to fight – and I too was glad to be camping close by their fast fleet in the hope of capturing the balanced ships. But now I am terribly afraid of the swift-footed son of Peleus. Such is the violence of his spirit, he will not be content to stay here in the plain, where the Trojans and Achaians have been sharing between them the fury of battle on middle ground – but he will be making the fight for our city and our women. No, let us go back to the city. Believe me, it will be as I say. For the moment immortal night has stopped the swift-footed son of Peleus. But if he catches us out here tomorrow and comes against us in armed strength, then no-one will fail to be aware of him: we will be glad to reach sacred Ilios, those of us who escape, and the dogs and vultures will have many Trojans to feed on – may my ears never hear of such a thing! But if we follow my advice, hard though it is, we will keep our forces for the night in the market-place, and the city will be guarded safe by the walls and the high gateways with the great doors of planed timber joined tight and fitting closely in them. Then early in the morning, before the showing of dawn, we will arm in our weapons and take posts along the walls. Then it will be the worse for Achilleus if he comes out from the ships and tries to fight us for the wall. He will be on his way back again to the ships, when he has exhausted his strong-necked horses with constant running, chasing up and down below the city walls. His fury will not enable him to break inside, and he will never sack our city – before that the quick-running dogs will eat him.'

Then Hektor of the glinting helmet scowled at him and said: 'Poulydamas, what you say now is not to my liking, telling us to go back and coop ourselves in the city. Have you not all had your fill of being shut up inside our walls? Before now all mortal men would speak of Priam's city as rich in gold and rich in bronze: and now this great treasure has vanished from our houses, and many of our possessions have been sold and gone to Phrygia or lovely Maionia, after great Zeus' anger fell on us. But now when the son of devious-minded Kronos has granted me glory won by the ships, and the Achaians penned back against the sea, this is no time, fool, to put these thoughts of yours before the people. None of the Trojans will take your advice – I shall not let them. No, come, let us all do as I say. Now you should take your supper at your posts throughout the army – remember to set guards, and every one of you stay awake. And any Trojan who is too much concerned for his possessions can gather them up and give them to the people for common use – better that one of us enjoys them rather than the Achaians. Then early in the morning, before the showing of dawn, let us arm in our weapons and wake war's anger by the hollow ships. And if it is true that godlike Achilleus has stirred from the ships, then yes, it will be the worse for him if that is what he tries. I shall not run from him in the grim clash of war, but stand to face him direct, and see if he wins a great victory or I win it myself. The god of war takes no sides, and can kill the one who hopes to kill.'

So Hektor spoke, and the Trojans roared in approval – the fools:

Pallas Athene had taken away their wits. They applauded Hektor and his disastrous plan, and not one of them supported Pouludamas, who had given them good advice. So then they took their supper throughout the army. Meanwhile the Achaians mourned all night long in lamentation for Patroklos. The son of Peleus led their loud lament, placing his murderous hands on the breast of his companion and groaning incessantly, like some great bearded lion whose cubs have been stolen from the thick wood where he left them by a man out hunting deer: the lion comes back too late and is filled with anguish, and ranges through many of the mountain hollows tracking after the man's footsteps in the hope of finding him, and bitter fury grips him. So Achilleus, groaning heavily, spoke to the Myrmidons: 'Oh, it was an empty promise I made on that day when I was comforting the hero Menoitios in his house! I said that I would bring his son back to Opoëis in glory — that he would sack Ilios and come home with his share of the booty. But Zeus does not bring about all that men intend: and both of us are fated to redden the same earth here in Troy, as I shall not return home either to be welcomed in his house by the old horseman Peleus or my mother Thetis, but the earth will cover me here. But now, Patroklos, since I shall be going under the ground after you, I shall not give you burial until I have brought here the armour and the head of Hektor, the great man who murdered you. And at your pyre I shall cut the throats of twelve splendid Trojan children, in my anger for your killing. But until then you will lie by my beaked ships as you are now, and deep-breasted Trojan and Dardanian women will keen for you with their tears falling day and night long, the women we worked hard to win with our own strength and our long spears when we were sacking the rich cities of mortal men.'

So speaking godlike Achilleus called to his companions to set a great tripod over the fire, so they could wash the clotted blood from Patroklos without delay. They placed a three-legged cauldron on the burning fire, and poured water into it, and brought firewood to kindle under it. The fire worked on the belly of the cauldron, and the water warmed. Then when the water had boiled in the gleaming bronze, they washed him and rubbed him thickly with oil, and filled his wounds with long-stored ointment. Then they placed him on a bier, and covered him from feet to head with a soft sheet of fine linen, and over that a white cloak. Then all night long the Myrmidons gathered round swift-footed Achilleus and mourned in lamentation for Patroklos. And Zeus spoke to Hera, his sister and wife: 'So you have achieved it in the end, ox-eyed queen Hera – you have stirred swift-footed Achilleus into action. It must be then that you are mother to all the long-haired Achaians, and they your children.'

Then the ox-eyed queen Hera answered him: 'Dread son of Kronos, what is this you are saying? Even men will achieve their purposes for other men, though they are mortal and without the knowledge that we have. How then, when my claim is to be the greatest of goddesses, for double reason, both by birth and because I am called your wife, and you are lord over all the immortals – how could I not weave trouble for the Trojans, when they have angered me?'

Such were their words to each other. Meanwhile silver-footed Thetis came to the house of Hephaistos – that imperishable house of star-bright bronze, a shining sight for the immortals, which the cripple-foot god had made with his own hands. She found him busy at his bellows and sweating as he plied them. He was making a set of twenty tripods to stand along the wall of his strong-built house, and had fitted them with golden wheels under each leg, so he could have them moving of their own accord, running by themselves to where the gods were gathered and then returning again to his house – a miraculous sight. They were so far finished, but the worked handles had not yet been added: he was fitting these, and forging the rivets. While he was working at these in the cunning of his craft, the silver-footed goddess Thetis came close. Charis came out of the house and saw her – the lovely shining-veiled goddess who was the wife of the famous lame god. She took her hand and spoke to her: 'What is it, Thetis, fine-robed goddess, that has brought you to our house? You are honoured and loved here, but before now you have not visited us often. But come inside with me, and let me give you hospitality.'

So speaking the queen among goddesses led her inside. She then sat her down on a beautiful chair, finely worked with silver studs, with a footstool underneath, and called to Hephaistos the famous craftsman and said: 'Hephaistos, come out here – Thetis is here with a request for you.' Then the famous lame god answered her: 'Oh, then, a goddess I revere and honour is in our house. She saved me, when I was in pain after the great fall brought on me by my own shameless mother, who wanted to hide me away because I was crippled. I would have suffered agonies at heart then, if Thetis had not taken me in and welcomed me to her bosom, Thetis and Eurynome, the daughter of the circling stream of Ocean. I lived with them for nine years, crafting jewellery in abundance – brooches and curved bracelets, earrings and necklaces –

down there in the hollow cave, surrounded by the foam and roar of Ocean streaming endlessly on: and no-one else among gods or mortal men knew of it, but only Thetis and Eurynome knew, as they had saved me. And now Thetis has come to our house – so I must do all that I can to repay lovely-haired Thetis the debt for my life. So you now set out fine food for our guest, while I put away my bellows and all my tools.'

So he spoke, and stood up from the anvil-block – a monstrous size, and limping: but his thin legs bustled quickly under him. He put the bellows away from the fire, and gathered all the tools he had been working with into a silver box. Then he used a sponge to wipe over his face and both his hands, his massive neck and hairy chest. He put on a tunic, took up a thick stick to lean on, and went limping to the door, where his maids ran to help their master. They are made of gold, looking like living girls: they have intelligent minds, and speech too and strength, and have learnt their handiwork from the immortal gods. So they busied themselves in support of their master. He came stumbling close to where Thetis was seated, and sat down on a shining chair, and took her hand and spoke to her: 'What is it, Thetis, fine-robed goddess, that has brought you to our house? You are honoured and loved here, but before now you have not visited us often. Say what is in your mind. My heart prompts me to do it, if I can and it is something possible.'

Then Thetis answered him with her tears falling: 'Hephaistos, is there any one of all the goddesses on Olympos who has endured such misery in her heart as all the sorrows that Zeus, son of Kronos, has given me beyond all others? Out of all the sea-goddesses he made me subject to a man, Peleus son of Aiakos, and I had to serve a mortal's bed, though much against my will. Now he lies in his house broken by painful old age, but there is more misery for me now. He gave me a son to bear and raise, to be the greatest of heroes, and he shot up like a young sapling. I tended him like a plant in the crown of a garden, and sent him out with the beaked ships, to fight the Trojans. But now I shall never welcome him back to Peleus' house – there will be no homecoming. And yet all the time I have him alive and looking on the light of the sun, he is suffering, and I can give him no help when I go to him. The girl that the sons of the Achaians chose out as his prize lord Agamemnon took back out of his hands. So he let his heart waste away in grief for her. And meanwhile the Trojans penned the Achaians back by the sterns of their ships, and would not let them break out.

The elders of the Argives came and pleaded with Achilleus, and named all the glorious gifts they would give him. Then he refused to go out himself to beat disaster from them, but he dressed Patroklos in his own armour and sent him out to war, and a large force to go with him. All day long they fought around the Skaian gates, and they would have sacked the city on that very day, if Apollo had not killed the brave son of Menoitios in the front ranks after he had done much damage, and he gave the glory to Hektor. So that is why I have come to beg at your knees, hoping that you will give my doomed son a shield and a fine pair of greaves fitted with ankle-pieces, and a corselet. The armour he had was lost with his trusted friend when he fell to the Trojans: and now my son is lying on the ground in agony of heart.'

Then the famous lame god answered her: 'Do not worry – do not let your heart be concerned about this. If only I could be as certain of hiding him away from grim death, when his cruel fate comes on him, as I am that there will be beautiful armour for him now, such that all the many men who see it will marvel at the sight.'

So speaking he left Thetis where she was and went back to his bellows: he turned them to the fire and ordered them to set to work. There were twenty bellows in all, and they began blowing on the crucibles, sending out a good blast at every strength he needed, ready to give their help when he was busy, and ready again to blow in whatever way suited Hephaistos' wish and the progress of the work. He threw unwearying bronze on the fire, and tin, and precious gold and silver: then he set the great anvil on the anvil-block, and gripped a mighty hammer in one hand and fire-tongs in the other.

First he began to make a huge and massive shield, decorating it all over. He put a triple rim round its edge, bright and gleaming, and hung a silver baldric from it. The body of the shield was made of five layers: and on its face he elaborated many designs in the cunning of his craft.

On it he made the earth, and sky, and sea, the weariless sun and the moon waxing full, and all the constellations that crown the heavens; Pleiades and Hyades, the mighty Orion and the Bear, which men also call by the name of Wain: she wheels round in the same place and watches for Orion, and is the only one not to bathe in Ocean.

And on it he made two fine cities of mortal men. In one there were marriages and feasting, and they were escorting the brides from their houses through the streets under the light of burning torches, and the wedding-song rose loud. The young men were whirling in the dance, and among them reed-flutes and lyres kept up their music, while the women all stood at the doors of their houses and looked on admiring. The men had gathered in the market-place, where a quarrel was in progress, two men quarrelling over the blood-money for a man who had been killed: one claimed that he was making full compensation, and was showing it to the people, but the other refused to accept any payment: both were eager to take a decision from an arbitrator. The people were taking sides, and shouting their support for either man, while the heralds tried to keep them in check. And the elders sat on the polished stone seats in the sacred circle, taking the rod in their hands as they received it from the loud-voiced heralds: then each would stand forward with the rod, and give his judgment in turn. And two talents of gold lay on the ground in the middle of their circle, to be given to the one who spoke the straightest judgment.

The other city had two encamped armies surrounding it, their weapons glittering. There was debate among them, with support for either view, whether to storm the city and sack it, or to agree with the inhabitants a division of their property, taking half of all the possessions contained in the lovely town. But the defenders were not ready to yield, and had secretly armed for an ambush. Their dear wives and young children and the men overtaken by old age stood on the walls to defend them, while the others set out. They were led by Ares and Pallas Athene, both shown in gold, and dressed in golden clothing, huge and beautiful in their armour, and standing out, as gods will, clear above the rest: and the people with them were of smaller size. When they reached the place that suited their ambush, down by a river, where all the cattle came to water, they took up their position there covered in shining bronze. Then two scouts were posted at a distance from the main body, to wait for sight of the sheep and twist-horned cattle. Soon they appeared, and with them two herdsmen playing on their pipes, with no thought for danger. The men in ambush saw them coming and rushed out on them, then quickly surrounded the herds of cattle and fine flocks of white-woolled sheep, and killed the shepherds with them. But when the besiegers heard the great commotion among their cattle from where they sat in their assembly-place, they immediately mounted behind their high-stepping horses and went in pursuit and quickly overtook them. Then they formed for battle and fought it out by the banks of the river, casting at each other with their bronze-tipped spears. And Strife and Confusion were in their company, and cruel Death – she gripped one man alive with a fresh wound on him, and another one unwounded, and was dragging a dead man by the feet through the shambles: the cloak on her shoulders was deep red with men's blood. The figures closed and fought like living men, and dragged away from each other the bodies of those who were killed.

And he made on it a field of soft fallow, rich ploughland, broad and triple-tilled. There were many ploughmen on it, wheeling their teams and driving this way and that. Whenever they had turned and reached the headland of the field, a man would come forward and put a cup of honey-sweet wine in their hands: then they would turn back down the furrows, pressing on through the deep fallow to reach the headland again. The field darkened behind them, and looked like earth that is ploughed, though it was made in gold. This was the marvel of his craftsmanship.

And he made on it a king's estate of choice land, where workers were reaping the corn with sharp sickles in their hands. The crop fell to the ground in handful after handful along the swathe, while binders tied the cut trusses into sheaves with twine. There were three sheaf-binders standing ready, and boys working behind the reapers kept them constantly supplied, gathering the cut corn and bringing it in armfuls to them. And among them the king holding his sceptre stood quietly by the swathe, with delight in his heart. To one side his heralds were preparing a feast under an oak, busy with a great ox they had slaughtered: and the women were pouring out an abundance of white barley for the workers' meal.

And he made on it a vineyard heavy with grapes, a beautiful thing made in gold: but the clusters on the vines were dark, and the rows of poles supporting them were silver: and all around the plot he set a ditch worked in blue enamel, and a fence of tin. A single path led in to the vineyard, and along it went the pickers at the time of the grape-harvest. Girls and young men, innocent-hearted, were carrying out the honey-sweet crop in woven baskets. In their midst a boy was playing a lovely tune on a clear-sounding lyre, and to it sweetly singing the Linos-song in his delicate voice: they followed him with singing and shouting, and danced behind him with their feet beating time to his music.

And he made on it a herd of straight-horned cattle. The cows were fashioned in gold and tin, and were mooing as they hurried from the farmyard to their pasture by a purling river, beside the beds of swaying reeds. Four herdsmen in gold walked along with the cattle, and there were nine quick-footed dogs accompanying them. But at the head of the cattle two fearsome lions had caught a bellowing bull, and he was dragged away roaring loud. The dogs and the young men went after him. The lions had broken open the great ox's hide and were gulping its inwards and black blood. The herdsmen could only set their quick dogs at them and urge them on. The dogs would always turn back before biting the lions, but they stood close and barked at them, while keeping clear.

And the famous lame god made on it a great pasture-ground for white-woolled sheep in a beautiful valley, with steadings and covered huts and sheepfolds.

And the famous lame god elaborated a dancing-floor on it, like the dancing-floor which once Daidalos built in the broad space of Knosos for lovely-haired Ariadne. On it there were dancing young men and girls whose marriage would win many oxen, holding each other's hands at the wrist. The girls wore dresses of fine linen, and the men closely-woven tunics with a light sheen of olive oil: and the girls had beautiful garlands on their heads, and the men wore golden daggers hanging from belts of silver. At times they would run round on their skilful feet very lightly, as when a potter sits to a wheel that fits comfortably in his hands and tries it, to see if it will spin smoothly: and then they would form lines and run to meet each other. A large crowd stood round enjoying the sight of the lovely dance: and two acrobats among the performers led their dancing, whirling and tumbling at the centre.

And he made on it the mighty river of Ocean, running on the rim round the edge of the strong-built shield.

Then when he had finished the huge and massive shield, he made him a corselet brighter than the light of burning fire, and he made him a heavy helmet to fit close round his temples, a beautiful finely-worked thing, and he added a golden crest on top, and he made him greaves of fine-beaten tin.

Then when the famous lame god had worked all the armour, he took it up and laid it before the mother of Achilleus. And she plunged down like a hawk from snowy Olympos, carrying with her the glittering armour from Hephaistos.

BOOK 19
ACHILLEUS AND AGAMEMNON RECONCILED

Dawn was now rising in her yellow robe from the streams of Ocean, to bring light to deathless gods and mortal men, when Thetis reached the ships carrying with her the gifts from the god. She found her dear son lying prostrate over Patroklos, weeping loud, and many of his companions stood mourning round him. The queen among goddesses came among them, and took his hand and spoke to him: 'My child, we must let him be now, for all our grief – now that he has finally been brought down through the gods' will, let him lie. And you take this glorious armour given by Hephaistos, armour so fine that no man has ever worn its like on his shoulders.'

So speaking the goddess laid the armour down in front of Achilleus, and all the decorated metal-work rang out loud. Fear took hold of all the Myrmidons, and none dared to look full at the armour, but they all shrank back. But when Achilleus saw it, then the anger reached deeper into his heart, and his eyes glared out from his lids as if they were flames: and he was delighted to hold the splendid gifts from the god in his hands. When he had given his heart full pleasure in looking at the beautiful work, he spoke to his mother with winged words: 'Mother, the god has given me armour which is truly the work that immortals would make – no mortal man could have created it. So now I shall arm myself for battle. But I am terribly afraid for the brave son of Menoitios during this time – flies may crawl into the wounds cut in him by the bronze and breed worms there to foul his body, now that the life is killed from him, and so all his flesh will rot.'

Then the silver-footed goddess Thetis answered him: 'Child, do not let your heart be concerned about this. I shall make sure to keep away from him the cruel swarms of flies that feed on the bodies of men killed in war. Even if he lies here for a year's full circle, his flesh will always remain as it is, or even firmer than now. So you call the Achaian fighting men to assembly, and declare the end of your anger against Agamemnon, shepherd of the people – then arm immediately for battle, and clothe yourself in your fighting power.'

So speaking she put a fearless strength of courage in him. And then she dripped ambrosia and red nectar into Patroklos through his nostrils, to preserve his flesh as it was.

Meanwhile godlike Achilleus went along the shore of the sea, shouting fearfully, and calling out the fighting men of the Achaians. And even those who before now had stayed among the gathered ships, the helmsmen who had charge of the ships' steerage, and the stewards who stayed on the ships and rationed the food, even these came this time to the assembly, now that Achilleus had appeared after long absence from the cruel fighting. And two came limping along, two of Ares' men-at-arms, the staunch son of Tydeus and godlike Odysseus, leaning on their spears as their wounds still pained them. They came and sat down at the front of the assembly. Last of all to come was Agamemnon, lord of men, and he too had a wound on him: Koön son of Antenor had stabbed him with his bronze-tipped spear in the battle's fury. Then when all the Achaians were gathered together, swift-footed Achilleus stood up and spoke to them: 'Son of Atreus, could we possibly say that this has proved good for both of us, for you and for me, that the two of us in our passions quarrelled in heart-consuming anger over a girl? I wish that Artemis had killed her with an arrow on board my ships, on that day when I destroyed Lyrnessos and won her. Then all those many Achaians would not have sunk their teeth in the broad earth, brought down by enemy hands in the time of my great anger. For Hektor and the Trojans this has been their gain: but I think the Achaians will long remember the quarrel between us. But all this is past and we should let it be, for all our pain, forcing down the passion in our hearts. And now, as for me, I am ending my anger – it is wrong to go on in stubborn rage for ever. So come, urge the long-haired Achaians quickly into battle, so that I can go out to face the Trojans again and see whether they will still want to camp out by our ships – but I rather think that many of them will be right glad to take their rest, if they come out alive from the grim battle and untouched by my spear.'

So he spoke, and the well-greaved Achaians were overjoyed that the great-hearted son of Peleus had declared an end to his anger. And then Agamemnon, lord of men, spoke to them, rising in his place where he was, and not moving to stand in the centre: 'Friends, Danaan heroes, Ares' men-at-arms, when a man is standing to speak, it is proper to listen, and not right to interrupt him – this is troublesome for even an experienced speaker. But when people are making a great uproar, how can anyone hear or speak? This frustrates even the clearest of speakers. Now I shall address the son of Peleus: but the rest of the Argives should listen, and mark well what I say, every one of you. The Achaians before this have often said the same to me as you say now, and criticised me for it. But I am not to blame, but rather Zeus and Fate and Erinys that walks in darkness: they put a cruel blindness in my mind at the assembly on that day when by my own act I took away his prize from Achilleus. But what could I do? It is god who brings all things to their end. This blindness is Ate, eldest daughter of Zeus, the accursed goddess who blinds all men. Her feet are soft – she does not walk on the ground, but she treads across men's heads bringing folly to mankind, and ensnaring one or other of them. Even Zeus was blinded by her once, and he is said to be the greatest of gods and men. But Hera, female though she is, tricked even Zeus with her cunning, on the day when Alkmene was about to give birth to the mighty Herakles in Thebes with the strong circle of walls. Zeus made a declaration then to all the gods: "Listen to me, all you gods and all you goddesses, so I can tell you what my heart within me urges. Today Eileithyia, goddess of birth-pains, will reveal to the light a man who will be king over all those who live around him, and he will be born of the race of those who come from my blood." Then queen Hera said to him with deceitful intent: "You will prove a liar – in the end you will not give effect to what you say. So come then, Olympian, swear me now a binding oath, that kingship over all those who live around him will indeed come to the child who this day drops between a woman's feet, and is born to those who are of your stock by blood." So she spoke: and Zeus had no idea of her cunning, but swore a solemn oath, and that was his great blindness. Hera then darted away from the peak of Olympos and came quickly to Achaian Argos, where she knew the strong wife of Sthenelos, son of Perseus, was pregnant with a son, and in her seventh month: but Hera brought this child out to the light before its full time, and delayed Alkmene's childbirth and kept the Eileithyiai from bringing on her pains. Then she went to bring the news herself to Zeus son of Kronos: "Father Zeus, master of the bright lightning, I will tell you the news I have for you. Today there was born that great man who will be king over the Argives – Eurystheus, child of Sthenelos the son of Perseus, your stock: so it is only right that he should rule the Argives." So she spoke, and sharp pain struck into Zeus' deep heart. He immediately seized the goddess Ate in his heart's fury, catching her by the shining hair on her head, and swore a great oath that never again would Ate, who brings blindness on all, return to Olympos and the starry heaven. So speaking he swung her round with his arm and hurled her out of the starry heaven: and soon she landed in the world of men. And Zeus would always groan to think of her, whenever he saw his own dear son put to shaming labour in his tasks for Eurystheus. So it has been for me in my case now. When great Hektor of the glinting helmet kept destroying the Argives by the sterns of the ships, I could not forget Ate and the blindness she brought on me on that first day. But since I was blinded and Zeus took away my wits, I am ready to take it back and offer the appeasement of limitless reparation. So rise now for battle, and rouse the rest of our people. As for the gifts, I am here ready to offer all that godlike Odysseus promised yesterday when he came to your hut. Or if you like, hold your eagerness for war while my servants fetch the gifts from my ship and bring them here, so that you can see how my offer will please your heart.'

Then swift-footed Achilleus answered him: 'Most glorious son of Atreus, Agamemnon, lord of men, do as you will with the gifts – either give them, as is right, or keep them with you. But now our spirits should fill for battle, and straightaway. We should not stay here making delays and wasting time in talk – there is still a great task to be done. So once more men will see Achilleus in the front lines destroying the ranks of Trojans with his bronze spear. Have this in your minds, all of you, when you are fighting your man.'

Then resourceful Odysseus answered him: 'No. You are a brave man, godlike Achilleus, but we have had no food: do not send the sons of the Achaians against Ilios to fight the Trojans like this, because the battle will not be short-lasting once the ranks of men have clashed and god breathes strength into both sides. No, give orders for the Achaians to take food and wine by the fast ships – this gives strength and courage. A man will not be able to stand and fight all day long to the setting of the sun if he has gone without food: his heart may be eager for the fight, but without his knowing his body grows heavy, and thirst and hunger come over him, and his legs weaken as he goes on. But when a man has had his fill of food and wine and then fights the enemy day-long, he has a heart within him full of courage, and his body does not flag until all break off the fighting. So come, dismiss the men and tell them to prepare their meal. And Agamemnon, lord of men, should bring the gifts into the middle of our assembly, so that all the Achaians can see them with their own eyes, and your heart can have its pleasure. And he should stand up before the Argives and swear an oath, that he has never mounted the girl's bed and lain with her, as is the way, my lord, between men and women. And you too should allow your heart within you to be reconciled. And then he should appease you with a rich feast in his hut, so that you can have all that is due to you. And you, son of Atreus, will be readier after this to give others their due: there can be no blame in a king giving a man recompense, when he was the first to grow angry.'

Then Agamemnon, lord of men, answered him: 'Son of Laertes, I welcome what you have said: you have dealt completely and properly with every aspect. I am willing to take the oath you ask, and my heart urges me to take it: I shall not swear falsely before the god. Let Achilleus stay here for the while, despite his eagerness for war: and all the rest of you stay gathered here, until the gifts come from my hut and we can make a sacrifice to seal my oath. This is a task I am giving for your own care, to choose the best young men from all the Achaians and fetch from my ship all the gifts that we promised yesterday to give Achilleus, and bring the women too. And let Talthybios be quick to prepare me a boar in the broad Achaian camp, for sacrifice to Zeus and the Sun.'

Then swift-footed Achilleus answered him: 'Most glorious son of Atreus, Agamemnon, lord of men, another time would be better for busying ourselves with this, when there is a pause in the fighting and my heart is not so full of fury. But now there are torn bodies lying there, the men brought down by Hektor, son of Priam, when Zeus gave him the glory, and you two are urging us to think of food. My orders to the sons of the Achaians would be to fight now, hungry and unfed, and make a large dinner afterwards when the sun sets and we have paid back for our disgrace. Before that no food or drink will pass down my own throat, when my friend is dead and lies torn by the sharp bronze in my hut, his feet turned towards the door, and his companions mourning round him. So what you speak of is of no interest to my heart, but my thought is on blood and slaughter and the groans of men in pain.'

Then resourceful Odysseus answered him: 'Achilleus, son of Peleus, far the greatest of the Achaians, you are a greater man than I and not a little stronger with the spear, but I might claim to surpass you in judgment by far, since I was born older than you and have greater knowledge. So your heart should consent to hear what I say. Men grow tired of battle quickly – war is a field where the bronze drops straw in plenty on the ground, but there is little harvest, when Zeus, who holds the issue of men's fighting, inclines his scales. Starving the belly is no way for the Achaians to mourn a dead man. Too many are falling, an endless succession day after day – when would a man ever have relief from the hardship of fasting? No, we must bury those who die, hardening our hearts and giving them the tears of a day. And those of us who survive the hateful fighting must take thought for food and drink, to give us more strength to fight the enemy relentlessly on and on, our bodies clothed in unwearying bronze. And none of our people should hold back waiting for another call to battle. This is the summons now, and it will go hard with any man left behind by the Argives' ships. Let us attack in full strength and wake war's anger against the horse-taming Trojans.'

So he spoke, and took with him the sons of glorious Nestor, and Meges son of Phyleus, and Thoas and Meriones and Lykomedes son of Kreion and Melanippos: and they went on their way to the hut of Agamemnon son of Atreus. No sooner was the command given than the task was done. They brought out from the hut the seven tripods promised to Achilleus, and twenty gleaming cauldrons and twelve horses: and then they brought out seven women skilled in excellent handcraft, and the beautiful Briseïs as the eighth. Odysseus weighed out ten talents of gold in all, and led the way back, with the young men of the Achaians carrying the gifts behind him. They set them down in the middle of the assembly, and Agamemnon stood up. Talthybios, whose voice was like the gods', stood beside the shepherd of the people holding the boar in his hands. The son of Atreus drew the knife which always hung beside his sword's great scabbard, and cut hairs from the boar's head to begin the sacrifice, then lifted up his hands in prayer to Zeus: 'Let my witness now be Zeus first of all, highest and greatest of gods, and Earth and Sun and the Erinyes who punish men below the earth, when any has falsely sworn. I swear that I never laid hand on the girl Briseïs, either in overt desire for her bed or for any other reason, but she has remained untouched in my huts. If any of this is falsely sworn, may the gods heap on me the misery they give to a man who offends them with his oath.'

So he spoke, and cut the boar's throat with the pitiless bronze. Talthybios swung the boar round and hurled it into the great expanse of the grey sea, food for the fish. Then Achilleus stood up and spoke to the war-loving Argives: 'Father Zeus, you do bring great blindness on men. Otherwise the son of Atreus would never have roused my heart to such lasting anger in my breast, or taken the girl from me in stubborn crossing of my will. But Zeus must have wished that death should come to great numbers of the Achaians. But go now to take your meal, so that we can then join battle.'

So he spoke, and dismissed the assembly without delay. The men scattered, each to his own ship, and the great-hearted Myrmidons took care of the gifts, carrying them back to godlike Achilleus' ship. They stowed them in his huts, and settled the women there, while his proud lieutenants drove the horses to join his own herd.

Then when Briseïs, lovely as golden Aphrodite, saw Patroklos lying there, torn by the sharp bronze, she threw herself over him and shrieked loud, and her hands tore at her breasts and soft neck and beautiful face. And the woman beautiful as the goddesses cried out in lament for him: 'Patroklos, more than any the pleasure of my poor heart, you were alive when I went away from the hut and left you, and now I come back, leader of your people, and find you dead. So it is always in my life, pain following pain. My father and honoured mother gave me to a husband, and I saw him torn by the sharp bronze in front of our city, and my three brothers, borne by the same mother, my beloved brothers all met the day of destruction. But when swift Achilleus killed my husband and sacked the city of godlike Mynes, you would not let me even weep, but you said you would make me godlike Achilleus' wedded wife, and take me back in your ships to Phthia, and celebrate my marriage-feast among the Myrmidons. And so I weep endlessly for your death. You were always gentle.'

Such was her lament, and the women joined with their keening – the cause was Patroklos, but each of them wept over her own sorrows. The elders of the Achaians gathered round Achilleus, begging him to take food, but he refused with a groan: 'I beg you, if any of you dear companions will do as I wish, do not urge me to satisfy my heart with food or drink now, now that this grievous pain has come on me. I shall wait and hold out despite all until the sun sets.'

So speaking he sent away the rest of the kings, but the two sons of Atreus stayed with him, and so did godlike Odysseus, and Nestor and Idomeneus and the old horseman Phoinix, trying to comfort him in his deep anguish: but his heart could feel no comfort until he entered the jaws of bloody battle. As he thought of Patroklos he sighed constantly for him and said: 'Oh, there was a time when you, poor ill-fated man, dearest of my companions, you yourself would set out a pleasing meal in my hut, so quick and ready, whenever the Achaians were eager to carry the misery of war against the horse-taming Trojans. But now you lie there torn, and my heart goes without food and drink, though it is here in plenty, out of longing for you. There could be no worse suffering for me, not even if I heard of the death of my father, who must now be weeping soft tears in Phthia for the loss of such a son, while I am in a foreign land, fighting the Trojans for hateful Helen's sake – or the death of my dear son, godlike Neoptolemos, who is being brought up for me in Skyros – if indeed he still lives. Before this my heart within me had hoped that I alone would die here in Troy, away from the horse-pasture of Argos, and that you would get back to Phthia, so you could take my son from Skyros in your fast black ship and show him all that is mine, my property and my servants and the great high-roofed house. Because I think Peleus by now will either be dead and utterly gone, or perhaps living on a shadow of life in the pain of hateful old age, and always expecting the terrible news when he will learn that I am dead.'

Such was his lament, and the elders joined with their mourning, as each remembered what he had left behind in his own home. Seeing them mourn the son of Kronos felt pity for them, and at once spoke winged words to Athene: 'My child, you have now utterly deserted the man you favour. Have you no longer any concern at all in your heart for Achilleus? He is sitting there in front of the horned ships grieving for his dear companion: the rest have now gone for their meal, but he is without food and fasting. So go then and distil nectar and lovely ambrosia into his breast, so that hunger does not come over him.'

With these words he urged on Athene what she herself already desired: and she plunged down from the heaven through the upper air in the form of a falcon with long wings and screaming voice. The Achaians had begun at once to arm throughout the camp: and Athene distilled nectar and lovely ambrosia into Achilleus' breast, so that grim hunger should not come over him and weaken his knees. Then she went back to her mighty father's house, and the Achaians streamed out away from their fast ships. As when the snowflakes fly thick from Zeus, driven cold under the blast of the north wind, child of the clear air, so thick was the mass of the bright-shining helmets moving out from the ships then, and the bossed shields and strong-plated corselets and ash spears. The glitter struck into the sky, and all the earth around them smiled in the gleam of bronze: and a thunder swelled under the feet of the men. In their midst godlike Achilleus began to arm himself. The noise of grinding came from his teeth, and his eyes glowed like the light of a fire, and grief past endurance entered into his heart. With fury for the Trojans he dressed himself in the gifts of the god, the work of Hephaistos' labour. First he placed the greaves on his legs, a fine pair, fitted with silver ankle-pieces. Next he put the corselet round his chest. Over his shoulders he slung the bronze sword, the hilt nailed with silver, and then he took up the great massive shield, with the light from it shining far like the moon's. As when sailors out at sea catch sight of the gleam from a burning fire, a fire burning high in the mountains in a lonely farmstead: but the winds are against them and carry them over the fish-filled sea away from their families – so the gleam from Achilleus' beautiful, finely-worked shield struck far into the upper air. Then he lifted the massive helmet and set it over his head. The helmet with its plume of horse-hair shone out like a star, and the golden hairs that Hephaistos had set thick along the crest shimmered round it. Godlike Achilleus tried himself in the armour, to see if it fitted him and his splendid body ran free in it: and the armour became like wings to the shepherd of the people and lifted him. Then he pulled from its casing his father's spear, the huge, heavy, massive spear which no other Achaian could wield, but Achilleus alone had the skill to handle it, the spear of Pelian ash from the height of Pelion which Cheiron had given to his dear father to be the death of fighting men. Automedon and Alkimos worked at the yoking of the horses. They settled the fine breast-straps over them, and fixed the bits between their jaws, and drew the reins back into the strongly-made chariot. Then Automedon took the shining whip firm-fitting in his hand and jumped up into the chariot. And behind him went Achilleus armed, bright in his armour like Hyperion the beaming sun, and he called in a terrible voice to his father's horses: 'Xanthos and Balios, Podarge's famous children, let it be different this time. Mind that you bring your charioteer safe back to the mass of Danaans when we have finished fighting, and not the way you left Patroklos, lying dead there on the field.'

Then from under the yoke the flashing-foot horse Xanthos spoke to him, and bowed down his head so that all his mane spilled down from the yoke-pad by the yoke and fell to the ground – the white-armed goddess Hera had given him speech: 'Yes, we shall still bring you back safe this time, mighty Achilleus. But your day of destruction is near: and it is not we who will be to blame, but a great god and strong Fate. It was not through any lack of speed or any slackness in us that the Trojans took the armour from Patroklos' shoulders – but the greatest of gods, child of lovely-haired Leto, killed him among the front-fighters and gave the glory to Hektor. We two could run even with the speed of the west wind's blowing, which men say is the fastest of all things: but it is your own fate to be brought down in battle by a god and a man.'

When he had said this, the Erinyes stopped his voice. Swift-footed Achilleus answered him in great anger: 'Xanthos, why prophesy my death? There is no need. I know well myself that it is my fate to die here, away from my dear father and mother. But even so I shall not stop until I have driven the Trojans to their fill of war.'

So he spoke, and with a shout he drove his strong-footed horses on among the leaders.

BOOK 20
THE RETURN OF ACHILLEUS

So the Achaians armed themselves by the beaked ships around you, son of Peleus, in your insatiable lust for battle. And the Trojans armed on the other side, at the rise of the plain. Meanwhile, from the peak of valleyed Olympos, Zeus ordered Themis to call the gods to assembly: and she went all round and told them to go to Zeus' house. None of the rivers was absent, apart from Ocean, and none of the Nymphs who live in the lovely woods, or the springs of rivers, or the grassy water-meadows. They all came to the house of Zeus the cloud-gatherer, and sat down in the porticoes of polished stone which Hephaistos had built for father Zeus in the cunning of his craft.

So they were assembled inside Zeus' house. And the Earthshaker too did not fail to hear the goddess' summons, but came out of the sea to join them, and sat in the middle of them, and asked Zeus his purpose: 'Why is it, master of the bright lightning, that you have once more called the gods to assembly? Have you some thought about the Trojans and Achaians? Because now the conflict between them is close to blazing out in battle.'

Then Zeus the cloud-gatherer answered him: 'You have realised the purpose in my mind, Earthshaker, the reason why I called you together – I do care for them even as they die. But now I shall stay here, sitting in a fold of Olympos where I can look on and delight my heart: but the rest of you go down now to join the Trojans and Achaians and give help to either side, as each of you is minded. If Achilleus is left alone to fight the Trojans, they will not be able to hold the swift-footed son of Peleus even for a short while. Even before now they used to tremble with fear at the sight of him, and now that there is terrible anger for his companion in his heart I am afraid that he may even reach beyond fate and storm the wall.'

So the son of Kronos spoke, and this was the waking of relentless war. The gods went down into the fighting, their intentions divided. Hera went to the assembly of ships, with Pallas Athene and Poseidon the encircler of the earth and Hermes the kindly, greatest of the gods in his mind's subtlety; and with them went Hephaistos, exulting in his strength – he limped, but his thin legs bustled quickly under him. But Ares of the glinting helmet went over to the Trojan side, and with him Phoibos the unshorn and Artemis the archer-goddess, and Leto and Xanthos and smiling Aphrodite.

Now while the gods still kept away from the mortal men, the Achaians were winning great glory, now that Achilleus had appeared after long absence from the cruel fighting: and fearful trembling came over every Trojan's body, in terror at the sight of the swift-footed son of Peleus blazing in his armour like Ares, the curse of men. But when the Olympians came among the company of men, then Strife, the rouser of armies, broke out in strength, and Athene kept up her shout, now standing by the ditch dug outside the wall, and now shouting loud along the thunderous sea-shore. And Ares, like a black storm-wind, shouted on the other side, giving his piercing call to the Trojans from the height of the city, and then again running to the hill Kallikolone by the side of Simoeis.

So the blessed gods drove on both sides and brought them to the clash: and they broke out bitter conflict among themselves. The father of men and gods thundered fearfully from on high, and beneath them Poseidon shook the limitless earth and the high peaks of the mountains. All the foothills and the peaks of Ida with the many springs were shaken, and the Trojans' city and the ships of the Achaians. And down below Aïdoneus, the lord of the dead, was terrified, and leapt screaming from his throne for fear that Poseidon the earthshaker would break open the earth above him, and the dwellings of the dead be revealed to mortals and immortals, the ghastly places of mould which the gods themselves hold in horror – such was the crash that arose as the gods joined in conflict. Lord Poseidon was opposed by Phoibos Apollo with his winged arrows, and the bright-eyed goddess Athene set herself against Ares Enyalios: against Hera there stood Artemis of the golden distaff, goddess of the loud hunt, the archer-goddess and sister of Apollo the far-shooter: against Leto stood Hermes the kindly, the strong one, and against Hephaistos the great deep-swirling river which the gods call Xanthos, but men's name for it is Skamandros.

So the gods went on to clash, god against god. Meanwhile Achilleus was urgent above all to enter the fighting against Hektor, son of Priam – his was the blood more than any that his heart pressed him to feed full to Ares, the fighter with the bull's-hide shield. But it was Aineias whom Apollo, the rouser of armies, set straight against the son of

Peleus, and filled him with strength and courage. Apollo, son of Zeus, made his voice like that of Priam's son Lykaon, and spoke to Aineias in his form: 'Aineias, counsellor of the Trojans, where are those threats of yours, those promises you made as you drank wine with the kings of Troy, that you would fight face to face with Achilleus, son of Peleus?'

Then Aineias answered him: 'Son of Priam, why urge me to fight against the high-hearted son of Peleus, when I have no will for it? This will not be the first time I have faced swift-footed Achilleus, but before now there was a time when he drove me away from Ida with his spear, when he came to attack our cattle and sacked Lyrnessos and Pedasos. But Zeus protected me then, spurring strength in me and speed to my legs. Otherwise I would have gone down at the hands of Achilleus and of Athene, who went in front of him bringing him safety, and urged him on to kill Leleges and Trojans with his bronze spear. It is not possible, then, for any man to fight against Achilleus – there is always one of the gods at his side to keep him from destruction. And even without that, his spear flies straight, and never stops until it has passed through a man's flesh. But if god were to pull the issue of battle level and fair between us, he would not win so easy a victory, even if he claims he is made all of bronze.'

Then lord Apollo, son of Zeus, said to him: 'Well, hero, make a prayer then yourself to the ever-living gods. You too have a divine mother: they say you were born to Zeus' daughter Aphrodite, while Achilleus is the son of a lesser goddess – Aphrodite is a child of Zeus, and Thetis of the old man of the sea. So take your tireless bronze straight for him, and do not let his sorry taunts and menaces deter you at all.'

So speaking he breathed great strength into the shepherd of the people, and Aineias strode through the front ranks helmeted in gleaming bronze. Now white-armed Hera did not fail to notice the son of Anchises moving through the throng of men to attack the son of Peleus. She brought together her fellow-gods and spoke to them: 'Think now, Poseidon and Athene, both of you, and give your minds to what should be done in this case. Here is Aineias come helmeted in gleaming bronze to attack the son of Peleus, set to it by Phoibos Apollo. So come, let us ourselves turn him back where he stands. Or else one of us too could stand by Achilleus and give him great strength and not let him fail in courage, so that he can know he is loved by the greatest of the immortals, while those who have before now kept war's destruction from the Trojans are nothing, empty as the wind. We have all come down from Olympos to engage in this battle, so that Achilleus should come to no harm among the Trojans on this day – then after this he will suffer what Fate spun for him with her thread as he was born, at the moment his mother gave birth to him. But if Achilleus does not learn of this through a voice from the gods, he will be afraid when a god comes to face him in the fighting – gods are dangerous when they are revealed open to men's sight.'

Then Poseidon the earthshaker answered her: 'Hera, do not let your anger run away beyond sense – that would be wrong. I myself would not want to drive god against god in conflict. No, we should rather move out of the way of the fighting and sit down where we can watch, letting the men see to the war. But if Ares or Phoibos Apollo begin to fight, or block Achilleus and prevent him from fighting, then we too will join issue there and then and battle with them – and I do not think it will be very long before they break away and go back to join the company of the other gods on Olympos, overcome by the force of our hands.'

So speaking the dark-haired god led the way to the rampart of godlike Herakles, the high mound of piled earth that the Trojans and Pallas Athene had built for him as a refuge to escape from the sea monster when it drove him inland away from the shore. There Poseidon and the other gods sat down, and wrapped impenetrable mist around their shoulders. And the gods on the other side sat on the brows of the hill Kallikolone around you, lord Apollo, and Ares the sacker of cities.

So the gods sat there on either side thinking over their intentions. Both sides were reluctant to start the misery of war, and Zeus held control from his seat high above them.

Meanwhile the whole plain was filled with the men and their horses, and shone bright with bronze: and the earth shuddered under their feet as they charged towards each other. And two men of outstanding prowess came together into the ground between the two sides, eager for battle, Aineias son of Anchises and godlike Achilleus. Aineias was the first to stride out in defiance, his heavy helmet nodding over his head: he held his mighty shield in front of his chest, and shook his bronze spear. On the other side the son of Peleus sprang out to face him like a lion, a marauding beast that has made the men of a whole village gather in a hunt to kill him: at first he pays them no attention and goes on his way, but when one of the quick young hunters has hit him with a spear, he gathers himself in a crouch, open-jawed, foam gushes over his teeth, and his brave heart snarls within him: he lashes his ribs and both flanks with his tail, spurring himself on to rage for the fight, and then springs straight for them in glaring fury, to kill one of the men or perish himself in the first attack. So Achilleus' fury and his proud heart spurred him to go out against great-hearted Aineias. When these two had advanced to close range, swift-footed godlike Achilleus was the first to speak: 'Aineias, why have you come so far out from your ranks to take your stand here? Does your heart urge you to fight me in the hope that you will take Priam's royal position over the horse-taming Trojans? But if you do kill me, that is no reason for Priam to hand you this honour – he has sons of his own, and he is sound, his mind is not feeble. Or it may be that the Trojans have set aside for you the finest piece of land, rich in vineyard and ploughland, to be your own domain, if you kill me? But I think you will not find that easy. There was a time before now, I think, when I scared you away with my spear. Or do you not remember when I cut you off alone from your cattle and sent you running down the mountains of Ida with all speed of your legs? You ran away quickly then, without looking back at all. Then you took refuge in Lyrnessos. But I came after you and sacked the town with the help of Athene and father Zeus, and took the day of freedom from the women I carried away captive: but you were saved by Zeus and the other gods. But I do not think they will save you now, as you imagine in your heart. No, go back, I tell you, back into the crowd, and do not oppose me, before you come to harm: it is only the fool who learns too late.'

Then Aineias answered him and said: 'Son of Peleus, do not think you will frighten me with words as if I were a baby – I too know how to deal insults and slighting talk. We both know each other's birth, and we know each other's parents, from hearing the tales that mortal men have long made famous – though I have never seen your parents with my eyes, nor you mine. They say that you are the child of the excellent Peleus, with Thetis for your mother, the lovely-haired daughter of the sea: and I am proud to call myself the son born to great-hearted Anchises, and my mother is Aphrodite. And now one or other of these pairs will be mourning their dear son today – since I cannot think we will part and leave the battle with no more exchange than this childish talk. But if you want to hear of it and learn the history of my family, it is something that many men know. In the beginning Dardanos was born a son to Zeus the cloud-gatherer, and he founded Dardania, when sacred Ilios had not yet been built in the plain as a city of mortal men, but they still lived on the slopes of Ida with the many springs. Then Dardanos had a son, king Erichthonios, who became the richest of all mortal men. He had three thousand horses herded in the fens, all mares, proud with their soft young foals. The north wind fell in love with these mares as they grazed there, and coupled with them in the form of a dark-maned stallion: and they conceived and gave birth to twelve foals. When these foals played over the grain-giving ploughland, they could run across the tops of the ears of corn without bruising the crop: and when they played on the sea's broad back, they would run along the surface of the waves where the grey sea breaks. Erichthonios fathered Tros to be king over the Trojans. And then to Tros three excellent sons were born, Ilos and Assarakos and godlike Ganymedes, who was the most beautiful of all mortal men: and so the gods snatched him away to be Zeus' wine-pourer because of his beauty, so he should live among the immortals. Then Ilos fathered the excellent Laomedon: and Laomedon's sons were Tithonos and Priam and Lampos and Klytios and Hiketaon, branch of Ares. Assarakos fathered Kapys, and he had Anchises as son: Anchises is my father, and Priam is father to godlike Hektor. This is the family and blood I am proud to call mine. As for men's strength in war, it is Zeus who increases or diminishes it according to his will, as he is the most powerful of all. But come, enough of this talk – we are standing here at the centre of a furious battle and wrangling on like little boys. Both of us could find insults enough to hurl at the other – a hundred-oared ship could hardly carry that cargo. Man's tongue is a versatile thing: it contains every sort of varied speech, and its words can range at large, this way or that. Speak one way, and that is the way you will be spoken to. But what need is there for us to raise a quarrel out here and fling insults in each other's face, like a pair of women who have flown into a rage in some squabble that eats out their hearts, and come out into the middle of the street to squall abuse at each other, a torrent of truth and untruth, with anger prompting the false? I am ready for battle, and you will not deter me with words, not until we have fought it out face to face with bronze. So quickly now, let us try each other with our bronze-tipped spears.'

So he spoke, and hurled his heavy spear into that mighty, awesome shield: and the shield rang loud all over at the impact of the spearhead. The son of Peleus held the shield away from him with his massive hand – he was frightened, thinking that the long-shadowed spear of great-hearted Aineias would easily force through it: the fool, he did not realise in his heart and mind that the glorious gifts of the gods are not easily overcome by mortal men and will not fail before them. And now the warrior Aineias' heavy spear did not break the shield – the gold stopped it, the gift of the god. Aineias drove his spear through two layers, but there were still three more, since the cripple-foot god had beaten five layers over it, two of bronze, and two on the inside of tin, and a single gold layer between, where the ash spear was held.

Then after him Achilleus let fly his long-shadowed spear, and hit the even circle of Aineias' shield, at the very edge of the rim where the bronze ran thinnest, and there was the thinnest layer of ox-hide backing it. The spear of Pelian ash shot straight through, and the shield screeched under it. Aineias huddled down and held the shield above him at arm's length, terrified: and the spear pressed on over his back and stuck in the earth, after ripping open the two layers of his covering shield. The long spear had missed him, but Aineias stood there while a huge wave of shock flooded over his eyes, horrified that the shot had struck so close to him. But Achilleus drew his sharp sword and charged in on him in fury, shouting fearfully. And Aineias took up a boulder in his hand, a huge great thing, that two men could not carry between them, of the folk that live now – but he swung it easily on his own. And then as Achilleus rushed to attack, Aineias would have struck him with the stone on his helmet or shield, which would have saved him from grim death, and the son of Peleus would have closed and taken the life from Aineias with his sword, if Poseidon the earthshaker had not quickly seen it, and immediately spoken to the immortal gods with him: 'Oh, I feel sorrow for great-hearted Aineias! In a moment he will be brought down by the son of Peleus and go on his way to Hades, because he followed the prompting of Apollo the far-shooter – the fool, Apollo will not protect him from grim death. But why does this innocent man now suffer, because of other people's troubles and no cause of his own – and he always makes gifts which are pleasing to the gods who hold the wide heaven. So come, let us take him out of death's way, or it may be that the son of Kronos too will be angry, if Achilleus kills this man: it is fated that he should survive, so that the line of Dardanos should not perish without seed or trace, since the son of Kronos loved Dardanos more than all the other children borne to him by mortal women. The son of Kronos has come to hate Priam's line: and now the mighty Aineias will be king over the Trojans, and his children's children born in future time.'

Then the ox-eyed queen Hera answered him: 'Earthshaker, you must think in your own mind about Aineias, whether you will rescue him or let him go down, brave man though he is, under Achilleus son of Peleus. Because we two, I and Pallas Athene, have sworn many oaths before all the immortals that we will never keep the evil day away from the Trojans, not even when all Troy is ablaze with devouring fire, and the warrior sons of the Achaians are burning it.'

When Poseidon the earthshaker heard this, he went down through the fighting and the flurry of spears and came to the place where Aineias and famous Achilleus were meeting. Then immediately he cast a dark mist over the eyes of Achilleus son of Peleus: and he pulled the bronze-headed ash spear out from great-hearted Aineias' shield and laid it at Achilleus' feet. Then he lifted Aineias high off the ground and sent him flying through the air, so that, sped from the god's hand, Aineias leapt right over rank after rank of fighting men and horses and landed at the far edge of the seething battle, where the Kaukones were arming to enter the fight. Poseidon the earthshaker then came up close and spoke winged words to him: 'Aineias, which of the gods has put you to this madness, telling you to fight against the high-hearted son of Peleus, who is both a stronger man than you and dearer to the immortals? No, you must withdraw whenever you are thrown together with that man, so that you do not enter the house of Hades beyond what is fated for you. But when Achilleus has met his death and doom, then you can take courage and fight among the leaders – no other Achaian will kill you.'

So speaking Poseidon left him there, when he had made all this clear to him: and then he quickly scattered the miraculous mist away from Achilleus' eyes. Then Achilleus stared out with straining eyes, and spoke to his own great heart in vexation: 'Oh, this is a great astonishment for my eyes! Here is my spear lying on the ground, and I cannot see anything of the man I was eager to kill with my cast. It seems that Aineias too is loved by the immortal gods, and I thought that his claims were mere empty boasting. Well, let him go: he will not have the heart to try me again, now that he has been lucky to escape death this time. Come then, I shall urge on the war-loving Danaans and go to meet the other Trojans, to see how they fare.'

So he spoke, and leapt back to the Danaan ranks and urged on every man: 'No more keeping your distance from the Trojans now, godlike Achaians, but let me have every one going for his man and furious for the fight. Strong though I am, it is hard for me to keep pressure on such a number of men and fight with them all. Not even Ares, who is an immortal god, or Athene could face the jaws of such a battle as this and fight on through. But I shall do all that is in the power of my hands and feet and strength, and I tell you I shall not now hold back at all, but I am going straight through their line, and I think any Trojan who comes near my spear will be sorry.'

So he spoke, urging them on. And glorious Hektor called in a shout to the Trojans, thinking he would go to face Achilleus: 'You high-hearted men of Troy, do not be afraid of the son of Peleus. I too could fight with words, even against the immortals – though it would be hard with the spear, since they are much stronger than us. But even Achilleus will not give effect to all that he says – he will achieve part, and part will be thwarted in mid-course. Now I am going to face him, even if his hands are like fire, his hands like fire and his strength like gleaming iron.'

So he spoke, urging them on, and the Trojans raised their spears for the attack. Then the two sides joined their fury, and the clamour rose. But then Phoibos Apollo came up to Hektor and said to him: 'Hektor, on no account now must you challenge Achilleus out in the open, but stay within the mass of your troops and wait for him in the main seethe of battle, or he will take you with a spearcast or a blow from his sword close in.'

So he spoke, and Hektor sank back into the throng of men in fear, when he heard the voice of the god speaking to him. But Achilleus leapt on the Trojans, his heart clothed in courage, and shouting fearfully. The first he killed was Iphition, brave son of Otrynteus and leader of many people, borne by a water-nymph to Otrynteus, sacker of cities, below snowy Tmolos, in the rich land of Hyde. As he rushed straight for him Achilleus struck him with his spear in the middle of his head: the head was smashed completely in two, and he fell with a crash. Godlike Achilleus spoke in triumph over him: 'There you lie, son of Otrynteus, most formidable of all men. This is where you die, though your birth was by the Gygaian lake, where your family has its land by the fish-filled river Hyllos and the swirling water of Hermos.'

So he spoke in triumph, and darkness covered over Iphition's eyes. He then was cut in pieces by the wheel-rims of the Achaians' chariots in the first attack, and Achilleus went on to Demoleon, a brave defender in battle, and son of Antenor. He struck him in the temple, through his bronze-cheeked helmet: the bronze of the helmet could not hold, but the spear-point pushed on through it and smashed the bone, and all his brains were spattered inside, and the man brought down in his fury. Then when Hippodamas had jumped down from his chariot and was fleeing before him, Achilleus stabbed him with his spear in the back. He gasped out his life and bellowed, as a bull bellows when he is dragged round the altar of Poseidon, lord of Helike, and the Earthshaker delights in the young men who drag him – so he bellowed as his proud spirit left his bones. But Achilleus went with his spear after godlike Polydoros, son of Priam. His father always forbade him to fight, because he was the youngest of the sons born to him, and the one he loved most: and he was the fastest of all on his feet. And now in his young folly he was displaying the speed of his legs and racing through the front-fighters, until he lost the life that was in him. As he came dashing past, swift-footed godlike Achilleus hit him with his spear in the middle of the back, where the belt's golden buckles joined and the corselet opposed a double layer. The point of the spear held on right through and came out by his navel. He screamed, and dropped on his knees, and a dark cloud enfolded him: he sank down holding in his entrails with his hands.

When Hektor saw his brother Polydoros clutching his entrails and sinking to the ground, a mist spread down over his eyes: he could not bear to keep himself at a distance any longer, but went straight for Achilleus like a flame, shaking his sharp spear. The moment Achilleus saw him, he sprang to face him, and said in triumph: 'Here is the man who above all has touched right to my heart, when he killed my beloved friend. So there will be no more shrinking away from each other along the avenues of battle.'

So he spoke, and scowled at godlike Hektor and said: 'Come closer now, to meet your doomed end the sooner.'

Undismayed, Hektor of the glinting helmet replied: 'Son of Peleus, do not think you will frighten me with words as if I were a baby – I too know how to deal insults and slighting talk. I know that you are a great fighter, and I am much your inferior. But these things lie in the lap of the gods: lesser man though I am, I may yet take the life from you with my spear-cast, since my weapon too has proved sharp before now.'

So he spoke, and steadying his spear he let it fly. But Athene blew it away from glorious Achilleus, with the lightest puff of her breath, so that it came back to godlike Hektor and dropped in front of his feet. Achilleus charged in in fury, shouting fearfully and ready to kill him – but Apollo snatched Hektor away with the ease of a god, and wrapped him in thick mist. Three times then swift-footed godlike Achilleus charged in with his bronze spear, and three times he struck into deep mist. But when for the fourth time he had flung himself on like a god, he shouted winged words after Hektor in a terrible voice: 'Dog, this time you have escaped death once more – but your end came very close. This time Phoibos Apollo protected you – doubtless you pray to him when you set out for the thud of spears. I promise I shall finish you next time we meet, if any god has aid for me too. For now, I shall attack any I can catch of the others.'

So speaking he struck Dryops with his spear full in the neck, and he crashed down at his feet. Achilleus let him lie there, and then halted the approach of Demouchos, son of Philetor, a tall, brave man, stopping him with a spear-cast in the knee – then he took the life from him with a stab of his great sword. Then he sprang at Laogonos and Dardanos, two sons of Bias, and knocked both of them out of their chariot to the ground, hitting one with his spear-cast and the other with a blow from his sword close to. Then Tros, son of Alastor – he came to take hold of Achilleus' knees, in the hope that Achilleus would spare him, taking him prisoner and releasing him alive, and would not kill him out of pity for a man of his own age: the fool, he did not realise that Achilleus would never listen – this was no sweet-minded man, no gentle heart, but a man in full fury. So then Tros reached his hands out for Achilleus' knees intent on begging mercy, and Achilleus stabbed him in the liver with his sword: his liver slid out and the black blood pouring from it filled his lap – darkness covered over his eyes as the life deserted him. Achilleus then came up to Moulios and struck him in the ear with his spear, and the bronze point came straight out through the other ear. Now he caught Echeklos, son of Agenor, with a blow from his hilted sword full on the head, so the whole blade warmed with his blood: over his eyes came the surge of death and strong fate took him. Then he struck Deukalion, the bronze spear-point piercing through his arm where the tendons join at the elbow. Deukalion waited for him with his arm crippled, looking at his death there before him. Achilleus struck at his neck with his sword, and sent his head in its helmet dropping far away: the marrow spurted out from his vertebrae, and he lay there stretched flat on the ground. Then Achilleus went after the excellent son of Peiras, Rhigmos, who had come from fertile Thrace: he hit him in the middle with his spear, and the bronze fixed in his belly. He crashed from his chariot: and as his lieutenant Areïthoös turned the horses back, Achilleus stabbed him in the back with his sharp spear, knocking him out of the chariot, and the horses bolted.

As monstrous fire rages through the deep valleys on a parched mountainside, and the thick forest burns as the wind drives the flames billowing all over, so Achilleus stormed with his spear all over the field like some inhuman being, driving men on and killing them: and the black earth ran with blood. As when a man yokes together oxen, male and broad-browed, to tread white barley on a well-made threshing-floor, and the grains are quickly husked under the feet of the lowing oxen, so as great-hearted Achilleus drove them on his strong-footed horses trampled on bodies and shields alike: and all the axle beneath and the rails round the car were spattered with blood, flung up in gouts from the horses' hooves and the rims of the wheels. And the son of Peleus pressed onwards, urgent to win glory, with blood spattering his invincible hands.

BOOK 21
THE BATTLE OF THE GODS

But when they came to the fording-place of the lovely stream of the swirling river Xanthos, whose father is immortal Zeus, there Achilleus split the Trojans in two. He sent some running out over the plain towards the city, where the Achaians themselves had been driven back terror-struck on the day before, when glorious Hektor was raging there: this way then one group of Trojans streamed on in panic, and Hera spread a deep fog in their way to hamper them. But half of the Trojans were crowded into the deep silvery swirls of the river, and fell into the water with a great crash, so the rushing stream resounded and the banks echoed loud all round at the clamour of the men whirling in the eddies and trying to swim one way or the other. As when locusts rise in a swarm before the onrush of fire to take refuge in a river: the fire breaks out suddenly and burns on tireless, while they huddle away from it in the water – so then before the pursuit of Achilleus the roaring stream of deep-swirling Xanthos was filled with a mingled mass of men and horses.

Then god-born Achilleus left his spear there on the bank, leaning it against the tamarisks, and leapt in like some inhuman being, armed only with his sword: his heart was set on murder, and he began cutting all round him. Terrible groans arose from the men as they died under his sword, and the water reddened with blood. As the other fish flee before a great-bellied dolphin, and crowd into the nooks of a sheltered harbour in their terror of him, as he will certainly eat any fish he catches, so the Trojans cowered close under the overhangs all along the stream of that terrible river. But when Achilleus had tired his hands with killing, he rounded up twelve young Trojans and took them out of the river alive, to be the payment for the death of Patroklos son of Menoitios. He brought them out on to the bank, stupefied with fear like fawns, and tied their hands behind them with their own belts of well-cut leather which they wore with their twilled tunics. Then he gave them to his companions to take back to the hollow ships, and flung himself back at the Trojans furious for slaughter.

Then he came across a son of Dardanian Priam, Lykaon, as he was getting clear of the river. He had caught this man before on a night expedition, and taken him captive from his father's orchards: he was cutting young shoots from a fig-tree with the sharp bronze, to make the rails of a chariot, when the sudden disaster of godlike Achilleus came on him. At that time Achilleus took him on board ship to well-founded Lemnos and sold him there, and the son of Iason bought him. From there he was ransomed by a guest-friend of his family, Eëtion of Imbros, who gave a great sum for him and sent him to noble Arisbe: but he ran away from his refuge there and came back to his father's house. For eleven days after his return from Lemnos he could give his heart the enjoyment of his friends: but on the twelfth day god cast him once more into the hands of Achilleus, who this time would send him on a journey he could not want, down to the house of Hades. Now when swift-footed godlike Achilleus saw him there, unarmed, without helmet or shield, and no spear in his hand – he had thrown them all on the ground, weary and sweating from his escape from the river, and his knees were overcome with exhaustion – he spoke to his own great heart in vexation: 'Oh, this is a great astonishment for my eyes! Now all the great-hearted Trojans I have killed will rise up again from the murky darkness below – the way this man now has escaped the pitiless hour and come back, when he was sold in sacred Lemnos: but the deep of the grey sea could not hold him away, though it confines many other men whatever their will. Well now, he will taste the point of my spear this time, so that I can see and make certain in my mind whether he will equally come back even from that place as well, or whether the life-giving earth will hold him down, as she holds even the strongest of men.'

Such were his thoughts as he waited. And Lykaon came up to him, stunned with terror, and desperate to grasp Achilleus' knees, his heart filled with the desire to escape vile death and black fate. Godlike Achilleus lifted up his long spear ready for the thrust, but Lykaon ran in under the blow, crouching, and took hold of his knees – the spear passed over his back and fixed in the earth, eager for its fill of human flesh. Lykaon began to beg for mercy, grasping Achilleus' knees with one hand, and with the other he took hold of the sharp spear and would not let it go: and he spoke to him with winged words: 'Achilleus, I am entreating you by your knees – respect my claim and have mercy on me. I count as your suppliant, my lord, with a claim that should be honoured – because you were the first man with whom I ate the grain of Demeter on that day when you captured me in our well-laid orchard, and took me away from my father and friends and sold me in sacred Lemnos. I fetched you the worth of a hundred oxen, and I was freed for a ransom three times as much. This is the twelfth day since I came back to Troy after great hardship – and now cruel fate has put me once more in your hands. I think father Zeus must hate me, to have given me up to you a second time, and it was a short life that my mother Laothoë bore me to, the daughter of the old man Altes, Altes who is king of the war-loving Leleges and lives in steep Pedasos by the river Satnioeis. His daughter was taken to wife by Priam, but he has many other wives. There were two of us born to her, and you will have butchered both. You brought down godlike Polydoros among the leading foot-fighters with a cast of your sharp spear: and now the end will come for me here – I do not think I shall escape from your hands, now that god has brought me to them. But I say one thing more to you, and you mark it well in your mind. Do not kill me, because I am not from the same womb as Hektor, who killed your kind and strong friend.'

So the glorious son of Priam spoke to him with words of entreaty, but the answer he heard was hard: 'Fool, do not offer me ransom or talk of it. Before Patroklos met the day of his fate, then perhaps it was more my mind's liking to spare Trojans, and there were many I took alive and sold elsewhere. But now there is no-one who will escape death when god puts him into my hands in front of Ilios, none among all the Trojans, and above all none of the sons of Priam. No, friend, you die too – why all this moaning? Patroklos died also, a far better man than you. Do you not see how fine a man I am, and how huge? And I am the son of a great father, and a goddess was the mother who bore me. And yet I tell you death and strong fate are there for me also: there will be a dawn, or an evening, or a noonday, when some man will take my life too in the fighting with a cast of his spear or an arrow from the string.'

So he spoke, and Lykaon's strength and spirit collapsed there and then. He let go of the spear and sat down with both his arms out-stretched. Achilleus drew his sharp sword and struck him on the collar-bone by the neck, and the whole length of the two-edged sword sank inside him. He fell forward and lay stretched on the earth: and the dark blood ran from him, soaking the ground. Achilleus took him by the foot and flung him to float in the river, and spoke winged words in triumph over him: 'Now lie there among the fish. They will lick the blood from your wound and give you no loving burial. Your mother will not lay you out on the bier and lament for you, but Skamandros will be your bearer, swirling you out into the broad lap of the sea. And fish rising through the swell will dart up under the dark ruffled surface to eat the white fat of Lykaon. Death take you all, all the way till we reach the city of sacred Ilios, you Trojans running in flight and I behind you cutting you down! And your lovely silver-swirling river will not save you, for all the many bulls you have long sacrificed to it and the strong-footed horses you have thrown alive into its eddies. No, for all that you will die a vile death, until all of you have paid for the killing of Patroklos and the ravage of the Achaians you slaughtered by the fast ships when I was not with them.'

So he spoke, but the river had anger deepening in his heart, and pondered in his mind how he might stop godlike Achilleus in his murderous work, and protect the Trojans from destruction. Meanwhile the son of Peleus, holding his long-shadowed spear and furious to kill, leapt at Asteropaios, son of Pelegon: Pelegon had been born to the broad river Axios and Periboia, eldest of the daughters of Akes-samenos, when the deep-swirling river had lain with her. Achilleus sprang forward to attack Asteropaios, and he stood facing him from the river with two spears in his hands: and Xanthos put courage in his heart, as he was angered at the carnage of the young men whom Achilleus was slaughtering along his stream without pity. When these two had advanced to close range, swift-footed godlike Achilleus was first to speak: 'Who are you, that dare to come against me, and where are you from? Misery comes to the parents of those who face my strength.'

Then the glorious son of Pelegon answered him: 'Great-hearted son of Peleus, why do you ask of my birth? I come from fertile Paionia, far away, bringing men of Paionia with me, fighters with the long spear: and this is the eleventh day since I came to Ilios. My own descent is from the river Axios, Axios whose water is the loveliest that streams over earth. He fathered Pelegon, and I am called Pelegon's son. But now, glorious Achilleus, let us fight.'

So he made his challenge, and godlike Achilleus raised his spear of Pelian ash. But the hero Asteropaios threw with both spears at once, as he was ambidextrous. With one spear he hit Achilleus' shield, but did not break through it – the gold stopped it, the gift of the god. And with the other he grazed Achilleus' right arm at the elbow, so that the dark blood spurted out, and the spear, eager to taste flesh, passed over his body and stuck in the ground. Then after him Achilleus hurled his straight-flying ash spear at Asteropaios, furious to kill, but missed the man and struck the high river-bank, driving the ash spear to bury half its length in the bank. Then the son of Peleus drew his sharp sword from beside his thigh, and charged at him in fury. But Asteropaios could not pull Achilleus' spear out of the bank with his massive hand. Three times he budged it as he struggled to pull it clear, and three times he relaxed his effort. On the fourth attempt he was trying to bend Achilleus' ash spear and break it off, but before that Achilleus closed with him and took his life with his sword. He struck him in the belly by the navel: and all his guts gushed on the ground, and darkness covered over his eyes as he gasped in death. Achilleus trod on his chest and pulled off his armour, and spoke in triumph over him: 'Yes, lie there! It is hard, you see, even for one descended from a river to contend with the children of the almighty son of Kronos. You said that you were the stock of a broad-flowing river, but I can claim myself sprung from great Zeus himself. My father is a man, king over many Myrmidons, Peleus the son of Aiakos: but Aiakos was the son of Zeus. So just as Zeus is greater than the rivers that flow into the salt sea, so the stock of Zeus is greater than the stock of a river. Look, here is a river beside you now, a great river, if there is any help he can give. But there is no fighting with Zeus the son of Kronos – not even lord Acheloïos can equal him, or the great strength of Ocean's deep stream, from which all rivers and all the sea and all springs and deep wells take their flow: but even he is frightened of the lightning of great Zeus and his fearful thunder when it bursts crashing from the sky.'

So speaking he pulled his bronze spear out of the bank, and now that he had taken the life from him he left the man there, lying where he was on the sand, with the dark water lapping him. And eels and fish were his busy attendants, tearing and nibbling at the fat around his kidneys. Then Achilleus went on after the Paionian horsemen, who were still running in panic along the swirling river after they had seen their greatest man in the battle's fury beaten down under the hands and sword of the son of Peleus. Then he killed Thersilochos and Mydon and Astypylos and Mnesos and Thrasios and Ainios and Ophelestes. And now swift Achilleus would have killed yet more of the Paionians if the deep-swirling river had not spoken to him in his anger, taking the form of a man, and the voice came from the depths of a pool: 'Achilleus, of all men you are the strongest, and you do the greatest violence – the gods themselves are always helping you. If the son of Kronos has granted you the destruction of all the Trojans, then at least drive them away from me and do your grim work on the plain. My lovely stream is packed with corpses, and I cannot pour my waters through anywhere to reach the holy sea, choked as I am with dead bodies while you continue your murderous slaughter. Come then, leader of your people, leave off now – this is a horror to me.'

Then swift-footed Achilleus answered him: 'Lord Skamandros, what you ask shall be done. But I shall not stop killing the proud Trojans until I have penned them in their city and made the trial of battle with Hektor, whether he beats me down or I him.'

So speaking he charged at the Trojans like some inhuman being. And then the deep-swirling river called to Apollo: 'Shame on you, lord of the silver bow, child of Zeus, you have done nothing to uphold the wishes of the son of Kronos – he gave you full orders to stand by the Trojans and protect them, until evening comes on with the falling of dusk, and shadows over the fertile ploughland.'

So he spoke, and Achilleus the famous spearman sprang from the bank and jumped into mid-stream. But the river rushed on him in a seething swell, and whipped up all his waters into a turmoil, and pushed away the many bodies killed by Achilleus which were heaped in his course: roaring like a bull, he flung these out on to the dry land, and the living he kept safe along his lovely stream, hiding them in his huge deep pools. The water seethed and rose round Achilleus in a fearful wave, and beat down on his shield as it broke over him. He could not stand firm on his feet, but caught hold of a great full-grown elm-tree. The tree came away by the roots and tore open the whole of the bank: it blocked the lovely stream with a mass of branches, and dammed the entire river, crashing full-length into it. Achilleus jumped up out of the whirling water and, terrified, made a dash to go flying across the plain with all the speed of his legs. But the great god would not leave off, and rose up after him in a darkening swell, to stop godlike Achilleus in his murderous work, and protect the Trojans from destruction. The son of Peleus sped away as far as a spear carries, with the speed of a black eagle's swoop, the hunting eagle, which is both the strongest and the fastest of all flying creatures: this was how he darted away, and the bronze clashed grimly on his chest as he tried to run clear, away from the advancing water, but the river streamed on in pursuit, crashing loud behind him. As when a man channels water from a dark-welling spring and directs its flow among his plants and garden-plots, knocking the dams from its trench with a mattock in his hand: as the water starts to flow it clears all the pebbles from its path, then gathers speed and runs gurgling down over the sloping ground, outstripping the man who guides it. So the river's rolling wave was always overtaking Achilleus, however fast he ran – but gods are stronger than mortals. Every time swift-footed godlike Achilleus tried to stand and fight back, and see whether all the immortals who hold the wide heaven were driving him in flight, then the huge wave from the Zeus-fed river would crash down over his shoulders. In agony of heart he tried to jump clear, but every time the river shackled his legs under him with the violence of its current, and washed the ground from under his feet. The son of Peleus looked up into the wide heaven and cried out: 'Father Zeus, so none of the gods will take pity on me and move to save me from the river! After this I would be ready to suffer any fate. I do not blame any of the heavenly gods as much as my own mother, who has fooled me with lies – she told me that I would meet my death under the armed Trojans' wall, killed by the quick arrows of Apollo. I wish that Hektor had killed me, the greatest man born in this country – then one brave man would have killed another. But now I am doomed to be taken by a miserable death, caught in a great river like a little boy herding pigs who is swept away by a torrent when he tries to cross it in a storm.'

So he spoke, and very quickly Poseidon and Athene came and stood close by him, taking human form, and took his hands in theirs and spoke reassurance to him. Poseidon the earthshaker was the first to speak: 'Son of Peleus, do not be too much afraid. No need for your fear, such is the help that we two gods will give you, I and Pallas Athene, with the approval of Zeus. Because it is not your fate to be brought down by a river, but this one will soon abate, and you will see it for yourself. And we shall give you sound advice for you to follow. Do not hold your hand from cruel battle until you have penned all the Trojan people who escape you inside the famous walls of Ilios: and then go back to the ships after taking the life from Hektor. We are granting you the achievement of this glory.'

So speaking the two of them went away to join the immortals: and Achilleus went on into the plain under the strong spur of the gods' command. The whole plain was deep in flood water, and there floated there a mass of fine armour from the young men killed, and dead bodies. Achilleus stepped high and pressed on right forward against the stream, and the river could not hold him now with the wide spread of his waters, as Athene had put great strength in him. But Skamandros did not abate his fury, but grew yet more angry at the son of Peleus, and reared up his stream in a high crested wave, and called in a shout to Simoeis: 'Dear brother, let the two of us join together to contain the strength of this man, because he will soon attack king Priam's great city, and the Trojans will not face him in battle. So come quickly and help me against him. Fill your stream with water from your springs, summon up all your mountain torrents, and raise up a huge wave, sweeping a great tumult of timber and boulders, so that we can stop this savage man who is now mastering all and raging to equal the gods. I tell you, his strength will not save him, nor his beauty, nor that fine armour of his, which will lie somewhere at the very bottom of my flood covered deep in slime: and I shall wrap his body in sand, and pile an infinite wealth of silt over it, so the Achaians will not know where they can gather his bones, such is the covering of mud I shall heap over him. Yes, and that will serve as his grave-mound, so there will be no need for the Achaians to raise a barrow for his burial.'

So he spoke, and rose high in a seething turmoil to attack Achilleus, his water boiling with foam and blood and corpses. A heaving wave surged up from the Zeus-fed river to tower over the son of Peleus, and was ready to overwhelm him. Hera gave a great shout in terror for Achilleus, afraid that the great deep-swirling river would wash him away, and called at once to Hephaistos, her own dear son: 'Up now, cripple-foot god, my child! We had always thought that swirling Xanthos was the proper match for you in battle. So come quickly and help Achilleus against him, and kindle a great fire, while I go and raise a fierce storm from west and bright south winds to blow in from the sea, which can spread your destroying flames and burn up the bodies and the armour of the Trojans. And you burn the trees along the banks of Xanthos, and set the river himself on fire – and do not let him turn you back with any soft words or threats. Do not abate your fury until I call to you with a shout – then you should stop your tireless fire.'

So she spoke, and Hephaistos created a monstrous fire. First the fire blazed in the plain and burnt the many bodies killed by Achilleus which were heaped there in great numbers. And all the plain was dried up and the glittering water held back. As when the autumn north wind quickly dries a freshly-watered garden, and the man tending it is pleased, so the whole plain was dried, as Hephaistos burnt up the dead bodies – and then he turned his glaring flames to the river. The elms and willows and tamarisks were burnt, and burnt too the clover, the rushes, and the galingale that grew in abundance around the lovely stream of the river. And the eels and the fish in the pools were afflicted, and plunged about this way and that in the lovely water as they suffered under the blast of resourceful Hephaistos' breath. The river in all his strength was being burned, and called out to him: 'Hephaistos, none of the gods can match you, and I too could not fight against you when you burn with fire like this. Stop your fighting now, and godlike Achilleus can go right on and drive the Trojans out of their city – what need for me to take part in this battle?'

So he spoke as the fire burned him, and his lovely waters were bubbling in the heat. As a cauldron comes to the boil with a good fire speeding it, melting down the lard of a fatted hog which bubbles up all round as the dry logs burn underneath, so the river's lovely stream was burnt by the fire and the water boiled – it would not flow onwards but was held back, overcome by the force of the hot blast from resourceful Hephaistos. Then the river called to Hera with winged words, in urgent appeal: 'Hera, why has your son attacked in persecution of my stream above others? I am not so much to blame as all the others who give help to the Trojans. Well, I shall stop, if that is your wish, but he must stop too. And I shall swear this oath as well, that I shall never keep the evil day away from the Trojans, not even when all Troy is ablaze with devouring fire, and the warrior sons of the Achaians are burning it.'

When the white-armed goddess Hera heard this, she called at once to Hephaistos, her own dear son: 'Hephaistos, stop, my glorious child! It is not right to maltreat an immortal god like this for the sake of mortal men.'

So she spoke, and Hephaistos quenched his monstrous fire, and the stream ran back again along its lovely channel.

So when the might of Xanthos had been beaten back, those two then ceased their fighting, stopped by Hera, despite her continued anger. But on the other gods there fell the cruel weight of conflict, and they were divided by the fury storming in their hearts. They joined with a great crash, so the wide earth roared under them, and the great heaven rang loud like a trumpet. Zeus heard it where he sat on Olympos: and his heart within him laughed for joy, when he saw the gods joining in conflict. Now they did not hold off from each other any longer. Ares the shield-breaker began it, and sprang to attack Athene with his bronze spear in his hand, and spoke scornfully to her: 'Why are you again driving the gods to conflict, you dogfly, with that gall that always runs strong in you? Why has your great heart set you at it this time? Do you not remember when you put up Tydeus' son Diomedes to wound me, and openly took his spear in your own hand and drove it straight for me, and tore my lovely skin? So now I think you will pay for all you did then.'

So speaking he thrust at the tasselled aegis, that fearful thing which not even Zeus' thunderbolt can break: and Ares the murderer struck there with his long spear. Athene stepped back and picked up in her massive hand a stone that was lying on the plain, a black stone, huge and jagged, which men of an earlier time had set there to mark the boundary of a field. With this she hit furious Ares on the neck, and collapsed his strength. He covered seven acres where he fell, and sullied his hair in the dust, and his armour clattered about him. Pallas Athene laughed and spoke winged words in triumph over him: 'You poor fool, you cannot have thought at all how much greater strength I can claim than you, if you try to match your power against me. So this can be payment for your mother's curses – she is angry and wishes you ill, because you have deserted the Achaians and give your help to the proud Trojans.'

So speaking she turned her shining eyes away. And Aphrodite, daughter of Zeus, took Ares by the hand and led him away, groaning constantly and only just gathering back his senses. Now when the white-armed goddess Hera saw her, she immediately spoke winged words to Athene: 'Look, Atrytone, daughter of Zeus who holds the aegis, there is that dogfly again leading Ares, the curse of men, through the fighting and taking him out of the grim battle. Go after her!'

So she spoke, and Athene sped in pursuit, delighted in her heart. She came up to her and dealt her a blow on the breasts with her massive hand: and Aphrodite's strength and spirit collapsed there and then. So now both of them lay there on the nourishing earth, and Athene spoke winged words in triumph over them: 'Now may all those who help the Trojans be just as good as these, with all the bravery and endurance shown by Aphrodite when she came to aid Ares and face my fury! Then we should long ago have come to the end of our fighting and sacked the well-founded city of Ilios.'

So she spoke, and the white-armed goddess Hera smiled. And now the Earthshaker, powerful lord, called to Apollo: 'Phoibos, why are we two still keeping our distance? It is hardly right when others have begun, and it would be shameful if we have done no fighting when we return to Olympos and the bronze-floored house of Zeus. Begin, then, since you are the younger – it would not be fair for me to start, as I was born older than you and have greater knowledge. You fool, how forgetful your heart has been! Have you no memory now of all the misery we two suffered at Ilios, alone and away from the gods, when we were sent by Zeus to work for proud Laomedon and were his labourers for a year? Our hire was settled: he was our master and gave us his orders. Then I built the Trojans a wall around their city, a wide and magnificent wall to make the city impregnable: and you, Phoibos, were a herdsman with his shambling twist-horned cattle along the spurs and many valleys of wooded Ida. But when the glad seasons were bringing the term of our hire to its completion, then cruel Laomedon robbed us of all our wages and sent us away with threats. He threatened to bind our feet and hands and send us to distant islands to be sold as slaves: and he claimed he would lop the ears from both of us with the bronze. So we returned with fury in our hearts, angered for the payment he had promised and would not make good. And now it is his people you are favouring, and you will not join us in working for the utter destruction of the proud Trojans in a miserable fate, together with their children and their honoured wives.'

Then lord Apollo the far-worker said to him: 'Earthshaker, you would not say I was in my right mind if I do battle with you for the sake of wretched mortals, who are like leaves – for a time they flourish in a blaze of glory, and feed on the yield of the earth, and then again they fade lifeless. No, let us withdraw from battle immediately, and leave the mortals to fight on by themselves.'

So speaking he turned away, as respect would not let him lift his hands to join in combat with his father's brother. But he was berated by his sister, Artemis of the wild, mistress of wild creatures, who spoke scornfully to him: 'So you are running away, far-worker! You have yielded the whole victory to Poseidon, and given him a triumph he did nothing to earn. You poor fool, why then do you carry a bow which is nothing more than wind? May I never now hear you boasting in our father's house among the immortal gods, as you have before, that you could fight face to face with Poseidon.'

So she spoke, and Apollo the far-worker gave her no answer. But Hera, the honoured wife of Zeus, was angry at the archer-goddess and berated her with scornful words: 'And how do you now dare, you shameless bitch, to stand against me? I tell you it is hard to match strengths with me, even though you have your bow and Zeus has made you a lion to women, with leave to kill any woman you please. Better to go on slaughtering wild beasts and deer in the mountains than try full battle with your betters. But if you want to learn about fighting, seeing that you are challenging me – come on then, so you can discover how much stronger I am.'

So she spoke, and grabbed both Artemis' arms with her left hand, holding them at the wrists, and with her right hand she pulled the bow and quiver off her shoulders and used her own weapons to box her about the ears, smiling as Artemis writhed and twisted, and her quick-flying arrows came scattering from the quiver. The goddess ducked away and fled in tears, like a pigeon driven before a hawk which flies into a cave and finds a hollow – so it is not after all her fate to be caught. So Artemis ran away in tears, and left her bow and arrows there on the ground. And now Hermes the guide, the slayer of Argos, spoke to Leto: 'Leto, I will not fight with you – it is a dangerous business to come to blows with the wives of Zeus the cloud-gatherer. No, you are fully welcome to boast among the immortal gods that you overpowered me with your strength and beat me.'

So he spoke, and Leto gathered up the curved bow and the arrows that lay scattered all over in the swirling dust. She then went back with her daughter's weapons in her hands. But Artemis came to Olympos and the bronze-floored house of Zeus, and the girl sat in her father's lap with her immortal robe shaking to her tears. Her father the son of Kronos held her to him, and asked her with a gentle laugh: 'Which of the heavenly gods was it, dear child, who did this naughty thing to you, as if you were openly doing something wicked?'

Then the lovely-crowned goddess of the loud hunt answered him: 'It was your wife, white-armed Hera, who beat me about, father. It is her doing that quarrels and fighting have taken hold among the immortals.'

Such were their words to each other. Meanwhile Phoibos Apollo entered sacred Ilios. He was concerned for the wall of the strong-built city, afraid that the Danaans might go beyond fate and storm it on that very day. But the rest of the ever-living gods went back to Olympos, some in anger and others exulting, and they took their seats beside the Father, the lord of the dark clouds. And meanwhile Achilleus continued to slaughter the Trojans, men and strong-footed horses alike. As when the smoke goes up to reach the broad sky from a city that is burning, when the gods' anger has set it to burn, and brought hardship on all and loss to many, so Achilleus brought hardship and loss on the Trojans.

Now the old man Priam had gone to stand on the god-built tower, and saw the monstrous Achilleus, and the Trojans being driven in utter panic before him, with no spirit left in them. He groaned, and came down from the tower to the ground, giving urgent orders to the glorious gate-keepers beside the wall: 'Hold the gates wide open in your hands, until our people reach the city in their flight. Achilleus is close here behind them, driving them on, and now I think there will be grim work. As soon as they are crowded inside the walls and can recover breath, close the tight-fitting doors again – I am afraid that this murderous man may hurl himself inside our walls.'

So he spoke, and they pushed back the bars and opened the gates: and the spreading open of the gates brought saving light to the Trojans. And Apollo also leapt out to meet them, to keep disaster from the Trojans. They were running straight for the city and its high wall, parched with thirst and dust-covered from the plain: and behind them Achilleus drove them on with the violence of his spear, overpowering madness all the time gripping his heart, and urgent to win glory.

And now the sons of the Achaians would have taken high-gated Troy, if Phoibos Apollo had not set godlike Agenor against him, an excellent and powerful man, the son of Antenor. Apollo put courage in his heart, and stood by him himself to keep the heavy fates of death away from him, leaning against the oak-tree and hidden in thick mist. When Agenor saw the approach of Achilleus, sacker of cities, he stood his ground, but his heart was in a turmoil as he waited there. In dismay he spoke to his own great heart: 'What am I to do? If I run from mighty Achilleus along the way where the others are crowding in terror, he will catch me even so, and butcher a coward. But if I leave them to be driven on by Achilleus son of Peleus, and run by another way away from the walls to the Ilian plain, until I reach the spurs of Ida and can hide in the bushes: then in the evening I could return to Ilios after washing in the river and drying off the sweat – but what need for this debate in my heart? He may see me as I make my way to the plain away from the city, and chase after me and catch me with the speed of his legs. And then there will be no escaping death – he is too strong, stronger than any man. But suppose I go to face him in front of the city. Even his flesh can be wounded by the sharp bronze: there is only one life in him, and men say that he is mortal – only Zeus the son of Kronos is granting him glory.'

So speaking he drew himself in and waited for Achilleus, and the brave heart in him was eager for battle. As a leopard comes out of a dense thicket to face a huntsman, and has no fear in her heart or thought of flight when she hears the barking of the dogs: and if the man hits her first with a thrust or cast of his weapon, even though she is pierced through with his spear she does not slacken her fighting spirit until she is on him, or brought down herself. So the son of Antenor, godlike Agenor, would not run before making trial of battle with Achilleus. But he held the even circle of his shield in front of him, took aim with his spear at Achilleus, and shouted out loud to him: 'You must have thought in your heart, glorious Achilleus, that you would sack the proud Trojans' city this very day. You fool – there is still pain in plenty to be suffered over her yet. There are many of us in her, brave men who will fight in front of our dear parents and our wives and sons to defend Ilios – but you will meet your doom here, formidable man and brave fighter though you are.'

So he spoke, and let fly the sharp spear from his massive hand, and did not miss, hitting Achilleus on the shin below his knee. The greave of new-worked tin rang out fearfully on his leg: but the bronze point rebounded where it struck the greave, and could not pierce it, beaten back by the armour the god had given. Then after him the son of Peleus charged to attack godlike Agenor: but Apollo denied him this glory, and snatched Agenor away, covering him in thick mist and then sending him off silently out of the battle. And then Apollo tricked the son of Peleus to keep him away from the Trojan people. The far-worker made himself like the real Agenor in every way, and stood there in front of Achilleus' feet, and Achilleus sprang forward to run in pursuit. He chased him across the plain where the wheat grows, turning him off along the deep-swirling river Skamandros, as Apollo kept running just a little in front of him and luring him on, so that all the time he was deluded into thinking he could catch him with his speed. In this time the rest of the Trojans in a mass came running in panic-stricken, glad to reach their city, and they crowded it full. They did not even have the courage to wait for each other outside the city and the wall, and find out who might have got clear and who had died in the fighting, but they poured into the city in all haste, those of them whose legs and knees had brought them back safe.

BOOK 22

THE DEATH OF HEKTOR

So the Trojans, panicked like deer, spread through the city. They leaned against the fine battlements, and dried the sweat from their bodies and drank and slaked their thirst. And meanwhile the Achaians came up closer to the wall, sloping their shields against their shoulders. Then his cruel fate shackled Hektor to stay there outside, in front of Ilios and the Skaian gates. Meanwhile Phoibos Apollo spoke to the son of Peleus: 'Son of Peleus, why are you chasing me with all the speed of your legs when you are a mortal and I an immortal god? So you have not yet seen me for a god, and are still hot in your fury to catch me. You must be forgetting the work you have with the Trojans. You sent them running in panic, but look, they have crowded into their city while you swung away out here. You will never kill me – I am no creature of fate.'

Then swift-footed Achilleus said to him in fury: 'You have thwarted me, far-worker, deadliest of all gods, by turning me out here now away from the wall – otherwise many more would have sunk their teeth into the earth before they could reach Ilios. But now you have robbed me of great glory, and rescued the Trojans in all unconcern, as there is no revenge you had to fear for the future. I would surely pay you back, if only I had the power.'

So speaking he set out for the city with high thoughts in his mind, moving at speed like a champion horse pulling a chariot, who runs lightly at the gallop over the plain. So Achilleus set his legs and knees running fast.

The old man Priam's eyes were the first to see him, as he rushed on over the plain glittering like the star that comes in late summer, and its light is seen the clearest among the many stars in the darkness of the night: men call this star Orion's Dog, and it is the brightest of stars, yet a sign of evil, bringing much fever on poor mortals. Such was the shining of the bronze on his breast as he ran. The old man groaned aloud, and lifted his hands above him and beat his head: and with great groans he called out in entreaty to his dear son, who was standing firm in front of the gates, relentless in his fury to fight with Achilleus. The old man stretched out his arms and spoke pitiably to his son: 'Hektor, please, dear child, do not face this man alone, away from the others – so you do not go down under the son of Peleus and quickly meet your doom, you stubborn man, because he is far stronger than you. If only the gods had the same love for him as I do! Then he would soon be lying dead and the dogs and vultures eating him, and a terrible sorrow would be gone from my heart. He has left me bereaved of many brave sons, killing them or selling them to slavery in distant islands. And even now there are two of my sons I cannot see among the Trojans crowded into the city, Lykaon and Polydoros, sons borne to me by Laothoë, queen among women. If they are held alive in the Achaian camp, then we shall ransom them in time for bronze and gold – it is there in our house, as her old father, famous Altes, gave much wealth with his daughter. But if they are already dead and gone down to the house of Hades, there is sorrow for my heart and for their mother, we who are their parents – for the rest of our people the sorrow will be shorter-lived, unless you too are brought down by Achilleus and killed. No, come inside the walls, my child, so you can save the men and women of Troy. Do not give a great triumph to the son of Peleus and have your own dear life taken from you. And have pity on me too – I still live and feel, but my life is pain and I am fated to misery. Father Zeus will destroy me at the edge of old age with a cruel doom, when I have lived to see many horrors, my sons killed and my daughters dragged off captive, their houses looted and their little children smashed on the ground in the havoc of war, and the wives of my sons hauled away in the murderous hands of the Achaians. And then myself last of all – the dogs will tear me in front of my doors and eat me raw, when some man has taken the life from my body with a blow or cast of his sharp bronze. The dogs that I reared in the house and at my own table to guard the doors will lie in the gateway with their hearts excited by drinking my blood. In a young man all is decent if he is killed in war and lies there torn by the sharp bronze – though he is dead all that is revealed of him is beautiful. But when an old man has been killed and the dogs are mutilating his grey head and grey beard and private parts, this is the most pitiful sight that poor mortals can see.'

So the old man spoke, and began pulling out his grey hairs with his hands, tearing them out of his head: but he could not move Hektor's heart. His mother now wailed and wept tears beside Priam, and opened the fold of her dress and held out a breast in her hand, and then with her tears falling she called to him in winged words: 'Hektor, my child, respond to this and have pity on me, if ever I gave you the breast to soothe your trouble. Remember those times, dear child, and fight off your enemy from inside the wall – do not go out to challenge him, obstinate man. If he kills you, I shall not then be able to lay you on the bier and mourn for you, dear creature, my own child, nor will your dowered wife – but far away from both of us, out by the Argive ships, the quick dogs will feed on you.'

So those two called to their dear son in tears, imploring him over and over again. But they could not move Hektor's heart, but he waited there for huge Achilleus as he came closer. As a mountain snake in his hole waits the approach of a man, when he has eaten poisonous herbs and savage anger has sunk deep into him, and he glares out malevolently, coiling round in his hole: so Hektor kept his fury unabated and would not give back, leaning his bright shield against a jutting buttress. But he spoke in dismay to his own great heart: 'What am I to do? If I go back inside the gates and the wall, Poulydamas will be the first to lay blame on me, because he urged me to lead the Trojans back to the city during this last fatal night, when godlike Achilleus had roused himself. But I did not take his advice – it would have been far better if I had. Now that I have destroyed my people through my own arrant folly, I feel shame before the men of Troy and the women of Troy with their trailing dresses, that some man, a worse man than I, will say: "Hektor trusted in his own strength and destroyed his people." That is what they will say: and then it would be far better for me to face Achilleus and either kill him and return home, or die a glorious death myself in front of my city. But suppose I put down my bossed shield and heavy helmet, and lean my spear against the wall, and go out as I am to meet the excellent Achilleus, and promise to return Helen and all her property with her to the sons of Atreus for their keeping, all that Alexandros brought away in his hollow ships to Troy and was the first cause of our quarrel: and also to share equally with the Achaians all the rest of the property stored in this city – then afterwards I could make the Trojans take an oath in their council that they will hide nothing, but divide everything in two parts, all the possessions that the lovely city contains within it. But what need for this debate in my heart? I fear that if I go up to him he will not show me any pity or regard for my appeal, but will simply kill me unarmed like a woman, when I have taken off my armour. There can be no sweet murmuring with him now, like boy and girl at the trysting-tree or rock, the way a boy and girl murmur sweetly together. Better to close and fight as soon as can be. We can see then to which of us the Olympian is giving the victory.'

Such were his thoughts as he waited. And Achilleus came close on him like Enyalios the god of war, the warrior with the flashing helmet, shaking his terrible spear of Pelian ash over his right shoulder: and the bronze on his body shone like the light of a blazing fire or the sun when it rises. And trembling took hold of Hektor when he saw him. Now he no longer had the courage to stand his ground where he was, but he left the gates behind him and ran in terror: and the son of Peleus leapt after him, confident in the speed of his legs. As a hawk in the mountains, quickest of all flying things, swoops after a trembling dove with ease: she flies in terror before him, but he keeps close behind her, screaming loud, and lunging for her time after time as his heart urges him to kill. So Achilleus flew straight for Hektor in full fury, and Hektor fled away from him under the walls of Troy, setting his legs running fast. They sped past the look-out place and the wind-tossed fig-tree, keeping all the time to the wagon-track a little way out from the wall, and came to the two well-heads of lovely water: here the twin springs of swirling Skamandros shoot up from the ground. One spring runs with warm water, and steam rises all round it as if a fire were burning there. But the other even in summer flows out cold as hail, or frozen snow, or water turned to ice. There close beside these springs are the fine broad washing-troughs made of stone, where the Trojans' wives and their lovely daughters used to wash their bright clothes, in earlier times, in peace, before the sons of the Achaians came. The two men ran past here, one in flight, the other chasing him. A brave man was running in front, but a far greater one was in pursuit, and they ran at speed, since it was no sacrificial beast or ox-hide shield they were competing for – such as are the usual prizes that men win in the foot-race – but they were running for the life of Hektor the tamer of horses. As when champion strong-footed horses wheel round the turning-posts running at full stretch, when a great prize is there to be won, a tripod or a woman, in the funeral games for a man who has died: so those two raced round the city of Priam, circling it three times with all the speed of their legs, and all the gods looked on. The father of men and gods was the first of them to speak: 'Oh, I love this man who is being pursued around the wall under the gaze of my eyes. My heart is saddened for Hektor, who has burned the thigh-bones of many oxen to me on the peaks of valleyed Ida, and again on the city's height. But now godlike Achilleus on his swift feet is chasing him round the city of Priam. Well then, give thought to it, gods, and consider whether we shall save him from death, or bring him down now, for all his bravery, at the hands of Achilleus son of Peleus.'

Then the bright-eyed goddess Athene said to him: 'Father, master of the bright lightning and the dark clouds, what is this you are saying? Do you intend to take a man who is mortal and long ago doomed by fate, and release him from grim death? Do it then – but we other gods will not all approve you.'

Then Zeus the cloud-gatherer answered her: 'Do not worry, Tritogeneia, dear child. I do not speak with my heart in full earnest, and my intention to you is kind. Do as your purpose directs, and do not hold back any longer.'

With these words he urged on Athene what she herself already desired, and she went darting down from the peaks of Olympos.

And swift Achilleus kept driving Hektor on with his relentless pursuit. As when a dog has started the fawn of a deer from its lair in the mountains, and chases it on through the hollows and the glens: even if it takes to cover and crouches hidden under a bush, the dog smells out its track and runs on unerringly until he finds it. So Hektor could not throw off the swift-footed son of Peleus. Whenever he tried to make a dash for the Dardanian gates, to get under the well-built walls and give the men above a chance of defending him with their weapons, every time Achilleus would be there in time to block his way and head him back out towards the plain, while he himself kept always on the city side as he flew onwards. As a man in a dream is unable to pursue someone trying to escape, and the other cannot run away just as he cannot give chase: so Achilleus could not catch him with his running, nor Hektor get away. And how could Hektor have kept clear of the fates of death, if Apollo had not come close to him for the last and final time, and spurred strength in him and speed to his legs? And godlike Achilleus had been shaking his head at his own people to stop them shooting their bitter arrows at Hektor, in case one of them should win the glory with a hit, and he himself reach Hektor too late. But when they came round to the well-heads for the fourth time, then the Father opened out his golden scales. In the pans he put two fates of death's long sorrow, one for Achilleus and one for Hektor the tamer of horses, and he took the scales in the middle and lifted them up: and Hektor's day of doom sank down, away into Hades, and Phoibos

Apollo left him. Then the bright-eyed goddess Athene came to the son of Peleus, and stood close by him and spoke winged words to him: 'Now, glorious Achilleus loved of Zeus, now I think that we two will bring great glory for the Achaians back to the ships – we will kill Hektor, for all his lust for battle. There is no possibility now that he can escape us any longer, even if Apollo the far-worker goes through agonies of grovelling before father Zeus who holds the aegis. So you stand still now and get your breath, while I go and persuade him to fight with you face to face.'

So Athene spoke, and Achilleus was happy at heart, and did as she told him: so he stood there leaning on his bronze-barbed ash spear. She then left him and caught up with godlike Hektor, taking the form and tireless voice of Deïphobos. She came close and spoke winged words to him: 'Brother, swift Achilleus is pressing you very hard now, chasing you round the city of Priam with all his speed. Come then, let us face him together and beat him off where we stand.'

Then great Hektor of the glinting helmet said to her: 'Deïphobos, you have always been the brother I loved far the most of all the sons born to Hekabe and Priam. And now my heart is minded to honour you yet more highly, since you have had the courage, when your eyes saw my trouble, to come outside the wall on my account, while all the others stay inside.'

Then the bright-eyed goddess Athene said to him: 'Brother, our father and honoured mother, and my friends around me, did indeed beseech me one after the other, and implored me again and again to stay where I was inside – such is the terror on them all. But my heart within me was chafed with painful sorrow for you. Now let us charge straight in and fight, and not be sparing with our spears, so we can see whether Achilleus will kill us both and carry away our bloody spoils to the hollow ships, or else be beaten down under your spear.'

So speaking Athene led him forward in her treachery. When the two men had advanced to close range, great Hektor of the glinting helmet was first to speak: 'Son of Peleus, I shall not run from you any more, as I did when you chased me three times round the great city of Priam, and I did not dare to stop and take your attack. But now my heart prompts me to stand and face you – I shall kill or be killed. But first let us swear here before our gods – they will be the best witnesses to keep watch on our agreement. I swear that I will inflict no outrage on you, if Zeus grants me the endurance and I take away your life: but after I have stripped you of your famous armour, Achilleus, I will give your body back to the Achaians – and you do the same.'

Then swift-footed Achilleus scowled at him and said: 'Hektor, do not talk to me of agreements, you madman. There are no treaties of trust between lions and men: wolves and lambs share no unity of heart, but are fixed in hatred of each other for all time – so there can be no friendship for you and me, there will be no oaths between us, before one or the other falls and gives his glut of blood to Ares, the fighter with the bull's-hide shield. Call to mind now all your fighting skills: now is the time above all to show yourself a spearman and a brave warrior. But I tell you there is no escape for you any longer, but soon Pallas Athene will beat you down under my spear. And now you will make me lump payment for the pain of my companions' deaths, all those you killed when your spear was raging.'

So he spoke, and steadying his long-shadowed spear he let it fly. But glorious Hektor had looked ahead and avoided it. He watched it come and crouched down, and the bronze spear flew over him and fixed in the earth: and unseen by Hektor, shepherd of the people, Pallas Athene pulled up the spear and gave it back to Achilleus. Hektor then spoke to the excellent son of Peleus: 'You missed! So, godlike Achilleus, it seems you knew nothing from Zeus about my death – and yet you said you did. No, you turn out a mere ranter – all your talk is bluff, to frighten me and make me lose my courage for the fight. Well, I shall not run and let you fix your spear in my back, but you must drive it through my chest as I charge straight for you, if that is what god has granted you. But now you try to avoid this bronze spear of mine – how I hope you take it entire in your flesh! Then the war would go lighter for the Trojans, with you dead, their greatest danger.'

So he spoke, and steadying his long-shadowed spear he let it fly, and did not miss, hitting in the centre of the son of Peleus' shield: but the spear rebounded far from the shield. Hektor was angered that his swift spear had flown wasted from his hand, and stood there in dismay, as he had no second ash spear. He called in a great shout to Deïphobos of the white shield, and asked him for a long spear. But Deïphobos was not there near him. Then Hektor realised in his heart, and cried out: 'Oh, for sure now the gods have called me to my death! I thought the hero Deïphobos was with me: but he is inside the wall, and Athene has tricked me. So now vile death is close on me, not far now any longer, and there is no escape. This must long have been the true pleasure of Zeus and Zeus' son the far-shooter, and yet before now they readily defended me: but now this time my fate has caught me.

Even so, let me not die ingloriously, without a fight, without some great deed done that future men will hear of.'

So speaking he drew the sharp sword that hung long and heavy at his side, gathered himself, and swooped like a high-flying eagle which darts down to the plain through the dark clouds to snatch up a baby lamb or a cowering hare. So Hektor swooped to attack, flourishing his sharp sword. And Achilleus charged against him, his heart filled with savage fury. In front of his chest he held the covering of his lovely decorated shield, and the bright four-bossed helmet nodded on his head, with the beautiful golden hairs that Hephaistos had set thick along the crest shimmering round it. Like the Evening Star on its path among the stars in the darkness of the night, the loveliest star set in the sky, such was the light gleaming from the point of the sharp spear Achilleus held quivering in his right hand, as he purposed death for godlike Hektor, looking over his fine body to find the most vulnerable place. All the rest of his body was covered by his bronze armour, the fine armour he had stripped from mighty Patroklos when he killed him. But flesh showed where the collar-bones hold the join of neck and shoulders, at the gullet, where a man's life is most quickly destroyed. Godlike Achilleus drove in there with his spear as Hektor charged him, and the point went right through his soft neck: but the ash spear with its weight of bronze did not cut the windpipe, so that Hektor could still speak and answer Achilleus. He crashed in the dust, and godlike Achilleus triumphed over him: 'Hektor, doubtless as you killed Patroklos you thought you would be safe, and you had no fear of me, as I was far away. You fool – behind him there was I left to avenge him, a far greater man than he, waiting there by the hollow ships, and I have collapsed your strength. Now the dogs and birds will maul you hideously, while the Achaians will give Patroklos full burial.'

Then with the strength low in him Hektor of the glinting helmet answered: 'I beseech you by your life and knees and by your parents, do not let the dogs of the Achaian camp eat me by the ships, but take the ransom of bronze and gold in plenty that my father and honoured mother will offer you, and give my body back to my home, so that the Trojans and the wives of the Trojans can give me in death my due rite of burning.'

Then swift-footed Achilleus scowled at him and said: 'Make me no appeals, you dog, by knees or parents. I wish I could eat you myself, that the fury in my heart would drive me to cut you in pieces and eat your flesh raw, for all that you have done to me. So no man is going to keep the dogs away from your head, not even if they bring here and weigh out ten times or twenty times your ransom, not even if Dardanian Priam offers to pay your own weight in gold. Not even so will your honoured mother lay you on the bier and mourn for you, her own child, but the dogs and birds will share you for their feast and leave nothing.'

Then, dying, Hektor of the glinting helmet said to him: 'Yes, I can tell it – I know you well, and I had no chance of swaying you: your heart is like iron in your breast. But take care now, or I may bring the gods' anger on you, on that day when for all your bravery Paris and Phoibos Apollo will destroy you at the Skaian gates.'

As he spoke the end of death enfolded him: and his spirit flitted from his body and went on the way to Hades, weeping for its fate, and the youth and manhood it must leave. Then godlike Achilleus spoke to him, dead though he was: 'Die! I shall take my death at whatever time Zeus and the other immortal gods wish to bring it on me.'

So he spoke, and pulled his bronze spear out of the body and laid it on one side, then stripped the blood-stained armour from Hektor's shoulders. And the other sons of the Achaians came running round, and stared with admiration at the size and wonderful looks of Hektor – and none who came up to the body left without stabbing it. And a man would glance at his neighbour and say: 'Look, Hektor is much milder to handle now than when he fired our ships with burning flame.'

This is what they said as they came up and stabbed him. When swift-footed Achilleus had stripped the body, he stood up and spoke winged words to the Achaians: 'Friends, leaders and lords of the Argives, now that the gods have granted us the mastering of this man, who has done so much harm, more than all the rest of them together, come then, let us test them with an armed attack around the city, to see if we can now find out what is in the Trojans' minds – whether they will abandon their citadel now that this man has fallen, or are determined to stay there even though Hektor is no longer with them. But yet how can my heart debate like this, when a dead man is lying by the ships unwept and unburied – Patroklos. I shall not forget him, as long as I am in the company of the living and there is lift in my knees – and if the dead forget their dead in the house of Hades, yet even there I shall remember my dear companion. So come now, young Achaians, let us return to the hollow ships singing a song of victory, and carrying this body with us. We have won great glory – we have killed glorious Hektor, whom the Trojans venerated like a god in their city.'

So he spoke, and then he put glorious Hektor to shameful treatment. He cut through behind the tendons of both feet from heel to ankle, and pulled straps of ox-hide through them which he tied fast to his chariot, so the head would be left to drag. Then he mounted the chariot and lifted the famous armour into it, and whipped the horses on, and they flew eagerly on their way. As Hektor was dragged behind, a cloud of dust arose from him, his dark hair streamed out round him, and all that once handsome head was sunk in the dust: but now Zeus had given him to his enemies to defile him in his own native land.

So Hektor's head was all sullied in the dust. And now his mother tore her hair, and flung the shining mantle away from her head, and raised a great wail when she saw her son. And his dear father groaned pitiably, and around them and all through the city the people were overcome with wailing and groans of lamentation. It was just like it would be if all of beetling Ilios were fired and smouldering from top to bottom. The people could hardly hold back the old man in his anguish, as he tried urgently to get out through the Dardanian gate. He rolled there in the dung and implored them all, calling on each man by name: 'Let me be, friends, for all your care for me – let me go out of the city alone and come to the ships of the Achaians, so I can make supplication to this monstrous man, this criminal. He might have respect for my years and pity my old age: he too has a father old like me, Peleus, who sired and reared him to be a curse on the Trojans – and it is on me above all that he has brought the most sorrow, so many are the sons of mine in their bloom that he has killed. But all my grief for these, much though I mourn them, is less than my grief for one, and piercing sorrow for him will bring me down into Hades – for Hektor. How I wish that he could have died in my arms! Then we could have satisfied our desire for weeping and mourning, I and his mother who bore him in a cruel fate.'

So he spoke with his tears falling, and the townspeople joined with their mourning. And Hekabe led the women of Troy in the loud lament: 'Child, oh, my misery! Why should I live now, when I have suffered the agony of your death? Day and night you were my pride in the city, and the benefactor of all the men and women throughout Troy, who welcomed you like a god, since you were their great glory too, when you were alive – but now death and fate have overtaken you.'

So she spoke with her tears falling. But Hektor's wife had not yet heard anything. No messenger had come to bring her clear news that her husband had stayed outside the gates, but she was in a corner of their high house working at a web of purple cloth for a double cloak, and weaving a pattern of flowers in it. She had told the lovely-haired maids in her house to set a great three-legged cauldron over the fire, so there could be hot water for Hektor's bath when he came home from battle – poor child, she did not know that far away from any baths bright-eyed Athene had brought him down at the hands of Achilleus. But now the sound of wailing and lamentation reached her from the tower. Her body shook, and the shuttle dropped to the ground from her hands. She called once more to her lovely-haired maidservants: 'Come, two of you come with me, so I can find out what has happened. I could hear the voice of my husband's honoured mother, and the heart in my own breast is leaping up to my mouth, and my legs are freezing under me – some disaster must be coming on Priam's children. May my ears never hear such a thing as I say, but I am terribly afraid that Achilleus may have caught my brave Hektor alone and cut him off from the city, driving him out to the plain, and now he may have put an end to that dangerous pride which always possessed him – he would never stay among the mass of men, but was always charging out far ahead and yielding to no-one in his fury.'

So speaking, she rushed out of the house like a woman in frenzy, her heart jumping: and her maids went with her. When she came to the tower and the crowd of men gathered there, she stood on the wall and stared out, and saw him being dragged in front of the city, and fast horses pulling him ruthlessly away to the hollow ships of the Achaians. Black night covered over her eyes, and she swooned backwards, and the spirit breathed out of her. And she flung away from her head her shining headdress, the frontlet and the cap, the woven hair-band, and the mantle that golden Aphrodite had given her on the day when Hektor of the glinting helmet led her as his wife from Eëtion's house, when he had given a countless bride-price for her. Her husband's sisters and the wives of his brothers crowded round her where she lay shocked almost to her death, and held her up between them. When she came to her senses and the spirit gathered back again in her heart, with bursts of sobbing she cried out her lament among the women of Troy: 'Hektor, my life is misery! So both of us were born under the same fate, you in Troy in Priam's house, and I in Thebe under wooded Plakos in the house of Eëtion, who brought me up when I was small, doomed father and doomed child – how I wish he had never fathered me! Now you are going down to the house of

Hades in the cellars of the earth, and leaving me behind in hateful mourning, a widow in your house. And our child is still only a baby, the son that was born to you and me, ill-fated parents. He will have no benefit from you, Hektor, now that you are dead, nor you from him. Even if he lives through the misery of war with the Achaians, for ever after there will be hardship and sorrow for this boy, and others will lay claim to his land. The day of his orphaning makes a child all friendless – all the time he hangs his head, and his cheeks are wet with tears, and in his need the child goes up to his father's friends, pulling at one by the cloak and another by the tunic: and if they pity him one will hold a cup to his mouth just for a moment, enough to wet his lips but not to wet his palate. And then some boy with living parents shoves him away from the feast with blows of his fists and sneering words: "Get out, and quick! You have no father dining with us here." So the child comes back in tears to his widowed mother – our Astyanax, who before now would sit on his father's knees and eat nothing but marrow and the rich fat of sheep: and then when sleep came over him and he had finished his playing, he would sleep in his bed, in the arms of his nurse, in a soft bed with his heart full of happiness. But now when he has lost his dear father there will be much suffering for him, for Astyanax, Lord of the City, the name the Trojans have given him, as you were the sole protection of their gates and long walls. And now out there by the beaked ships, far away from your parents, the wriggling worms will feed on you, when the dogs have had their fill, where you lie naked – and yet there are fine and lovely clothes stored for you at home, the work of women's hands. But now I shall burn them all in the blazing fire – not for your comfort, as you will never be laid out in them, but to do you honour in the sight of the men and women of Troy.'

Such was her lament, and the women joined with their keening.

BOOK 23
FUNERAL GAMES FOR PATROKLOS

So the Trojans lamented in their city. Meanwhile the Achaians reached the ships and the Hellespont. The rest scattered, each to his own ship, but Achilleus would not dismiss the Myrmidons, and spoke to his war-loving companions: 'My fast-horsed Myrmidons, loyal companions, let us not unyoke our strong-footed horses from the chariots yet, but drive up close to Patroklos as we are with our horses and chariots and mourn for him – such is the right of the dead. Then when we have had our pleasure in the sorrow of tears, we can release the horses and all take our supper here.'

So he spoke, and the whole gathering of the Myrmidons cried out in lamentation, led by Achilleus. Three times they drove their fine-maned horses around the body in grief for him, and Thetis roused in them all the desire for weeping. Tears wet the sands, and wet the men's armour: such was the warrior, the great creator of panic, whose loss they mourned. The son of Peleus led their loud lament, placing his murderous hands on the breast of his companion: 'Fare you well, Patroklos, even in the house of Hades. See, I shall fulfil now all that I promised you before, to drag Hektor's body here and give it to the dogs to eat raw, and cut the throats of twelve splendid Trojan children at your pyre, in my anger for your killing.'

So he spoke, and then he put godlike Hektor to shameful treatment, flinging him face down in the dust alongside the son of Menoitios' bier. Then they all took off their armour of gleaming bronze, and unyoked their high-neighing horses, and sat down beside the ship of the swift-footed son of Peleus in their thousands: and he gave them a funeral feast to please their hearts. Many sleek oxen plunged and fell under the iron slaughtering-knife, and many sheep and bleating goats, and many white-tusked hogs rich in fat were laid to singe across the flames of Hephaistos. All around the dead body the blood was poured in cupfuls.

But now their lord, the swift-footed son of Peleus, was brought to godlike Agamemnon by the kings of the Achaians, though his heart was still full of anger for his companion and they had trouble to persuade him. When they reached Agamemnon's hut, they immediately gave orders to the clear-voiced heralds to set a great tripod over the fire, thinking they would persuade the son of Peleus to wash away the clotted blood. But he refused stubbornly, and swore an oath as well: 'No, by Zeus who is the highest and greatest of gods, it is not right that water should come near my head, until I have laid Patroklos in the fire and heaped a burial mound over him, and cut my hair for him, since no second grief like this one will come to touch my heart as long as I am in the company of the living. For now let us yield to the cursed need for food. But in the morning, Agamemnon, lord of men, urge your people to gather in wood and bring all that a dead man should have on his journey to the murky darkness below, so that the tireless fire can soon burn him away from our sight, and the men go back to their duties.'

So he spoke, and they listened well and agreed. Then they busily prepared a meal and all set to eating, and no man's desire went without an equal share in the feast. When they had put away their desire for eating and drinking, the others went each to his own hut to sleep, but the son of Peleus, groaning deeply, lay down on the shore of the sounding sea, lying among the numbers of his Myrmidons, in a clear place, where the waves washed up on the beach. When sleep took hold of him, pouring its sweetness round him and dissolving the troubles of his heart – as his glorious body was utterly tired with his chase after Hektor up to windy Ilios – then the ghost of poor Patroklos came to him, in all ways the image of the living man, in size, and voice, and lovely eyes, and dressed in the clothes that he used to wear on his body. The ghost stood over his head and spoke to him: 'You are asleep, and you have forgotten me, Achilleus. You were never neglectful of me while I lived, but you are in my death. Bury me as quickly as can be, so I can pass through the gates of Hades. The ghosts, the phantoms of the dead, are keeping me away, they will not let me cross the river to join their number, but I am left wandering in vain along the broad-gated house of Hades. And give me your hand, I beg you with my tears – as I shall never again return from Hades, once you have given me my due rite of burning. No more, in the world of the living, will you and I sit down away from our dear companions and talk over our thoughts together. But the hateful doom that fell to me at my very birth has gaped for me and swallowed me: and it is your own fate too, godlike Achilleus, to be killed under the wall of wealthy Troy. And there is one more thing I will ask of you, if you will do it. Do not let my bones be laid away from yours, Achilleus, but let them be together, as we grew up together in your house, after Menoitios had brought me there from Opoëis when I was little, because of a dreadful manslaughter, on the day when I killed the son of Amphidamas – I was just a boy, I did not mean to, I was angry over a game of knucklebones. Then the horseman Peleus welcomed me in his house and brought me up lovingly and made me your lieutenant. So let the same urn hold the bones of both of us, the golden two-handled jar which your honoured mother gave you.'

Swift-footed Achilleus answered him: 'Why have you come to me here, dear head, and tell me all these things that I must do? I shall be sure to carry out all that you ask and do as you tell me. But stand closer to me now: let us embrace each other, if only for a short while, and have our pleasure in the sorrow of tears.'

So speaking Achilleus reached out with his arms, but could grasp nothing. The ghost vanished away under the earth like smoke, squeaking. Achilleus sprang up in amazement, and clapped his hands together, and spoke sadly to the Myrmidons: 'Ah, so there does remain something of a man even in the house of Hades, a ghost and a semblance of him, but without real being at all. All night long the ghost of poor Patroklos has stood over me weeping and lamenting, and has told me all that I must do – it looked wonderfully like the true man.'

So he spoke, and roused in them all the desire for weeping: and rosy-fingered Dawn came up on their lamentation around the pitiable body. Now lord Agamemnon gathered men and mules from all the huts and sent them out to fetch wood, with a fine man to take charge of them, Meriones, the lieutenant of kindly Idomeneus. They set out with wood-cutting axes in their hands and strong-woven ropes, and the mules went ahead of the men. On and on they went, upwards, downwards, sidewards, and zigzag. But when they finally came to the spurs of Ida with the many springs, they quickly set to felling high-branched oak-trees with their long-bladed bronze axes, working fast, and the trees came down with huge crashes. Then the Achaians split them into logs and tied them to the mules: and the mules churned up the ground with their feet as they strained towards the plain through the thick brushwood. And all the woodcutters carried logs – this was the order of Meriones, the lieutenant of kindly Idomeneus. They threw down the wood in a line along the shore, at the place where Achilleus intended a huge burial mound for Patroklos and for himself.

When they had piled a vast quantity of wood on all sides, they sat down there all together and waited. Achilleus then ordered the war-loving Myrmidons to arm themselves in their bronze and yoke the horses to every chariot. They set to and dressed in their armour, and mounted their chariots, drivers and fighting men. The horsemen went in front, and behind them followed a cloud of foot-soldiers, in their thousands: and in the middle of them Patroklos was carried by his companions. They covered the whole of his body with the locks of their hair they cut off and scattered on it: and behind them godlike Achilleus held the head, grieving for the excellent friend he was sending on his way to Hades.

When they reached the place that Achilleus had shown them, they set down the body, and quickly piled the wood as he wished it. Then swift-footed godlike Achilleus thought of one more act. He walked away from the pyre and cut off the lock of his fair hair that he had been growing long in dedication to the river Spercheios: and looking out over the sparkling sea he called out in distress: 'Spercheios, it was to no end that my father Peleus made his vow to you, that if I returned there to my dear native land I would cut off this hair for you and make you a full and holy offering, and sacrifice fifty entire rams right beside you into your waters, where you have your precinct and your altar fragrant with sacrifice. That is what the old man vowed, and you have not fulfilled his wish. Now, since I shall not return to my dear native land, let me give my hair to the hero Patroklos to go with him.'

So speaking he put the hair in the hands of his dear companion, and roused in them all the desire for weeping. And now the light of the sun would have gone down on their lamentation, if Achilleus had not soon come up to Agamemnon and said to him: 'Son of Atreus, you are the one the Achaian people will listen to most of all, and follow what you say. Men can have enough of lamentation, so send them away now from the pyre and tell them to prepare their meal. We who have the main concern to mourn the dead man will see to the work here – but the leaders of the Achaians should stay here with us.'

When Agamemnon, lord of men, heard this, he immediately dismissed the men to their balanced ships, but the mourners stayed there and piled up the wood. They built a pyre a hundred feet square, and with anguish in their hearts they laid the body at the top of the pyre.

In front of the pyre they skinned and prepared many sturdy sheep and shambling twist-horned cattle: great-hearted Achilleus took the fat from all of them and wrapped the body with it from head to foot, and piled the flayed carcasses around it. And he put two-handled jars of honey and oil there, leaning them against the bier: and groaning loud in his grief, he hurried to fling four strong-necked horses on the pyre. The lord Patroklos had nine dogs that he fed from his table, and Achilleus cut the throats of two of these and threw them on the pyre, and likewise twelve noble sons of the great-hearted Trojans, slaughtering them with the bronze for the grim purpose he had for them: and he set the iron strength of fire at work, to feed on them. Then he groaned out loud and called by name on his dear companion: 'Fare you well, Patroklos, even in the house of Hades. See, I am fulfilling now all that I promised you before. There are twelve noble sons of the great-hearted Trojans with you in the fire and it is consuming them all together with your body. But for Hektor's devouring, the son of Priam, I shall not give him to the fire, but to the dogs.'

Such was his threat. But the dogs did not busy themselves with Hektor, but Zeus' daughter Aphrodite kept them away from him day and night, and anointed him with immortal oil of roses, so that Achilleus' dragging of him should not tear his skin. And over him Phoibos Apollo brought down a dark cloud from the sky to the plain, and covered all the ground where the corpse lay, so that the power of the sun should not play round his body in the meantime and dry up the flesh of limb and sinew.

But the pyre of dead Patroklos would not burn: and then swift-footed godlike Achilleus thought of one more act. He walked away from the pyre and prayed to the two winds of the north and west, Boreas and Zephyros, and promised them splendid sacrifice: with many libations from a golden cup he begged them to come, so that the bodies could be burned in the fire without delay, and the wood start to kindle. Iris heard his prayers and went quickly to carry his message to the winds. Now they were all gathered at a feast in the stormy west wind's house. Iris came running and stood on the stone threshold. When they caught sight of her, they all leapt to their feet and each of them invited her to sit beside him. But she declined to sit down, and said to them: 'No time for sitting. I am on my way back to the stream of Ocean, to the land of the Ethiopians, where they are sacrificing hecatombs to the immortals, and I want to share in the sacrificial feast. But Achilleus is praying for Boreas and whistling Zephyros to come to him, and promising you splendid sacrifice, so you can set the pyre burning where Patroklos lies, mourned by all the Achaians.'

So speaking Iris went away, and the two winds rose with a tremendous roaring and whirled the clouds before them. In a moment they came blowing over the sea, and the waves reared up under their screaming breath. Then they reached the fertile land of Troy, and fell on the pyre, and the fire roared up in a monstrous blaze. All night long they beat together on the flames of the pyre with their shrill blasting: and all night long swift Achilleus drew wine from a golden mixing-bowl with a two-handled cup in his hand and poured it out on the ground till the earth was drenched, calling on the spirit of poor Patroklos. As a father weeps for his son as he burns his bones, a son newly married whose death brings anguish to his unhappy parents, so Achilleus wept for his companion as he burnt his bones, dragging his steps up and down beside the pyre in ceaseless lamentation.

At the time when the Morning Star comes bringing news of daylight to the earth, and after him Dawn in her yellow robe spreads over the sea, then the fire burnt low and the flames died away. And the winds went back on their way home out over the Thracian sea, and it seethed in a swell and roared under them. The son of Peleus turned away to one side of the pyre and sank down exhausted, and sweet sleep swept over him. But the son of Atreus and the others came crowding round, and the noise and tramp of their approach roused him. He sat up straight and spoke to them: 'Son of Atreus, and you other leading men of the Achaians, first you extinguish the pyre with gleaming wine, all of it that the fire's fury has reached. And then let us gather the bones of Patroklos son of Menoitios, making sure to tell them apart – they are easily distinguished, as he was lying at the centre of the pyre, and the others, horses and men together, were burnt away from him at the edge. And let us put his bones in a golden jar with a double fold of fat, until I myself am hidden in Hades. For his tomb I do not want you to build a huge mound, but just one that is fitting. Then afterwards the Achaians can make it broad and high, those of you who are left in the many-benched ships after my time.'

So he spoke, and they carried out the wishes of the swift-footed son of Peleus. First they extinguished the pyre with gleaming wine, all that the flames had reached, where the ash had fallen deep. Then with tears they gathered the white bones of his kind friend into a golden jar with a double fold of fat, and placed it in his hut and covered it with a soft sheet of fine linen. They marked out the circle for his grave-mound round the pyre, and fronted it with a groundwork of stones, then quickly heaped a pile of earth over it. When they had built the mound, they were ready to go back. But Achilleus kept the people there, and sat them down in a broad gathering, and brought from his ships prizes for the games – cauldrons and tripods, horses, mules, strong heads of cattle, and fine-girdled women and grey iron.

First he set out the splendid prizes the charioteers would race for. A woman skilled in excellent handcraft, and a tripod with handles holding twenty-two measures, for the winner to take: for the second the prize he set out was a mare six years old and unbroken, pregnant with a mule foal: for the third he put down a beautiful cauldron holding four measures, untouched by the fire and with its new brightness still on it: for the fourth he put down two talents of gold, and for the fifth a two-handled bowl untouched by the fire. Then he stood up and spoke to the Argives: 'Son of Atreus, and you other well-greaved Achaians, these prizes set out in your gathering here are the prizes that await the charioteers. Now if we Achaians were holding these games at any other man's death, I would certainly take first place and carry the prize away to my hut. You know how far my horses excel all others, as they are immortal horses, given by Poseidon to my father Peleus, and he then handed them to me. But I and my strong-footed horses will stay here, out of the race. They have lost their great and glorious charioteer, that gentle man who so often would pour soft olive oil down over their manes after washing them in bright water. So they stand there grieving for him, and their manes trail on the ground – there is sorrow in their hearts, and they will not move. But the rest of you get ready now, any Achaian in the camp who is confident in his horses and strongly-made chariot.'

So spoke the son of Peleus, and the fast charioteers gathered for the race. Far the first to rise was Eumelos, lord of men, the dear son of Admetos, who was outstanding for his horsemanship. Then Tydeus' son, strong Diomedes, rose after him, and brought under the yoke those horses of Tros' stock which he had taken that time from Aineias, though Apollo rescued their master. After him rose the son of Atreus, fair-haired Menelaos the king, and he brought a fast pair of horses under the yoke – Aithe, Agamemnon's mare, and his own Podargos. Aithe had been given to Agamemnon by Echepolos son of Anchises, a gift made so that he should not have to go with him to windy Ilios, but could stay at home and enjoy his life – Zeus had given him great wealth, and he lived in Sikyon where there are broad spaces for the dance. So Menelaos led this mare under the yoke, and she was avid for the race. The fourth to harness his fine-maned horses was Antilochos, the splendid son of the great-hearted lord Nestor, son of Neleus: the swift-footed horses pulling his chariot were of Pylian stock. His father came up close to him and gave advice for his benefit, words of wisdom to one who could think well for himself: 'Antilochos, young though you are, Zeus and Poseidon have favoured you and taught you every form of horsemanship: so there is no great need for me to instruct you – you know how to wheel properly round the turning-posts. But you see your horses are the slowest in the race, and I think this will be troublesome. The others have faster horses, but their drivers know no more of the skill than you do yourself. So then, my friend, your task is to use all the skill you can think of, so that the prizes do not slip past you. It is skill, you know, that makes the good woodcutter, much more than strength. By skill again the helmsman keeps his quick ship running straight over the sparkling sea, though the winds are buffeting. And it is by skill that charioteer beats charioteer. The driver who relies only on his horses and chariot is careless at the turn and wheels wide this way or that, and his horses wander on the straight, without control. But if a man has cunning, even though he is driving inferior horses, he always keeps his eye on the post and turns tight, and does not miss the proper use of ox-hide reins to stretch his horses from the start, but drives them on unswervingly and keeps close watch on the leader. Now I will tell you something to mark – it is clear to see, and you will not miss it. There is a dry stump of wood, oak or pine, standing about six feet out of the ground. The rain has not rotted it, and there are two white stones driven in on either side of it, at the place where the road narrows, and there is smooth going for horses round it – maybe it marks the grave of some man long dead, or was set up as a goal in earlier times. Well, swift-footed godlike Achilleus has made it the turning-post now. You must cut in very close as you drive your chariot and pair round the post, and let your own body, where you stand on the well-strung platform, lean a little to the left of the horses. Goad your right-hand horse and shout him on, and make sure your hands give him rein: and have your left horse cut close in to the post, so that the nave of your well-built wheel seems to be just touching it – but be careful not to hit the stone, or you will damage your horses and smash the chariot, and that would delight the others and bring shame on you. So, my friend, use your head and keep on your guard. If you can pass them at the turning-post as you come up behind them, then there is no-one who could close the distance to catch you or overtake you, even if he was driving the great Arion behind you, Adrestos' race-horse whose stock came from the gods, or Laomedon's horses, the greatest ever bred in Troy.'

So speaking, Nestor son of Neleus sat down again in his place, after telling his son the way to do it all.

Meriones was the fifth to harness his fine-maned horses. Then they mounted the chariots, and dropped their lots into a helmet. Achilleus shook it, and out jumped the lot of Nestor's son Antilochos: second place fell to lord Eumelos: the next lane was drawn by the son of Atreus, the famous spearman Menelaos, and after him Meriones: and then far the best of them all, Diomedes son of Tydeus, drew the last lane to drive in. They drew up in a row, and Achilleus showed them the turning-post far out in the plain. He had positioned an umpire beside it, godlike Phoinix, his father's follower, to note their courses and bring back an accurate account.

At the same moment they all raised their whips over their horses, then brought the lash down on them, and shouted them forward with urgent commands. At once they were speeding over the plain far away from the ships. Under their chests the dust rose and hung like a cloud or a thunderhead, and their manes streamed back in the rush of the wind. The chariots would bounce at one moment close to the nourishing earth, and then be leaping in the air off the ground. The heart of every driver standing in his car beat hard as he strained for victory: each man called to his own horses, and they flew on raising the dust over the plain.

But when the fast horses were now running the last part of the course back again to the grey sea, then the worth of each of the drivers began to show and the horses' pace was strained. Then the swift-footed horses of Eumelos, son of Admetos the son of Pheres, drew away in front. After them came Diomedes' stallions of Tros' stock, and they were not at all far behind, but very close on him: all the time it seemed that they were about to step into Eumelos' chariot, and his back and broad shoulders grew warm in their breath, as they flew along with their heads leaning right into him. And now Diomedes would have passed him or made it a dead heat, if Phoibos Apollo had not shown his anger for the son of Tydeus and knocked the bright whip out of his hands. Tears of fury poured from his eyes when he saw Eumelos' mares going yet more strongly and his own horses were slowed for running without the whip. But Athene had seen Apollo fouling the son of Tydeus, and she sped quickly after the shepherd of the people and gave him back his whip and put strength in his horses. Then the goddess went after Admetos' son in her anger and with her divine power smashed the yoke of his chariot. His mares ran off the road, the shaft dropped to the ground, and Eumelos himself was tumbled out of the chariot beside the wheel. The skin was ripped from elbows, mouth, and nose, and his forehead smashed in over his eyebrows: his eyes filled with tears, and his strong voice was blocked. The son of Tydeus swerved his strong-footed horses and drove on past, speeding far ahead of the others, as Athene put strength in the horses and gave glory to their driver. After him came the son of Atreus, fairhaired Menelaos. And Antilochos called out to his father's horses: 'Come on the pair of you – pull as fast as you can! I am not asking you to match those ones, the horses of Tydeus' warrior son – Athene has just now given them speed and granted glory to their driver. But catch up with the son of Atreus' horses and do not let them leave you behind – quick, or Aithe will cover you in shame, and she a female. Why are you falling behind, my fine horses? I tell you this, and it will certainly be done as I say. There will be no more keep for you from Nestor, shepherd of the people, but he will kill you on the spot with the sharp bronze, if your slackness makes me win a lesser prize. So after them now, and put out all your speed. My part will be to think out a way of getting past them where the road runs narrow – and I shall not fail.'

So he spoke, and they were frightened at their master's shout and ran more strongly for a little while. And then brave Antilochos saw a place where the road was sunk and narrow. There was a gulley in the earth, where the winter rain had gathered and broken away part of the road, making the whole area sink. Menelaos was driving through here and leaving no room for another to get abreast. But Antilochos pulled his strong-footed horses off the track and drove along a little to one side, pressing on in full pursuit. The son of Atreus was frightened and shouted to Antilochos: 'Antilochos, this is crazy driving – hold your horses in! The road is too narrow here – it soon widens for passing. Take care you do not crash your chariot into mine and wreck us both.'

So he spoke, but Antilochos drove yet more furiously, whipping his horses to greater speed, as if he had not heard. They ran on level for the length that a discus carries from an over-arm cast, when a powerful man flings it to test his young strength. But then the son of Atreus' horses slackened and dropped behind, as he himself deliberately eased his driving, in fear that the strong-footed horses might collide in the road and overturn the well-strung chariots, and then their urge for victory would leave the drivers sprawled in the dust. But fair-haired Menelaos called after Antilochos in disgust: 'Antilochos, there is no man viler than you! Curse you! We Achaians were wrong when we thought you a man of sense. But, I tell you, even so you will not take this prize without need for an oath.'

So speaking he called out to his own horses: 'No holding back now, no stopping, however pained you are at heart! Those horses will find their legs and knees tiring before yours – both of that pair have lost their youth.'

So he spoke, and they were frightened at their master's shout, and quickly came close up behind the others.

Meanwhile the Argives sitting assembled together were looking out for the horses, as they flew on raising the dust over the plain. Idomeneus, the leader of the Cretans, was the first to catch sight of the horses – he was sitting away from the main assembly and higher, in a place with a view all round. When the first driver was still far away he heard him shouting and recognised the voice, and he could make out the distinctive horse in front, who was chestnut all over, except that there was a white blaze on his forehead, round like the full moon. Idomeneus stood up and called to the Argives: 'Friends, leaders and lords of the Argives, am I the only one to see the horses, or can you too? It seems to me that other horses are in front now, and it looks like another charioteer. Eumelos' mares must have come to grief out there in the plain – they were in the lead on the way out. I saw them before dashing for the turn at the post, but now I cannot see them anywhere, though my eyes have been looking out all over the Trojan plain. Perhaps the charioteer lost hold of the reins, and could not control his horses properly round the post, and failed to make the turn. That is where I think he must have been thrown out and crashed his chariot, and the mares bolted away with their hearts sent wild. But stand up and look for yourselves – I cannot tell for sure, but it seems to me that the man in front is an Aitolian by birth, and king over the Argives, the son of horse-taming Tydeus, strong Diomedes.'

But quick Aias, son of Oïleus, scorned him with insulting words: 'Idomeneus, why are you always blustering on? Those prancing mares are far away with much ground still to cover. You are hardly the youngest of the Argives, and you do not have the sharpest pair of eyes in your head – but you always have some blustering speech to make. You have no business to bluster like this, when there are better men than you here. The same horses are in the lead as were before, Eumelos' mares, and there he is standing in the chariot with the reins in his hands.'

Then the leader of the Cretans answered him in anger: 'Aias, good for nothing but abuse, you stupid man, with your boorish mind, you are the lowest of the Argives in every way. Here then, let us both bet a tripod or a cauldron on which are the leading horses, and make Agamemnon son of Atreus our referee – then you will see, when you pay it over.'

So he spoke, and quick Aias son of Oïleus sprang up in fury to answer with stinging words. And now the quarrel would have gone yet further on both sides, if Achilleus himself had not stood up and spoken to them: 'No more now, Aias and Idomeneus, of this exchange of hard words: these insults are quite improper. Both of you would be angry with any other man who behaved in this way. No, you should sit down with the rest of the spectators and look out for the horses. They will be coming in soon enough, pressing hard for victory: and then each of you will be able to see which of the Argive horses are in the lead and which come second.'

So he spoke, and the son of Tydeus came driving in towards them, very close now, all the time lashing his horses on with the whip swung full from the shoulder: and they bounded on for him, springing speedily on their way. A constant spray of dust rained on their driver, and the chariot with its overlays of gold and tin came whirling at the heels of the fast-running horses, and there was hardly any track made by the wheel-rims in the fine dust behind them as they flew speeding on. Diomedes pulled up in the middle of the gathering, with a thick sweat welling on the neck and chest of his horses and dripping to the ground. He himself jumped down from his glittering chariot and leant his whip against the yoke. And the mighty Sthenelos, his lieutenant, was not slow to act – he quickly took hold of the prizes and gave them to his proud companions, telling them to lead the woman away and carry the handled tripod with them: then he unyoked the horses.

Next after him to drive in his horses was Antilochos of Neleus' stock, who had got ahead of Menelaos by craft, not speed – but even so Menelaos was driving his fast horses close behind. The gap between them was that of a horse from the chariot-wheel, when he is pulling his master at speed over the plain: the tip of his tail brushes against the wheel-rim, and the wheel spins close behind him, and there is little space between as he runs far across the plain. That was how far

Menelaos came in after the excellent Antilochos. At first he had been as much as a discus-throw behind, but he was quickly gaining on him, as Agamemnon's mare, the lovely-maned Aithe, put out her great strength: and if both had to run a longer course, Menelaos would have passed him and put the result beyond dispute. Then Meriones, Idomeneus' brave lieutenant, came a spear's throw behind Menelaos – his lovely-maned horses were the slowest, and he himself the weakest at driving a chariot in the race. Far the last of all came the son of Admetos, pulling his fine chariot himself and driving his horses in front of him. Seeing this swift-footed godlike Achilleus felt pity for him, and stood up in the gathering of Argives and spoke winged words to them: 'The best man is driving in his strong-footed horses last. Come then, let us give him a prize as he deserves – the second prize. And the son of Tydeus can take the first.'

So he spoke, and they all applauded his suggestion. And now he would have given Eumelos the mare, since the Achaians had approved, if Antilochos, great-hearted Nestor's son, had not stood up to make his objection in answer to Achilleus son of Peleus: 'Achilleus, I shall be greatly angry with you if you carry out what you now propose. You mean to rob me of my prize, on the basis that Eumelos' chariot and fast horses came to grief, and he himself too, though he is a fine driver – but he should have prayed to the immortals, and then he would not have come last of all in the race. If you are sorry for him and your heart is fond of him, then you have gold in abundance in your hut, you have bronze and sheep, serving-women and strong-footed horses. You can pick an even greater prize from this store to give him later, or indeed right now, and win the approval of the Achaians. But I will not give up the mare – anyone who wants to try me for her will have to fight me with his fists.'

So he spoke, and swift-footed godlike Achilleus smiled in delight at Antilochos, as he was a dear friend, and he spoke winged words in answer to him: 'Antilochos, if you want me now to give some extra prize to Eumelos from my own store, then I will do it. I will give him the corselet I took from Asteropaios. It is bronze, ringed round with an overlay of bright tin – it will be something of great value to him.'

So he spoke, and told his dear companion Automedon to bring the corselet from his hut. He went off and brought it back, and placed it in Eumelos' hands: and he accepted it with delight.

But then Menelaos too stood up in the company, bitter at heart and full of lasting anger at Antilochos. The herald put the sceptre in his hand, and called for the Argives to be silent. Then the godlike man spoke out among them: 'Antilochos, you used to be a man of sense before now, but look what you have done. You brought shame on my skill and fouled my horses by throwing your own horses across them, which were much slower than mine. Come then, leaders and lords of the Argives, give your judgment between the two of us openly, and without favour, so that some bronze-clad Achaian may never say: "Menelaos used lies to do down Antilochos and get away with the mare. His horses were far the slower, but he took the advantage of his rank and power." Or look, I shall propose the test myself, and I do not think that any Danaan will criticise me for it – straight justice will be done. Antilochos, come here, my lord, and take an oath, as custom decrees. Stand here in front of your horses and chariot, take the thin whip you drove with in your hands, then with a hand touching your horses swear by the encircler and shaker of the earth that it was no deliberate foul of yours that blocked my chariot.'

Then Antilochos, good man of sense, answered him: 'Enough now. I am much younger than you, lord Menelaos, and you are my senior and better. You know how a young man oversteps the mark – his mind works quickly, but his judgment is flimsy. So let your heart bear with me. I shall give up of my own accord the mare that I won. And if you asked for something yet more valuable from my own possessions, I would be willing to give it to you at once rather than fall out of your favour, my lord, for all my days, and make myself an offender against the gods.'

So he spoke, and then great-hearted Nestor's son led the mare across and gave her into Menelaos' hands. And his heart was melted like the dew on the ears of growing corn, when the fields are bristling with the crop – so your heart, Menelaos, was melted within you. Menelaos then spoke winged words to him: 'Antilochos, now I too will give way and forget my anger. You were never a reckless fool before now: but this time your young heart ruled your head. Another time you should take care not to cheat your betters. Any other Achaian would not have found it easy to mollify me. But you have been through much suffering and much trouble for my sake, as have your noble father and your brother. So I shall be swayed by your appeal, and I shall even give you the mare, mine though she is, so that all our friends here can see that my heart is never stubborn or unyielding.'

So he spoke, and gave the mare to Antilochos' companion Noëmon to lead away: and then he himself took the gleaming cauldron. Meriones took up the two talents of gold, as the fourth to drive his horses in. But the fifth prize, the two-handled bowl, was now left. Achilleus gave it to Nestor, carrying it through the gathering of the Achaians and saying as he came up to him: 'Here now, old man, here is a treasure for you too to keep, as a memory of the burial of Patroklos, as you will never see him again among the Argives. I give you this prize simply as a gift. You will not fight a boxing-match now, or wrestle, or enter the spear-throw, or race with your legs. Old age has its cruel hold on you now.'

So speaking he put the bowl in Nestor's hands. He accepted it with delight, and spoke winged words in answer: 'Yes, all that you say, my child, is right and true. My limbs are no longer firm as they were, dear friend, neither legs nor arms – my arms cannot now shoot supply out from my shoulders. Would that I were as young, and the power was still in me, as when the Epeians were burying lord Amarynkeus in Bouprasion, and his sons held funeral games for the king. Then there was no man to match me, either among the Epeians or my own Pylians or the great-hearted Aitolians. In the boxing I beat Klytomedes, the son of Enops, and at wrestling Ankaios from Pleuron, who challenged me. In the foot-race I outran Iphiklos, and he was a fine runner. And with the spear I threw further than Phyleus and Polydoros. Only in the chariot-race was I defeated, by the two sons of Aktor, who got ahead of me with their two-to-one advantage, and they were passionate for victory, as the greatest prize was left for that event. These two were twins. One drove all the time with the reins, all the time with the reins while the other laid on the whip. That is the man I was once. But now it is for younger men to face these trials, and I must bow to cruel old age, though then I was a hero among heroes. Well, you must go now and see to the games in honour of your own friend's burial. I gladly accept this gift, and my heart is happy that you always remember me as your kind friend, and you do not forget the honour that I should rightly be paid among the Achaians. May the gods give you your heart's desire in recompense for this.'

So he spoke, and the son of Peleus went back among the mass of the assembled Achaians, after listening to all the tale told by the son of Neleus. Then he set out the prizes for the painful boxing-fight. He led a hard-working mule into the assembly and tied it there, a female six years old and unbroken, the hardest to break in. And for the loser he set down a two-handled cup. Then he stood up and announced the event to the Argives: 'Son of Atreus, and you other well-greaved Achaians, we want two men, the best among you, to put up their fists and box it out for these prizes. The one granted endurance by Apollo and judged the victor by all the Achaians can lead the hard-working mule with him back to his hut: and the loser will take the two-handled cup.'

So he spoke, and immediately there stood up a huge, fine man and a skilful boxer, Epeios the son of Panopeus. He put his hand on the hard-working mule and said: 'Step forward the man who wants to take the two-handled cup. I tell you no other Achaian is going to outbox me and lead off the mule – I say I am the greatest. Is it not enough that I am less good in battle? It seems a man cannot be expert in all things. I tell you this, and it will certainly be done as I say – I will smash right through the man's skin and shatter his bones. And his friends had better gather here ready for his funeral, to carry him away when my fists have broken him.'

So he spoke, and they all stayed silent. Euryalos alone stood up to face him, a godlike man, the son of lord Mekisteus, son of Talaos: Mekisteus had once come to Thebes for the funeral games when Oidipous had fallen, and there he beat all the Kadmeians. Tydeus' son, the famous spearman, busied round Euryalos as his second, speaking encouragement to him and eager for his victory. First he put out a loin-cloth for him, then gave him the leather thongs well cut from the hide of a field ox. The two men belted themselves and walked out into the centre of the gathering. They faced each other and put up their massive fists together, then fell to, and there was a flurry of heavy hands meeting. There sounded a fearful crunching of jaws, and the sweat poured all over their bodies. Then as Euryalos peered for an opening godlike Epeios moved in for the punch and struck him on the cheek-bone – he did not stay on his feet long: his bright body collapsed under him where he stood. As when a fish leaps arching up through the north wind's ruffle in a weed-filled shoal, and then the dark wave covers him again, so Euryalos was lifted clear by the blow. And great-hearted Epeios took him in his arms and set him on his feet. His dear companions surrounded him, and carried him out through the assembly with his legs dragging, spitting out thick blood and lolling his head to one side. They took him off and set him down still dazed in their company, while they went themselves to collect the two-handled cup.

Then the son of Peleus quickly set out the prizes for the third event, the painful wrestling-match, and displayed them to the Danaans. For the winner a great tripod to stand over the fire, which the Achaians among themselves valued at twelve oxen's worth: and as the prize for the beaten man he brought a woman into the centre, one skilled in the range of handcraft, and they valued her at four oxen. Then he stood up and announced the event to the Argives: 'Stand up the two of you who will try now for this prize.' So he spoke, and then huge Aias, Telamon's son, stood up, and resourceful Odysseus rose too, the master of cunning. These two then belted themselves and walked out into the centre of the gathering. They gripped each other in the embrace of their massive arms like the rafters which a skilled builder fits locking together in the roof of a high house to keep out the force of the winds. Their backs creaked under the tight pressure of powerful hands, and the sweat ran pouring down. Weals swelling red with blood sprang up all over their sides and shoulders, as they struggled on hard for victory and the prize of the crafted tripod. Odysseus could not throw his opponent and bring him to the ground, nor could Aias, with Odysseus' great strength holding him. When at last they were beginning to bore the well-greaved Achaians, huge Aias, Telamon's son, said to Odysseus: 'Royal son of Laertes, resourceful Odysseus, either you lift me, or I will lift you – what follows then will be all for Zeus to decide.'

So speaking he lifted him off the ground. But Odysseus did not forget his cunning: he caught Aias with a kick behind the knee, which cut the legs from under him and threw him backwards, so that Odysseus landed on his chest. The people now looked on with admiration. Then much-enduring godlike Odysseus took his turn at the lift. He shifted Aias a little way from the ground, and could not lift him clear: but he gave him a knee-hook, and they both fell to the ground side by side and were dirtied in the dust. And now they would have sprung up and wrestled for the third throw, if Achilleus had not stood up himself and stopped them: 'No more struggling now – do not wear yourselves out with the pain of it. You have both won. Share the prizes, then, and go on your way, so that some other Achaians can enter the games.'

So he spoke, and they listened well and agreed. They brushed off the dust then and put on their tunics.

Then the son of Peleus quickly set out the prizes for the foot-race. The first was a mixing-bowl of worked silver. It held six measures, and it was far the loveliest thing in all the world. Craftsmen from Sidon had fashioned it beautifully, then men of Phoinicia had carried it over the hazy sea and given it to Thoas when they anchored in his harbour: and Iason's son Euneos gave it to the hero Patroklos as the price for Lykaon, son of Priam. Achilleus now made this the prize in memory of his companion, for the man who would be fastest in the speed of his legs. For the second he brought out a great ox rich in fat, and he set down half a talent of gold as the last prize. Then he stood up and announced the event to the Argives: 'Stand up those who will try now for this prize.' So he spoke, and immediately quick Aias, Oïleus' son, stood up, and resourceful Odysseus rose too, and then Nestor's son Antilochos – he was the best at running of the young men. They stood in line, and Achilleus showed them the turning-post. They set off at full stretch from the start, and then the son of Oïleus soon drew ahead. But godlike Odysseus was pressing him very close, close as the weaver's rod comes to the breast of a girdled woman when with the skill of her hands she pulls it in towards her and draws the bobbin through past the warp, keeping the rod close to her breast – so Odysseus kept running close, and his feet were hitting the tracks behind Aias before the dust could settle in them. Godlike Odysseus kept up his pace so that his breath was always streaming on the back of Aias' head: and all the Achaians shouted him on in his bid for victory, giving encouragement to a man who was already making every effort. But when they were now running the last part of the course, Odysseus quickly made a prayer to bright-eyed Athene in his heart: 'Listen, goddess, be a kind helper to me now and come to speed my feet.' So he spoke in prayer, and Pallas Athene heard him, and made his limbs light, his legs and his arms above. Then as they were just about to dash in for the prize, Aias slipped in mid-course – Athene had fouled him – in a place where dung had been dropped by the bellowing cattle which Achilleus had slaughtered for Patroklos' funeral. So Aias had his mouth and nostrils filled with cow-dung, while much-enduring godlike Odysseus came in past him and took up the mixing-bowl in his place – and glorious Aias took the ox. He stood there with his hand on a horn of the field ox, spitting out dung, and said to the Argives: 'Oh, I swear it was that goddess that fouled my feet, the one who is always at Odysseus' side taking care of him like a mother.'

So he spoke, and they all laughed happily at him. Then Antilochos carried off the last prize, smiling, and said to the Argives: 'Friends, I shall tell you something you all know – the immortals to this day are still favouring the older men. Aias is only a little older than I am, but this one belongs to another generation and another era. But, as they say, his is a green old age: and it is hard for us Achaians to rival his speed, except for Achilleus.'

So he spoke, in tribute to the swift-footed son of Peleus. Achilleus then answered him: 'Antilochos, your words of praise will not have been spoken for nothing. I shall add another half-talent of gold to your prize.'

So speaking he put the gold in Antilochos' hands, and he accepted it with delight. But then the son of Peleus brought a long-shadowed spear and set it down in the gathering, with a shield and helmet – the arms of Sarpedon, that Patroklos had taken from him. Then he stood up and announced the event to the Argives: 'We want two men, the best among you, to fight for these prizes. They are to put on their armour, take up spears of cutting bronze, and fight a duel here in front of the crowd. The first to make a hit in the other's fine body, and reach his inwards through his armour and his dark blood, will receive from me this sword with its silver-nailed hilt, a beautiful piece of Thracian work, which I took from Asteropaios. And both contestants can take this armour and share it: and we will give them both a fine feast in my hut.'

So he spoke, and then huge Aias, Telamon's son, stood up, and the son of Tydeus rose also, powerful Diomedes. So when these two had armed themselves on either side of the gathering, they both strode into the centre eager for the fight, glaring terror at each other – and anxious horror gripped all the Achaians. When they had advanced to close range, they made three charges, and three times they engaged close. Then Aias struck through the even circle of Diomedes' shield, but did not reach the flesh, as the corselet behind it saved him. Then over his great shield the son of Tydeus kept right at the neck of Aias with the point of his shining spear: and now the Achaians, terrified for Aias, shouted for them to stop and share the prizes equally. But the hero Achilleus brought the great sword and gave it to the son of Tydeus, together with its sheath and baldric of well-cut leather.

Now the son of Peleus set down a lump of pig-iron, which before then had been used as his discus by the mighty Eëtion: but swift-footed godlike Achilleus had killed him, and carried off the iron in his ships together with Eëtion's other possessions. He stood up then and announced the event to the Argives: 'Stand up those who will try now for this prize. The man who wins this iron will have the use of it for five succeeding years, even if his rich fields lie far out on their own – no shepherd or ploughman of his will go into town for lack of iron, but this will supply all their needs.'

So he spoke, and then there stood up the staunch fighter Polypoites, and the powerful lord Leonteus, godlike man, rose also, and Aias son of Telamon and godlike Epeios. They stood in order, and godlike Epeios took up the weight, swung it round, and hurled it – and all the Achaians laughed at him. Then second to throw was Leonteus, branch of Ares. Then huge Aias, Telamon's son, made the third cast from his massive hand, and threw beyond the marks of all those before. But when finally the staunch fighter Polypoites took up the weight, he out-threw the whole field by the distance a cowherd can reach with his throwing-stick, when he sends it spinning through the air among his herd of cattle. The Achaians shouted their applause, and the companions of strong Polypoites jumped up and carried their king's prize back to the hollow ships.

Then Achilleus put down blue-grey iron as prizes for the archers, setting out ten double-edged axes and ten single axes. And he set up the mast of a dark-prowed ship far out on the sands, and tethered a trembling dove to it by a thin cord round her foot. Then he invited them to shoot at the dove: 'Whoever hits the trembling dove can take up all the double axes and carry them home with him. And if a man misses the bird but hits the string, well, that will be less success, and he can take the single axes.'

So he spoke, and then there stood up the mighty lord Teukros, and Meriones rose too, Idomeneus' brave lieutenant. They took two lots and shook them in a bronze helmet, and Teukros' lot won him the right to shoot first. He quickly let fly a powerful shot, but he had not vowed to the archer-lord to make him a splendid sacrifice of first-born lambs. He missed the bird, then – Apollo grudged him that – but he hit the cord which tethered the bird, next to her foot, and the bitter arrow cut right through the cord. The dove then flew up into the sky, and the cord dangled towards earth. The Achaians cheered. But Meriones hurriedly grabbed the bow from Teukros' hand – he had had an arrow ready, while the other aimed. Quickly he vowed to Apollo the far-shooter to make him a splendid sacrifice of first-born lambs. Then high up under the clouds he saw the trembling dove, and as she circled there he shot her full in the body under the wing. The arrow passed clean through, and fell back to stick in the earth in front of Meriones' foot. The bird settled on the mast of the dark-prowed ship, then hung down her head and her thick wings drooped. The life fluttered fast from her body, and she dropped far down from the mast to the ground – and the people looked on in astonishment. Then Meriones took up all the ten double axes, and Teukros carried the single axes back to the hollow ships.

Then the son of Peleus brought a long-shadowed spear and put it down in the gathering, and a cauldron untouched by the fire, the worth of an ox, with a pattern of flowers on it: and the spear-throwers rose for the contest. Up stood the son of Atreus, wide-ruling Agamemnon, and Meriones rose too, Idomeneus' brave lieutenant. Then swift-footed godlike Achilleus said to them: 'Son of Atreus, we know how superior you are to all others, and how much you are the best in strength for the spear-throw. So you take this prize with you on your way to the hollow ships, and let us give the spear to the hero Meriones, if that might be the wish of your own heart – that is what I suggest.'

So he spoke, and Agamemnon, lord of men, did not fail to agree. The hero gave the bronze spear to Meriones, and then handed his own beautiful prize to his herald Talthybios.

BOOK 24
ACHILLEUS AND PRIAM

And the gathering broke up, and the people scattered, each group on their way to their fast ships. All others turned their minds to supper, and the enjoyment of sweet sleep. But Achilleus began to weep as he thought of his dear companion, and sleep that conquers all could not take him. He tossed this way and that, crying for the loss of Patroklos, his manhood and his brave strength, and all that he had worked through with him and the hardships they had suffered, threading the wars of men and dangerous seas. As he remembered all this he let the heavy tears fall, lying now on his side, now on his back, and now again on his face. Then he would leap to his feet and pace distraught up and down the length of the sea-shore – and he would see every dawn lightening over the sea and the beaches. He would harness the fast horses to his chariot, tie Hektor to it to drag behind the car, and pull him three times round dead Patroklos' tomb: then he would rest again in his hut, and leave Hektor flung face down in the dust. But Apollo pitied the man even in his death, and kept all disfigurement away from his flesh. He covered him over in the golden aegis, so that Achilleus' dragging of him should not tear his skin.

So Achilleus dishonoured godlike Hektor in his fury. But the blessed gods looked on and pitied Hektor, and they kept urging Hermes the sharp-sighted, the slayer of Argos, to steal the body. This found favour with all the other gods, but never with Hera or Poseidon or the bright-eyed girl. They persisted in the hatred they had from the beginning for sacred Ilios and Priam and his people, because of the blind folly of Alexandros, who had scorned the goddesses when they came to his sheepfold, and gave his choice for the one who offered him dangerous lust. But when the twelfth dawn came round from the day that Hektor died, then Phoibos Apollo spoke to the immortals: 'You are cruel, you gods, creatures of mischief! Did Hektor never burn for you the thigh-bones of oxen and goats without blemish? Yet now you will not bring yourselves to save even his corpse, for his wife to see him and his mother and his child, and his father Priam and his people, who would straightly burn him in the fire and give him full burial afterwards. But no, gods, you are determined to favour the deadly Achilleus. He has no decency in his heart, his mind cannot be turned in his breast, but his thoughts are savage like a lion's, who follows only his own great strength and his proud heart, and goes to make his meal on the flocks that men keep. So Achilleus has murdered pity, and there is no shame in him, which can both help and hurt a man. I suppose before now a man has lost one yet more dear to him – a brother from the same womb, or a son: yet he weeps and laments and then is done, since the Fates have put an enduring heart in humankind. But this man, after taking the life from him, ties Hektor to his horses and drags him round the tomb of his dear companion: and this does nothing to his honour or his good. Great man though he is, he should be wary of our anger – he is dishonouring the dumb earth now in his fury.'

Then white-armed Hera said to him in anger: 'Yes, there could be truth even in what you say, lord of the silver bow – if you gods mean to hold Hektor in equal honour with Achilleus. Hektor is a mortal, and sucked at a woman's breast. But Achilleus is child of a goddess, whom I myself brought up and reared and gave as wife to a man, Peleus, who of all men was dearest to the hearts of the immortals. All of you gods were there at the wedding: and you were among them too with your lyre at the feast – you coward-lover, you were always a traitor!'

Then Zeus the cloud-gatherer answered her: 'Hera, you must not be wholly angry with the gods. Certainly the honour shown the two men will not be the same. But Hektor too was dear to the gods, most of all the mortals who live in Ilios. So he was to me at least, since he never failed to make pleasing gifts – my altar was never without a share of the feasting, libation of wine and the smoke of sacrifice, which is our rightful honour. But as for stealing brave Hektor's body, we must let that go – and it cannot be done without Achilleus knowing, as his mother is by him all the time, day and night alike. But would one of the gods call Thetis to come here before me, so that I can put a sound plan to her, to see that Achilleus wins gifts from Priam and releases the body of Hektor.'

So he spoke, and storm-swift Iris sped to give his message. She leapt down into the dark sea between Samos and rocky Imbros, and the water crashed echoing round her. She plunged to the depths like the lead sinker set in a lure of field-ox horn which goes down bringing death to hungry fish. She found Thetis in a hollow cave, with the other sea-goddesses sitting gathered round her: and in their midst Thetis was weeping for the fate of her own excellent son, whom she was to see die in fertile Troy, far from his native land. Swift-footed Iris came close and spoke to her: 'Up now, Thetis! Zeus whose thoughts are deathless calls you.' Then the silver-footed goddess Thetis answered her: 'Why does he ask for me, the great god? I feel shame to mix with the immortals – I have misery enough in my heart. But I will go to him. No word that he says will be wasted.'

So speaking the queen among goddesses took up a blue-black veil, the darkest of all garments. She set on her way, and swift Iris with feet quick as the wind went before her: and the swell of the sea parted round them. They came out on to the shore, and darted up to the sky. There they found the wide-seeing son of Kronos, and all the other blessed gods sitting gathered round him. Thetis sat down beside father Zeus, and Athene made way for her. Hera put a lovely golden cup in her hand and spoke kind words of welcome: and Thetis drank and handed back the cup. Then the father of men and gods began to speak: 'You have come to Olympos, divine Thetis, for all your grief, and you have lasting sorrow in your heart – I know this. But even so I shall tell you why I have called you here. For nine days now there has been argument among the immortals over Achilleus, sacker of cities, and the body of Hektor – and they are urging Hermes the sharp-sighted, the slayer of Argos, to steal the body. But here is a means of glory I can grant to Achilleus, and preserve your respect and love for the future. You can go quickly to the camp and give this message to your son. Tell him the gods are enraged at him, and my own anger is the greatest among all the immortals, because in the madness of his heart he is keeping Hektor by the beaked ships and has not released him. He may then give Hektor back in fear of me. And I shall send Iris to great-hearted Priam, telling him to go to the ships of the Achaians and ransom his dear son, bringing gifts to Achilleus which will soften his heart.'

So he spoke, and the silver-footed goddess Thetis did not fail to obey. She went darting down from the peaks of Olympos, and came into her son's hut. She found him there in ceaseless lamentation, while around him his dear companions were busying themselves to prepare the morning meal: they had a great woolly sheep slaughtered there in the hut. His honoured mother sat down close beside him, and stroked him with her hand, and spoke to him, saying: 'My child, how long will you eat out your heart in sorrow and mourning, with no thought for either food or bed? It is a good thing to join with a woman in love – as I shall not see you live long now, but already death and strong fate are standing close beside you. Listen quickly to me now – I bring you a message from Zeus. He says the gods are enraged at you, and his own anger is the greatest among all the immortals, because in the madness of your heart you are keeping Hektor by the beaked ships and have not released him. Come, release him now, and accept a ransom for the body.'

Then swift-footed Achilleus answered her: 'So be it. The man who brings the ransom can take the body, if the Olympian himself in all earnest wishes it.'

So those two, mother and son, spoke deep together in winged words by the gathering of the ships. And the son of Kronos urged Iris off to sacred Ilios: 'Away with you, swift Iris, leave your home on Olympos and take my message to great-hearted Priam in Ilios. Tell him to go to the ships of the Achaians and ransom his dear son, bringing gifts to Achilleus which will soften his heart. He must go alone, and no other Trojan with him: but one of the older heralds may accompany him, to drive the mules with a strong-wheeled cart and carry back to the city the dead man killed by godlike Achilleus. And he should have no thoughts of death or terror in his mind – such is the escort we will give him, Hermes the slayer of Argos, who will guide him until he has brought him straight to Achilleus. And when he has brought him into Achilleus' hut, Achilleus will not kill him, and he will hold back all the others – he is not foolish or blind or godless, but will show a suppliant all kindness and spare him.'

So he spoke, and storm-swift Iris sped to give his message. She came into Priam's house, and found there crying and lamentation. The sons, sitting around their father in the courtyard, were soaking their clothes with their tears. And in their midst the old man sat shrouded tight in his cloak: and the dung lay heaped on the old man's head and neck, where he had rolled in it and gathered it up with his own hands. And his daughters and sons' wives were mourning throughout the rooms of the house, remembering those many brave men who had lost their lives and lay dead at the hands of the Argives. Zeus' messenger stood beside Priam and spoke to him, speaking softly, but even so trembling took over his limbs: 'Have courage in your heart, Priam, stock of Dardanos, and do not be afraid. I come here not with news of evil for you, but with kind intent. I bring you a message from Zeus, who though far away cares greatly for you and pities you. The Olympian tells you to ransom godlike Hektor, bringing gifts to Achilleus which will soften his heart. You must go alone, and no other Trojan with you: but one of the older heralds may accompany you, to drive the mules with a strong-wheeled cart and carry back to the city the dead man killed by godlike Achilleus. And you should have no thoughts of death or terror in your mind – such is the escort who will go with you, Hermes the slayer of Argos, who will guide you until he has brought you straight to Achilleus. And when he has brought you into Achilleus' hut, Achilleus will not kill you, and he will hold back all the others – he is not foolish or blind or godless, but will show a suppliant all kindness and spare him.'

So speaking swift-footed Iris left him, and he ordered his sons to get ready a strong-wheeled mule-cart, and fasten a wicker frame to it. He himself went down into the sweet-smelling storeroom, cedar-lined and high-roofed, which held many precious things. And he called in his wife Hekabe and said to her: 'Dear wife, an Olympian has come to me with a message from Zeus, that I must go to the ships of the Achaians and ransom our dear son, bringing gifts to Achilleus which will soften his heart. Tell me now, how does your heart see this? The urge of my own spirit and heart is terribly strong, telling me to go there to the ships and enter the broad camp of the Achaians.'

So he spoke, and his wife shrieked loud, and answered: 'Oh, where have your wits gone now, that wisdom for which you used to be famous among men from other lands as well as your own subjects? How can you think of going alone to the ships of the Achaians, into the eyes of a man who has killed many of your brave sons? Your heart must be of iron. If he gets you in his hands and sets his eyes on you – he is a savage beast and not to be trusted, he will not show you mercy, he will have no regard for your claim. No, we should sit by ourselves now in our own home and weep for Hektor. So strong Fate must have spun for him with her thread as he was born, at the moment I gave birth to him, that he should be food for the quick-running dogs, away from his parents, in the power of a mighty man – I wish I could sink my hands in that man's very liver and eat it! Then there would be some revenge for my son, as it was no coward that Achilleus killed, but he was standing in defence of the men of Troy and the deep-breasted women of Troy, with no thought of flight or shelter.'

Then the old man, godlike Priam, said to her: 'I will go. Do not try to hold me back, or make yourself a bird of ill omen in our house – you will not dissuade me. If it were a mortal man that told me this, one of the seers who divine from sacrifice, or the priests, we would rather call it false and reject it. But I have heard the god's voice with my own ears and looked at her face to face, so I shall go now, and her message will not be in vain. If it is my fate to die beside the ships of the bronze-clad Achaians, then I welcome it – Achilleus can kill me outright, once I have taken my son in my arms and filled my need to mourn him.'

So he spoke, and lifted up the beautiful lids of his store-chests. From them he took out twelve robes of great beauty, and twelve single cloaks, as many blankets, as many white mantles, and as many tunics to go with them. He brought out gold, weighing out ten talents in all, and two gleaming tripods, and four cauldrons, and a cup of great beauty, which the men of Thrace had given him when he went there on an embassy, a fine possession – but the old man did not spare even this treasure of his house, as his heart was filled with the desire to win release for his dear son. And he drove all the Trojans away from his portico with angry words to shame them: 'Get out, you wretched creatures, you disgraces! Have you not enough to mourn for in your own homes, without coming here to bring me misery? Or do you think it nothing that Zeus the son of Kronos has brought sorrow on me, the loss of the best of my sons? Well, you will feel it yourselves – you will be yet easier now for the Achaians to kill, now that he is dead. As for me, may I go down into the house of Hades before my eyes see our city sacked and plundered.'

So he spoke, and laid about the men with his stick: they fled outside under the old man's rage. Then he began to rail at his own sons, cursing Helenos and Paris and godlike Agathon, Pammon and Antiphonos and Polites, master of the war-cry, and Deïphobos and Hippothoös and proud Dios. The old man shouted at these nine and gave them his orders: 'Move now, you sorry children, you shameful blots! If only all of you had been killed together by the fast ships instead of Hektor! Oh, the utter misery of my fate! I fathered sons who were heroes in the broad land of Troy, and I tell you not one of them is left – godlike Mestor and Troïlos the horseman and Hektor, who was a god among men, and did not seem like the son of a mortal man, but rather of a god. Ares has killed them all, and I am left with all these disgraces, braggarts and dandies, heroes of the dance-floor, thievers of sheep and goats from their own people. Will you not fit me out a cart – quick! – and put all these things in it, so we can get on our way?'

So he spoke, and they were frightened at their father's shouting, and carried out a strong-wheeled mule-cart, a fine one fresh from the joiner's hands, and fastened a wicker frame to it, and took down from its hook the mule-yoke, made of box-wood and topped with a knob and well fitted with guide-rings: and together with the yoke they brought out its lashing-rope, nine cubits long. They settled the yoke carefully on the polished pole at the front end, and slipped the eye of the rope over the peg: they tied the rope three times round the knob, then lashed it all the way down the pole, and twisted it under the hook. Then they carried out from the store-room the unlimited gifts to ransom the head of Hektor, and piled them in the well-polished cart, and yoked to it the strong-footed draught-mules that the Mysians had once given as a splendid gift to Priam. And they brought under the yoke of Priam's chariot the horses which the old man kept for his own use and tended at his polished manger.

So the yoking went on in the high house for the herald and Priam, men with wise thoughts in their minds. And Hekabe came up close to them in distress of heart, holding cheering wine in a golden cup in her right hand, so they could pour a libation before going. She stood in front of the horses, and called Priam and said: 'Here, make a libation to father Zeus, and pray that you may return home again from the enemy, now that your heart is urging you on to the ships, though I would not have you go. So pray then to the son of Kronos, lord of the dark clouds, Zeus the god of Ida, who looks over all the land of Troy. Ask him for a bird of omen, a swift-flying messenger, the bird which he himself loves best and is the most powerful of all, to appear on the right, so that you can see it with your own eyes and go to the ships of the fast-horsed Danaans with your trust in the omen. But if wide-seeing Zeus will not give you his own messenger, I certainly would not then encourage you and advise you to go to the Argive ships, however strong your own desire.'

Then godlike Priam answered her: 'Wife, I shall not fail to do as you ask. It is a good thing to hold up one's hands to Zeus and pray for his mercy.'

So he spoke, and the old man told his housekeeper to bring pure water to pour over his hands: and the servant came to stand by him with a basin and a jug in her hands. Priam washed and took the cup from his wife. Then he stood in the middle of the yard to make his prayer, and poured out the wine looking up into the sky, and said: 'Father Zeus, ruling from Ida's height, greatest and most glorious: grant that my coming to Achilleus' hut may find kindness and pity,

and send me a bird of omen, a swift-flying messenger, the bird which
you yourself love best and is the most powerful of all, to appear on the
right, so that I can see it with my own eyes and go to the ships of the
fast-horsed Danaans with my trust in the omen.'

So he spoke in prayer, and Zeus the counsellor heard him, and he
immediately sent an eagle, surest omen of all flying things, the dark
one, the hunter known as the black eagle. His wings spread on either
side as wide as the doors that are built to a high-roofed room in a rich
man's house, and fitted with strong bolts. He showed swooping across
the city on the right: and they were all delighted when they saw him,
and their hearts warmed within them.

In haste now the old man mounted his chariot, and drove out
through the gateway and the echoing portico. In front went the mules
pulling the four-wheeled cart, driven by wise Idaios: and then behind
them the horses, which the old man plied with the whip and urged on
quickly through the city. And all his family went with him in constant
lamentation, as if he was going to his death. When they had come
down through the city and reached the plain, the others, his sons and
sons-in-law, turned back and went home to Ilios, and as the two men
showed out on the plain wide-seeing Zeus was watching them. He felt
pity for the old man when he saw him, and quickly spoke to Hermes,
his own dear son: 'Hermes, you above all take pleasure in befriending
a man, and you listen to any man you will. Away with you, then, and
guide Priam to the hollow ships of the Achaians, so that none of the
other Danaans sees him or is aware of him before he reaches the son of
Peleus.'

So he spoke, and Hermes the guide, the slayer of Argos, did not fail
to obey. Immediately he bound under his feet the beautiful sandals,
immortal and golden, which carried him over water and limitless earth
alike, fast as the wind's blowing: and he took up the rod with which he
lulls the eyes of mortal men as he wishes, and again wakes men from
their sleep. With this rod in his hands the mighty slayer of Argos flew
on his way, and quickly reached the land of Troy and the Hellespont.
There he set out in the form of a young prince with the first beard on
his lip, which is the loveliest time of youth.

Now when the two men had driven alongside the great tomb of Ilos,
they halted the mules and the horses at the river, so they could drink.
By now darkness had come over the earth. The herald looked out and
saw Hermes when he was close on them, and said to Priam: 'Take care,
stock of Dardanos! Here is something that needs thought and care. I

can see a man, and I think we shall soon be torn apart. Come then, let us make our escape in the chariot – or else we can take him by the knees and beg for his mercy.'

So he spoke, and the old man's mind was confounded, and he felt terrible fear: the hairs stood up along the flex of his body, and he stood there dazed. But the very god, the kindly one, came close to him, and took the old man by the hand and spoke to him with questions: 'Where is it, father, that you are driving your horses and mules through the immortal night, when other men are sleeping? Are you not frightened of the Achaians who breathe fury? They are your enemies and intend you harm, and they are close by. If any of them were to see you coming through the quick black night with so many treasures, what would become of you then? You are not young yourself, and your companion here is too old for defence against a man who starts a fight with you. But I will do you no harm, and indeed I will protect you from any who would – I look on you as my own father.'

Then the old man, godlike Priam, answered him: 'Yes, dear child, it is as you say. But still one of the gods has held his hand even over me, to send into my path a traveller such as you, a man of good omen, as you are with your wonderful size and good looks, and the good sense of your mind – you are the son of blessed parents.'

Then Hermes the guide, the slayer of Argos, answered him: 'Yes, all that you say, old man, is right and true. But come, tell me this, and tell me in clear truth. Are you sending these many fine treasures to people somewhere abroad, where they can be kept safe for you – or are all of you now deserting sacred Ilios in terror, such is the loss of your best man killed, your own son, who was never weak in battle with the Achaians?'

Then the old man, godlike Priam, answered him: 'Who are you, good sir, and who are your parents, that you could speak so well of the fate of my doomed son?'

Then Hermes the guide, the slayer of Argos, answered him: 'You are testing me, old man, and asking about godlike Hektor. I often saw him with my own eyes in the battle where men win glory, and I saw him when he had driven the Argives back on their ships and kept killing them there, cutting them down with his sharp bronze – we stood by and marvelled at him, as Achilleus would not let us fight, in his anger at the son of Atreus. I am a lieutenant of Achilleus, and the same strong-built ship brought us here. I am one of the Myrmidons, and my father is Polyktor, a rich man, and old now like you. He has six other sons, and I am the seventh: I shook lots with them, and it fell to me to come here with the expedition. But now I have come out to the plain from the ships, as in the morning the bright-eyed Achaians will start battle round the city. They are restless with sitting here idle, and eager for war – the kings of the Achaians cannot hold them back.'

Then the old man, godlike Priam, answered him: 'If then you really are a lieutenant of Achilleus, son of Peleus, come now, tell me the whole truth. Is my son still lying by the ships, or has Achilleus already cut him limb from limb and served him to his dogs?'

Then Hermes the guide, the slayer of Argos, answered him: 'Old man, he is not eaten yet by dogs or birds, but he still lies there in Achilleus' hut beside his ship, just as he fell. This is the twelfth day he has lain there, but his flesh is not decaying, nor the worms eating him, which feed on the bodies of men killed in war. Yes, Achilleus does drag him ruthlessly around the tomb of his dear companion every day, at the showing of holy dawn, but he cannot disfigure him. If you went there you could see for yourself how he lies there fresh as dew, and all the blood is washed from him, and there is no stain on him. All the wounds have closed where he was struck – there were many who drove their bronze into him. Such is the care the blessed gods have for your son, even for his dead body, as he is very dear to their hearts.'

So he spoke, and the old man was overjoyed, and answered: 'My child, it is indeed a good thing to give their proper gifts to the immortals, because my son – if ever he really was – never forgot in our house the gods who hold Olympos. So they have made him recompense, if only in the time of his death. But come now, take this lovely cup as a gift from me, and give me your protection: go with me, if the gods so will it, until I come to the son of Peleus' hut.'

Then Hermes the guide, the slayer of Argos, answered him: 'You are testing me, old man. I am younger than you, but you will not make me agree when you ask me to take your gifts without Achilleus' knowledge. He is a man I fear, and the shame is too deep in my heart for me to rob him – or there will be trouble for me afterwards. But I would go as your escort all the way to famous Argos, and attend you with every care on board a quick ship or by land – and no man would start a fight with you in scorn of your escort.'

So he spoke, and the kindly god sprang up into the chariot behind the horses and quickly took the whip and reins in his hands, and breathed strength and courage into the horses. When they came to the ditch and the towered wall around the ships, the guards there had just set about preparing their supper, but Hermes the guide, the slayer of Argos, shed sleep over all of them, and quickly opened the gates and pushed back the bars, and led Priam inside with the splendid gifts on the cart. Then they came to the son of Peleus' hut – a high building, which the Myrmidons had made for their king, cutting planks of pine to build it: and above they had roofed it with shaggy thatch gathered from the meadows. All round it they had made a great yard for their king, fenced with close-set stakes. The gate was held by a single bar of pine-wood. It needed three Achaians to push home this great door-bolt, and three to open it – three of the rest of the Achaians: but Achilleus could push it home by himself. And now it was Hermes the kindly god who opened it for the old man, and brought inside the glorious gifts for the swift-footed son of Peleus. He dismounted from the chariot onto the ground, and spoke to Priam: 'Old man, I am an immortal god that has come to you – I am Hermes. My father sent me to be with you as your escort. But I shall go back now, and I shall not come into the sight of Achilleus – it would cause anger in heaven for an immortal god to be entertained like that by mortals face to face. But you should go in and take the son of Peleus by his knees, and appeal to him in the name of his father and lovely-haired mother and his child, so as to move his heart.'

So speaking Hermes went away to high Olympos. Priam jumped down to the ground from his chariot, and left Idaios where he was. He stayed there holding the horses and mules, and the old man went straight for the house, where Achilleus loved of Zeus was sitting. He found him inside, and his companions sitting apart from him. Two only, the hero Automedon and Alkimos, branch of Ares, were busy close by him – he had just now finished his meal and done with eating and drinking: the table was still there beside him. Huge Priam came in unseen, and moving close to him took Achilleus' knees in his arms and kissed his hands, those terrible, murderous hands, which had killed many of his sons. As when a man is held fast by blind folly – he kills a man in his own country, and then comes to another land, to a rich man's house, and amazement takes those who see his entry. So Achilleus was amazed when he saw godlike Priam, and the others too were amazed, and looked at each other. And now Priam spoke to him in entreaty: 'Think of your father, godlike Achilleus, an old man like I am, at the cruel edge of old age. And it may be that he too is pressed by those who live around his home, and there is no-one to protect him from harm and destruction. But he at least can hear that you are alive, and feel joy in his heart, and look forward every day to seeing his dear son return from Troy. But my fate is utter misery – I fathered sons who were heroes in the broad land of Troy, and I tell you not one of them is left. I had fifty, when the sons of the Achaians came. Nineteen were from the womb of one mother, and the others were borne to me by the women in my house. Furious Ares has collapsed the strength of most of these. And the one son I had, who guarded our city and people, you have now killed as he fought to defend his country – Hektor. And it is for his sake that I come now to the ships of the Achaians, to win his release from you, and I bring unlimited ransom. Respect the gods, then, Achilleus, and have pity on me, remembering your own father. But I am yet more pitiable than he. I have endured to do what no other mortal man on earth has done – I have brought to my lips the hands of the man who killed my child.'

So he spoke, and he roused in Achilleus the desire to weep for his father. He took the old man by the hand and gently pushed him away. And the two of them began to weep in remembrance. Priam cried loud for murderous Hektor, huddled at the feet of Achilleus, and Achilleus cried for his own father, and then again for Patroklos: and the house was filled with the sound of their weeping. Then when godlike Achilleus had had his pleasure in mourning, and the desire for it had passed from his mind and his body, he stood up from his chair and raised the old man by his hand, in pity for his grey head and grey beard, and spoke winged words to him: 'Poor man, you have surely endured many sorrows in your heart. How could you bear to come alone to the ships of the Achaians, into the eyes of a man who has killed many of your brave sons? Your heart must be of iron. But come now, sit down here on a chair, and for all our sorrow let us leave the pain to lie still in our hearts – no good can come from chilling tears. This is the fate the gods have spun for poor mortal men, that we should live in misery, but they themselves have no sorrows. There are two jars standing on Zeus' floor which hold the gifts he gives us: one holds evils, the other blessings. When Zeus who delights in thunder mixes his gifts to a man, he meets now with evil, and now with good. But when Zeus gives from the jar of misery only, he brings a man to degradation, and vile starvation drives him over the holy earth, and he wanders without honour from gods or men. So it was with Peleus also. The gods gave him splendid gifts from his birth – he surpassed all other men in wealth and substance, and he was king over the Myrmidons: and mortal though he was they made a goddess his wife. But yet even on him god brought evil, because no line of royal children was born to him in his house, but he fathered a single son doomed to die all-untimely: and I cannot care for him as he grows old, since I am sitting here in Troy, far from my own country, bringing pain to you and your children. And you too, old man, we hear that you had fortune once – in all the land contained by Lesbos out to sea, where Makar reigned, and Phrygia far inland, and boundless Hellespont, they say that you, old man, surpassed all in wealth and sons. But now that the heavenly gods have brought this plague on you, all the time there is fighting round your city and the killing of men. But you must endure, and not grieve endlessly in your heart. You will not gain anything by mourning for your son: you will not bring him back to life, before yet more suffering has come on you.'

Then the old man, godlike Priam, answered him: 'Do not make me sit on a chair, my lord, while Hektor still lies untended in your hut, but release him now, so I can see him with my eyes. And for yourself accept this great ransom which we bring you – may you have joy of it, and may you return to your own native land, since now you have let me keep my life and see the light of the sun.'

Then swift-footed Achilleus scowled at him and said: 'Do not now provoke me more, old man. It is already my own mind to release Hektor to you – a message has come to me from Zeus, brought by my mother who bore me, the daughter of the old man of the sea. And what is more, you do not deceive me, Priam. I have the wit to see that one of the gods brought you to the fast ships of the Achaians. No mortal man – even with all the strength of youth – would dare to come here into the camp: and he could not get past the guards, or easily push back the bolt across our gates. So do not stir my heart any further in its grief, or I may not spare you either in my hut, old man, suppliant though you are – and so offend against Zeus' command.'

So he spoke, and the old man was afraid and did as he was ordered. Then the son of Peleus sprang like a lion to the door – not alone, but two lieutenants went with him, the hero Automedon and Alkimos, the two that Achilleus honoured most of his companions, after Patroklos was dead. They then released the horses and mules from the yoke, and brought in the herald, the old man's crier, and sat him down on a stool: and from the well-polished cart they lifted out the unlimited gifts to ransom the head of Hektor. But they left behind two cloaks and a closely-woven tunic, for Achilleus to wrap the body before he gave it to Priam to carry home. Achilleus called out his serving-women and told them to wash the body and anoint it all over, carrying it first to another room so that Priam should not see his son – in case in his anguish of heart he might not control his anger on seeing his son, and then Achilleus might have his own heart stirred to violence, and kill him, and so offend against Zeus' command. When then the serving-women had washed the body and anointed it with olive oil, and put the tunic and a beautiful cloak over it, Achilleus himself lifted it and placed it on a bier, and his companions helped him to lift it onto the well-polished cart. Then Achilleus groaned aloud, and called on his loved companion: 'Do not be angry with me, Patroklos, if you learn, even where you are in Hades, that I have released godlike Hektor to his dear father, as it was no unworthy ransom he gave me. But you will have from me all your proper share even of this.'

So he spoke, and then godlike Achilleus went back into his hut, and sat down against the opposite wall on the decorated chair which he had left, and spoke to Priam: 'Well, your son is released for you now, old man, as you asked, and he lies there on a bier. With the showing of dawn you will see him for yourself when you take him. But now let us think of our supper. Even lovely-haired Niobe, you know, thought of food, and she had twelve children killed in her house, six daughters, and six sons in the strength of their youth. Apollo killed the sons with his silver bow, in anger at Niobe, and Artemis the archer-goddess killed the daughters, because Niobe would compare herself with beautiful Leto – she said Leto had two children only, but she herself had borne many. But those two, though they were only two, destroyed all her many. For nine days they lay in their blood, and there was no-one to bury them, as the son of Kronos had turned the people into stones: but on the tenth day the heavenly gods buried them. And Niobe thought of food, when she was worn out with her weeping. Now she is somewhere among the rocks, in the lonely mountains, in Sipylos, where they say the goddesses sleep, the nymphs that dance by the stream of Acheloïos: there, though she is stone, she still broods on the pain the gods gave her. So come now, we too, godlike old man, should have our thought for food. Then afterwards you can weep for your dear son, when you have taken him to Ilios – and you will have many tears for him.'

So speaking swift Achilleus sprang up and slaughtered a shining white sheep. His companions flayed it and prepared the carcass properly, then chopped it deftly into pieces and threaded them on spits, roasted them carefully, and drew all the meat off. Automedon took bread and set it out on the table in fine baskets, and Achilleus served the meat. Then they put their hands to the food set prepared beside them. When they had put away their desire for eating and drinking, then Dardanian Priam gazed at Achilleus with admiration for the size of the man and his beauty – he looked like the gods face to face. And Achilleus gazed at Dardanian Priam, admiring his noble looks and the talk that he had heard. When they had taken their pleasure in looking at each other, the old man, godlike Priam, was the first to speak: 'Give me a bed now, my lord, as soon as may be, so that we can lie down at last now and enjoy the sweetness of sleep. My eyes have never yet closed under my lids since my son lost his life under your hands, but all the time I have been grieving and brooding on my countless anguish, rolling in the dung in the enclosure of my farmyard. Now I have both tasted food and let gleaming wine down my throat – before this I had tasted nothing.'

So he spoke, and Achilleus told his companions and serving-women to make beds under the portico and put fine purple rugs on them, and spread blankets above, and lay woolly cloaks on top for their covering. The women went out of the room with torches in their hands, and busied themselves to have two beds quickly spread. Then swift-footed Achilleus spoke to Priam, his words dissembling his thought: 'You must sleep outside, old man, in case one of the Achaian counsellors comes here – they are constantly joining me to discuss plans, as is the normal way. If one of them were to see you here in the quick black night, he would immediately report it to Agamemnon, shepherd of the people, and that would mean delay in the release of the body. But come, tell me this, and tell me exactly, how many days you wish for the burial of godlike Hektor, so that I can stay my own hand and hold back the army for that time.'

Then the old man, godlike Priam, answered him: 'If you are willing for me to give a full funeral to godlike Hektor, this is what you could do, Achilleus, as a kindness to me. You know how we are penned in our city, and it is a long way to bring wood from the mountain, and the Trojans are very much afraid. We would lament him for nine days in our houses, then bury him on the tenth day and hold the funeral feast for the people. On the eleventh day we would build the grave-mound over him, and on the twelfth day let us fight again, if that must be.'

Then swift-footed godlike Achilleus answered him: 'Yes, old Priam, all this shall be as you say. I will hold back the fighting for the time that you ask.'

So speaking he took the old man's right hand at the wrist, so he should feel no fear in his heart. So they then lay down there in the porch of the house, the herald and Priam, men with wise thoughts in their minds. And Achilleus slept in the corner of his well-built hut, and the beautiful Briseïs lay beside him.

The other gods, and the warrior men, slept the night long, mastered by sweet sleep. But sleep took no hold on Hermes the kindly god, as he pondered in his heart how he might bring king Priam away from the ships unseen by the strong guards at the gates. He stood over Priam's head and spoke to him: 'Old man, you have no thought of danger, the way you are sleeping on among your enemies, now that Achilleus has spared you. Now you have won the release of your dear son, and you gave much for him. But for you alive three times that ransom would be given by the sons you have left behind, if Agamemnon son of Atreus discovers you here, and all the Achaians learn of it.'

So he spoke, and the old man was afraid, and woke his herald. Hermes yoked the horses and mules for them, and drove them himself quickly through the camp. And no man was aware of them.

But when they came to the fording-place of the lovely stream of the swirling river Xanthos, whose father is immortal Zeus, Hermes then went away to high Olympos, and Dawn in her yellow robe was spreading over all the earth: and they drove the horses on towards the city with wailing and lamentation, while the mules carried the body. And no-one else saw them first, man or girdled woman, but only Kassandra, beautiful as golden Aphrodite, who had gone up to the height of Pergamos, and saw her dear father standing in the chariot and the herald, his town-crier, with him. And she saw Hektor lying there in the mule-cart on a bier. She shrieked aloud then and cried out to all the city: 'See, men and women of Troy, come and see Hektor, if ever you rejoiced to see him return from battle still living, since he was a great joy to our city and all our people.'

So she spoke, and no-one was left there in the city, man or woman. Uncontrollable grief came over all of them, and they met Priam close by the gates as he brought the body in. At their front Hektor's dear wife and his honoured mother tore their hair for him, and threw themselves at the strong-wheeled cart, to touch his head: and the crowd gathered round them weeping. And now they would have poured their tears in mourning for Hektor there in front of the gates all day long to the setting of the sun, if the old man had not spoken from his chariot to his people: 'Give me room now for the mules to pass.

You can have your fill of mourning afterwards, when I have brought him home.'

So he spoke, and they parted and made way for the cart. When they had brought him inside the great house, they then laid him on a fretted bed, and seated singers beside him to lead the laments. They sang the mournful dirge, and the women joined with their keening. White-armed Andromache began their lamentation, holding murderous Hektor's head between her hands: 'My husband, you are gone from life young, and you leave me behind a widow in your house. And our child is still only a baby, the son that was born to you and me, ill-fated parents, and I do not think he will reach his manhood. Before that this city of ours will be sacked from top to bottom: because you, her guardian, are dead – you used to protect the city, and keep safe her loved wives and little children. They will soon now be carried away in the hollow ships, and I among them. And you, child, you will go where I go, where you will be put to shaming work, slaving for a cruel master. Or some Achaian will catch you by the arm and fling you from the walls to a miserable death, in his anger because Hektor killed his brother, it may be, or his father or perhaps his son – there were very many of the Achaians who sank their teeth in the broad earth, brought down at Hektor's hands. Your father was not a gentle man in the misery of battle. And so the people are mourning him all through the city, and on your parents, Hektor, you have brought the curse of grief and lamentation. But it is I who will be left the greatest pain and misery – because when you died it was not in your bed, you did not hold out your arms to me or tell me some weighty last word, which I could remember for ever, all the nights and days when I weep for you.'

Such was her lament, and the women joined with their keening. And now Hekabe led their loud lamentation: 'Hektor, dearest to my heart by far of all my sons, when I had you alive you were loved by the gods, and now they have indeed cared for you, if only in the time of your death. Others of my sons swift-footed Achilleus would sell, if he caught them, sending them over the harvestless sea to Samos and Imbros and misty Lemnos. But when he had taken the life from you with the long-pointed bronze, he dragged you time after time around the tomb of his companion you had killed, Patroklos – yet for all this he did not bring him to life. But now I have you lying here in the house sweet and fresh as dew, looking like one whom Apollo of the silver bow has visited and killed with his gentle arrows.'

Such was her lament, and she set them to endless weeping. Then

Helen was the third to lead their lamentation: 'Hektor, dearest to my heart by far of all my husband's brothers – my husband is godlike Alexandros: he brought me to Troy, and how I wish that I had died before that! This is now the twentieth year since I came from there and left my own native land. But in all that time I have never heard a hard word from you or any rudeness. But if anyone spoke harshly to me in the house – one of your brothers or sisters or your brothers' fine-dressed wives, or your mother (though your father was always kind to me as a real father) – then you would speak winning words to them and stop them, through your own gentle-hearted way and your gentle words. And so I weep in anguish of heart both for you and for my own ill-fated self. There is no-one else now in the broad land of Troy to be kind to me and a friend, but they all shudder with loathing for me.'

Such was her lament, and the limitless crowd of townspeople joined with their mourning. Then the old man Priam spoke to his people: 'Bring wood now into the city, Trojans, and have no fear in your hearts of a massed ambush from the Argives. Achilleus promised me, when he sent me on my way back from the black ships, that they will do us no harm until the twelfth dawn comes.'

So he spoke, and they yoked oxen and mules to their carts, and quickly gathered then in front of the city. For nine days they brought in vast quantities of wood. But when the tenth dawn appeared bringing light for mortals, then they carried out brave Hektor with their tears falling, and placed his body at the top of the pyre, and put fire to it.

When early-born Dawn appeared with her rosy fingers, then the people collected around the pyre of famous Hektor. When they were all gathered together in one place, first they extinguished the pyre with gleaming wine, all of it that the fire's fury had reached. And then his brothers and companions gathered the white bones, mourning, and heavy tears fell from their cheeks. And they took the bones and put them in a golden box, wrapping them in soft purple cloths: and they quickly placed it in the hollow of a grave, and covered it over with great stones laid close together. Then they piled a grave-mound over it in haste, with look-outs set on all sides, in case the well-greaved Achaians made an early attack. When they had piled the mound they went back. And then they gathered again in due order and held a glorious feast in the house of Priam, the god-ordained king.

Such was the burial they gave to Hektor, tamer of horses.

INDEX

This index lists only the proper names occurring in the text of the *Iliad*. No references are made to the Introduction. Where a complete list of references would be impracticable (as for Achilleus) or unhelpful (as for Mount Ida), or both (as for Achaians), a reference to the first occurrence of the name is followed by 'etc.'.

(A) or (T) after a man's name indicates a combatant on the Achaian (A) or Trojan (T) side.

For ease of reference, the headings of some two dozen major entries are given in capital letters.

A

Abantes, people of Euboia: 76, 106

Abarbareë, nymph, mother of Aisepos (2) (T) and Pedasos (1) (T) to Boukolion: 130

Abas (T), son of Eurydamas, killed by Diomedes: 112

Abioi, northern tribe from Skythia or Thrace: 225

Ableros (T), killed by Antilochos: 130

Abydos, town on S. shore of Hellespont, N.E. of Troy: 83, 107, 306

Achaia, the general name for mainland Greece: 56 etc.

ACHAIANS, Greeks: 51 etc.; catalogue of Achaians, 75–81; their great numbers, 67, 89; contrasted with Trojans, 85, 105; slow to accept Hektor's challenge, 144–5; burial of dead, 151; wine-buying, 152; sink in Zeus' scales, 154; the ships fired, 275; stab the dead Hektor, 368; funeral for Patroklos, 374–8

—Achaian assemblies: 52–7, 67–8, 69–73, 150–51, 325–30

Achaian wall: 149, 151–2, 157; will be destroyed by Apollo and Poseidon, 214; fight for the wall, 219–24; flattened by Apollo, 264

Acheloïos (1), river in N.W. Greece, the largest river in Greece: 350

Acheloïos (2), river in Asia Minor (Lydia): 406

ACHILLEUS (A), son of Peleus and Thetis, leader of the Myrmidons: 51 etc.; grandson of Aiakos, 83 etc.; commander of men from Pelasgian Argos, Phthia, and Hellas, 79; handsomest of the

midons), 344, 362, 394 (Apollo), 397 (Hekabe)

sacking of cities: 23 cities, 173; Lesbos, 168, 172, 180; Lyrnessos, 79–80, 325, 330 (killed Mynes and Briseïs' brothers); Pedasos (2), 336; Skyros, 180; Tenedos, 209; Thebe, 79–80, 139 (killed Eëtion and all his sons), 170, 276

used to sell or ransom Trojans before Patroklos' death: 347, 348, 361, 409

—Calls assembly, 52, 325; killed Ennomos (1), 83; captured Isos and Antiphos (3), 197; brings the Myrmidons under arms, 276–8; 'useless burden on the earth', 312; curses quarrels and anger, 312; visited by Iris, 313–14; shouts at the ditch, 314–15; arms for battle, 331–2; dialogue with his horse Xanthos, 332–3; dominates the fighting, 342–5; slaughters Trojans in the river, 346–51; drives Trojans into Troy, 358; faced by Agenor, and tricked by Apollo, 358–60

Adamas (T), son of Asios (1) (T): 217; killed by Meriones, 237; 241–2

Admetos, son of Pheres, father of Eumelos (A) by Alkestis: 80, 81, 378, 380, 384

Adresteia, town to N.E. of Troy: 83

Adrestos (1), king of Sikyon: 77; father of Aigialeia, 118; father-in-law of Tydeus, 246; his race-horse Arion, 380

Adrestos (2) (T), son of Merops, joint leader of the Trojans from Adresteia, etc.: 83; killed by Diomedes, 202

Adrestos (3) (T), taken alive by Menelaos then killed by Agamemnon: 131

Adrestos (4) (T), killed by Patroklos: 288

Agakles, father of Epeigeus (A): 285

Agamede, daughter of Augeias, wife of Moulios (1): 211

AGAMEMNON (A), king of Mykene, son of Atreus, leader of the Achaian army: 51 etc.; leader of the largest Achaian contingent, 77; father of Orestes (2), Chrysothemis, Iphianassa, Laodike (2), 169, 172

—and Achilleus: quarrel, 53–7, 312; his responsibility for the quarrel, 73, 168, 227, 326–7; his offer of recompense, 168–9, 171–2; reconciled, 324–30; honoured by Achilleus, 392

and Klytaimestra, his wife: prefers Chryseïs to her, 53

and Menelaos, his brother: solicitude for Menelaos, 99–100, 144, 187; persuades him not to spare Trojans, 131; criticises him, 184

and Odysseus: 103–4, 245–6

criticism of him: by Achilleus, 54, 56; by Thersites, 69–70; by Diomedes, 166–7; by Nestor, 168; by Odysseus, 245–6

his despair: 99–100, 166, 182, 184, 245

dominates the fighting: 197–201

glorified by Zeus, 75; by Athene and Hera, 196

—Rejects Chryses, 51; sent false Dream by Zeus, 65–6; tests his troops, 66–8; admired by Priam, 88–9; solemnises oaths, 91; predicts destruction of Troy, 99; reviews his troops, 101–5; rallies the Achaians, 158; commends Teukros, 159; his armour and arming, 195–6; wounded by Koön, withdraws from the field, 200–201, 325; encouraged by Poseidon, 247; reconciled with Achilleus, 324–30

Agapenor (A), son of Ankaios (1), leader of the Arcadian contingent: 78

Agasthenes, son of Augeias and father of Polyxeinos (A): 78

Agastrophos (T), son of Paion, killed by Diomedes: 202, 203

Agathon (T), son of Priam, railed at by Priam: 398

Agaue, a Nereid: 311

Agelaos (1) (T), son of Phradmon, killed by Diomedes: 158

Agelaos (2) (A), killed by Hektor: 201

Agenor (T), son of Antenor: 106, 196, 216, 236, 238, 253, 263, 284; father of Echeklos (2) (T), 344; his stand against Achilleus, rescued by Apollo, 358–9

Aglaïa, mother of Nireus (A) to Charopos: 79

Agrios, son of Portheus: 246

Aiakos, father of Peleus, grandfather of Achilleus: 83 etc.; son of Zeus, 350

Aiantes, the two Achaians called Aias – Aias (1) son of Telamon, and Aias (2) son of Oïleus – when referred to as a pair: 73 etc.; the two distinguished, 76; commended by Agamemnon, 102; share name and courage, 309; hold off Trojans from body of Patroklos, 309, 313

AIAS (1) (A), son of Telamon, from Salamis: 54 etc.; his contingent, 77; best of the Achaians after Achilleus, 81; his quality as a fighter, 232, 299

—and Hektor: 146–9, 207, 243, 253, 256, 261, 271–2

and Teukros, his half-brother: 159–60, 221–2, 265–6

his shield: 147, 205, 206, 240, 295–6, 314

—Admired by Priam, 90; kills Simoeisios, 106; wins the lot to fight Hektor, 146; duel with Hektor, 146–9; chosen for embassy to Achilleus, 169; his appeal to Achilleus, 179; rescues Odysseus, 205–6; caused to retreat by Zeus, 207–8; defends the Achaian wall with Teukros, 221–2; spurred by Poseidon, 226; exchange of sneers with Hektor, 243; disables Hektor with stone, 253; fights in defence of the ships, 271–2; beaten back, 275; protects Patroklos' body, 295–6, 298–9; appeals to Zeus to lift fog, 307; competes in the wrestling-match, 388; competes in the fight in armour, 390; competes in the discus-throw, 390–91

Aias (2) (A), son of Oïleus (1), leader of the Locrians: 76 etc.; un-equalled in running, 255

—Spurred by Poseidon, 226; decapitates Imbrios, 229; inseparable from Aias (1), 240; kills Kleoboulos, 280; quarrel with Idomeneus, 382–3; competes in the foot-race, 389

Aïdoneus, another name for Hades (q.v.): 335

Aigai, town in Achaia, N. Peloponnese: centre of Poseidon's worship, 157, 225

Aigaion, the hundred-hander, also called Briareos: 60

Aigeus, father of Theseus: 57

Aigialeia, wife of Diomedes, daughter of Adrestos (1): 118

Aigialos, town in Paphlagonia: 83

Aigilips, place in Ithaka: 78

Aigina, island in the Saronic Gulf: 77

Aigion, town in Agamemnon's kingdom: 77

AINEIAS (T), son of Anchises (1) and Aphrodite, brought up by Alkathoös, 235; leader of the Dardanians, 82 etc.; his resentment against Priam, 235, cf. 338; fated to survive and be king of Trojans, 340, 341; leader of the fourth Trojan company, 216

—and Achilleus: earlier encounter, 336, 338; verbal exchange and fight, 337–41

his horses: 115, 116, 155, 378

protected by gods: Aphrodite, 116; Apollo, 116, 118–19, 120; Poseidon, 340–41

—Faces Diomedes with Pandaros, 113–16; wounded by Diomedes, 116; battle over Alkathoös, his brother-in-law, 235–7; urged on by Apollo, 300, 335–6; leads Trojan pursuit with Hektor, 309; gives genealogy of kings of Troy, 338–9

Ainios (T), Paionian killed by Achilleus: 350

Ainos, town in Thrace: 107

Aiolos, father of Sisyphos: 133

Aipeia, town in Messenia, S.W. Peloponnese: 169, 172

Aipy, town in Nestor's kingdom: 77

Aipytos, his tomb a landmark in Arcadia: 78

Aisepos (1), river flowing N.E. from Ida: 82, 98, 214

Aisepos (2) (T), son of Boukolion, killed by Euryalos: 130

Aisyëtes: his tomb, 82; father of Alkathoös (T), 234

Aisyme, town in Thrace: 159

Aisymnos (A), killed by Hektor: 201

Aithe, Agamemnon's mare, raced by Menelaos: 378, 381, 384

Aithikes, people in Thessaly: 81

Aithon, one of Hektor's horses: 157

Aithre, daughter of Pittheus, one of Helen's maids: 88

Aitolians, inhabitants of district in N. central Greece: 78, 127, 230, 262, 386; inhabitants of Kalydon, at war with the Kouretes, 177–8

Akamas (1) (T), son of Antenor: 82, 196, 216, 254; killed by Meriones, 280

Akamas (2) (T), son of Eüssoros, joint leader of the Thracians, Trojan allies: 83; impersonated by Apollo, 119; killed by Aias (1), 130

Akessamenos, father of Periboia: 349

Akrisios, king of Argos, father of Danaë: 251

Aktaia, a Nereid: 311

Aktor (1), son of Azeus, father of Astyoche: 76

Aktor (2), supposed father of Kteatos and Eurytos (2), the Moliones (*q.v.*), and grandfather of Amphimachos (1) (A) and Thalpios (A): 78, 211, 229, 386

Aktor (3), father of Menoitios: 212, 273

Aktor (4), father of Echekles: 277

Alalkomenaian, epithet of Athene: 96, 129

Alastor (1) (A), one of the Pylian leaders: 102

Alastor (2) (T), Lycian killed by Odysseus: 124

Alastor (3) (A), companion of Teukros (perhaps the same as Alastor (1)): 160, 234

Alastor (4), father of Tros (2) (T): 344

Alegenor, father of Promachos (A): 255

Aleïan plain, in Asia Minor, scene of Bellerophontes' wandering: 134

Alektryon, father of Leïtos (A): 306

Alesion, a town of the Epeians: 78, 211

Alexandros, *see* Paris

Alkandros (T), Lycian killed by Odysseus: 124

Alkathoös (T), son of Aisyëtes, son-in-law of Anchises (1): 216, 234–6; killed by Idomeneus, 234; brought up Aineias, 235

Alkestis, daughter of Pelias, mother of Eumelos (A) by Admetos: 80

Alkimedon (A), son of Laerkes, a leader of the Myrmidons: 277, 303–4; evidently also called Alkimos (*q.v.*), 332, 403, 405

Alkimos (A), evidently a shortened form of Alkimedon (*q.v.*): 332, 403, 405

Alkmaon (A), son of Thestor (2), killed by Sarpedon: 222

Alkmene, mother of Herakles by Zeus: 251, 326

Alkyone, her parents' name for Kleopatra (*q.v.*): 178

Aloëus, father of Otos and Ephialtes: 117

Alope, town in Pelasgian Argos: 79

Alos, town in Pelasgian Argos: 79

Alpheios, river in W. Peloponnese: 77, 210, 211; the god of the river, father of Ortilochos, 121

Altes, king of the Leleges, father of Laothoë: 348, 361

Boibeïs, Lake, lake in Thessaly: 80

Boiotia, district in central Greece: 124

Boiotians, inhabitants of Boiotia: 75–6, 240, 263

Boreas, the North Wind: 256, 376–7

Boros (1), father of Phaistos (2) (T): 110

Boros (2), son of Perieres, titular father of Menesthios (2) (A): 277

Boudeion, town of the Myrmidons: 285

Boukolion, son of Laomedon, father of Aisepos (2) (T) and Pedasos (1) (T): 130

Boukolos, father of Sphelos: 263

Bouprasion, district of Epeian territory in N.W. Peloponnese: 78, 211, 386

Briareos, the hundred-hander, also called Aigaion; 60

Briseïs, daughter of Briseus, captive awarded to Achilleus: 55, 168; taken from Achilleus by Agamemnon, 58; captured at sack of Lyrnessos, 79; Achilleus' love for her, 173, cf. 408; Achilleus wishes she had been killed, 325; untouched by Agamemnon, 328–9; her lament for Patroklos, 330; her husband (Mynes?) and brothers killed by Achilleus, 330; Patroklos promised her marriage to Achilleus, 330; back with Achilleus, 408

Briseus, father of Briseïs: 59, 169, 172

Bryseiai, town in Lakedaimon: 77

C

Caria, country in S. Asia Minor: 99

Carians, Trojan allies, inhabitants of Caria; 83, 191

Centaurs, wild creatures, half man and half beast, living around Mt. Pelion: destroyed by the Lapiths, 57, 81; Cheiron the most civilised of the Centaurs, 213

Chalkis (1), town in Euboia: 76

Chalkis (2), town in Aitolia: 78

Chalkodon, father of Elephenor (A): 76, 106

Chalkon, father of Bathykles (A): 286

Charis, goddess, wife of Hephaistos: 318

Charops, father of Nireus (A): 79

Charops (T), son of Hippasos (1), killed by Odysseus: 204

Cheiron, Centaur: gave medicines to Asklepios, 100; most civilised of the Centaurs, taught medicine to Achilleus, 213; gave Peleus his spear, 276, 332

Chersidamas (T), killed by Odysseus: 204

Chimaira, monster: killed by Bellerophontes, 134; reared by Amisodaros, 280

E

F

Fate(s): blamed for Agamemnon's folly, 326; blamed for Achilleus' death, 332; Fate the spinner, 337, 397; put endurance in men, 394

Folly (*see also* Ate): 176; (326–7)

Furies (*see also* Erinyes): 260

G

Galateia, a Nereid: 311

Ganymedes, son of Tros (1): most beautiful of men, taken to be Zeus' wine-pourer, 339; Zeus' compensation for him, 115

Gargaron, the central peak of Mt. Ida: 154, 250, 251, 259

Gerenian, epithet of Nestor: 72 etc.

Glaphyrai, town in Thessaly: 80

Glauke, a Nereid: 311

Glaukos (1) (T), son of Hippolochos (1), Trojan ally, joint leader of the Lycians: 84 etc., 142, 216, 220–21; and Diomedes, 132–5; wounded by Teukros, 222, 284; healed by Apollo, and rallies Trojans to fight for Sarpedon, 283–5; criticises Hektor, 296

Glaukos (2), son of Sisyphos, father of Bellerophontes: 133

Glisas, town in Boiotia: 76

Gonoessa, town in Agamemnon's kingdom: 77

Gorgo *or* Gorgon, monster: 125, 160, 195

Gorgythion (T), son of Priam, killed by Teukros: 159–60

Gortyn, city in Crete: 79

Gouneus (A), leader of Enienes and Peraibians from N.W. Greece: 81

Graces, goddesses: 116, 249–50, 294

Graia, town in Boiotia: 75

Grenikos, river of the Troad: 214

Gygaian lake (in Maionia), nymph of, mother of Mesthles (T) and Antiphos (2) (T) to Talaimenes: 83; perhaps also mother of Iphition (T) to Otrynteus, 342

Gyrtias, father of Hyrtios (T): 255

Gyrtone, town in Thessaly: 80

H

Hades, god of the dead (*see also* Aïdoneus, Zeus of the underworld): 51 etc.; son of Kronos and Rhea, 260; his allocation, 260; pitiless, the most hated god, 169; 'Zeus of the underworld', 175, cf. 178; wounded by Herakles, 117–18; his dog (Kerberos) captured by Herakles, 161; terrified by Poseidon's earthquake, 335

I

Ixion, husband of (Dia) mother of Peirithoös by Zeus: 251

K

Kabesos, town of unknown location, presumably in the Troad: 233

Kadmeians, inhabitants of Thebes (1): 104, 127, 188, 387

Kaineus, a Lapith: 57; father of Koronos, 81

Kalchas (A), son of Thestor (1), augur of the Achaians: explains Apollo's anger, 52–3; his prophecy at Aulis, 71–2; impersonated by Poseidon, 226

Kalesios (T), lieutenant of Axylos: 130

Kaletor (1), father of Aphareus (A): 237

Kaletor (2) (T), son of Klytios (1), killed by Aias (1): 265

Kallianassa, a Nereid: 311

Kallianeira, a Nereid: 311

Kalliaros, town in Lokris: 76

Kallikolone, a hill near Troy: 335, 337

Kalydnai islands, islands in S.E. Aegean: 79

Kalydon, town in Aitolia: 78, 230, 246; war over Kalydon between Kouretes and Aitolians, 177–8

Kameiros, city in Rhodes: 79

Kapaneus, father of Sthenelos (1) (A): 77 etc.

Kapys, son of Assarakos, father of Anchises (1): 339

Kardamyle, town in Messenia, S.W. Peloponnese: 169, 172

Karesos, river of the Troad: 214

Karystos, town in Euboia: 76

Kasos, island in S.E. Aegean: 79

Kassandra, daughter of Priam: 233, 408

Kastianeira, mother of Gorgythion (T) by Priam: 159

Kastor, brother of Helen and Polydeukes: 90

Kaukones, people of Asia Minor, Trojan allies: 191, 341

Kaÿstrios, river in Asia Minor: 75

Keas, father of Troizenos: 83

Kebriones (T), bastard son of Priam, brother of Hektor and his charioteer: 169, 206, 216, 242; killed by Patroklos, 289; the battle over his body, 289–90

Keladon, river bordering Arcadia and Pylos (?): 145

Kephallenia, island off W. Greece, part of Odysseus' kingdom: 78

Kephallenians, men from Kephallenia: 103

Kephisian Lake, Lake Kopaïs in Boiotia: 124

Kephisos, river flowing through Phokis: 76

Kerinthos, town in Euboia: 76

Kikones, Trojan allies, living to N.W. of Thrace: 83, 294

Kilikes, the people of Eëtion (1) in Thebe: 138, 139

Killa, town in the Troad: 52, 61

Kinyres, of Cyprus: gave corselet to Agamemnon, 195

Kisseus, father of Theano, grandfather of Iphidamas (T): 200

Kleitos (T), son of Peisenor, companion of Poulydamas, killed by Teukros: 265–6

Kleoboulos (T), killed by Aias (2): 280

Kleonai, town in Agamemnon's kingdom: 77

Kleopatra, wife of Meleagros, daughter of Idas and Marpessa, called Alkyone by her parents: 177–8

Klonios (A), leader of the Boiotians: 75; killed by Agenor, 263

Klymene (1), one of Helen's maids: 88

Klymene (2), a Nereid: 311

Klytaimestra, wife of Agamemnon: 53

Klytios (1), son of Laomedon, 339: Trojan elder, 88; father of Kaletor (2) (T), 265

Klytios (2), father of Dolops (1) (A): 201

Klytomedes, son of Enops (3), defeated at boxing by Nestor: 386

Knosos, city in Crete: 79, 323

Koiranos (1) (T), Lycian killed by Odysseus: 124

Koiranos (2) (A), charioteer of Meriones, killed by Hektor: 306

Koön (T), son of Antenor, killed by Agamemnon: 200–201; wounds Agamemnon, 200, 325

Kopai, town in Boiotia: 75

Kopreus, father of Periphetes (2) (A), lackey of Eurystheus: 270

Koroneia, town in Boiotia: 76

Koronos, son of Kaineus, father of Leonteus (A): 81

Kos, island in S.E. Aegean: 79, 249, 256

Kouretes, a people in Aitolia, living in Pleuron: their war with the Aitolians of Kalydon, 177–8

Kranaë, island where Paris first made love to Helen after abducting her: 94

Krapathos, island in S.E. Aegean: 79

Kreion, father of Lykomedes (A): 168, 329

Krethon (A), son of Diokles, killed by Aineias: 121

Krisa, town in Phokis: 76

Kroismos (T), killed by Meges: 267

Krokyleia, place in Ithaka: 78

Kromna, town in Paphlagonia: 83

Kronos, god, son of Ouranos, father of Zeus: 60 etc.; father, by Rhea, of Zeus, Poseidon, Hades, 260; father of Hera, 97

—Banished by Zeus, 248; confined in Tartaros, 163, 250, 261

see also Titans

Kteatos, supposed son of Aktor (2), real son of Poseidon, twin brother of Eurytos (2), father of Amphimachos (1) (A) (*see also* Moliones): 78, 229, (386)

Kyllene, mountain in Arcadia: 78, 267

Kymodoke, a Nereid: 311

Kymothoë, a Nereid: 311

Kynos, town in Lokris: 76

Kyparisseëis, town in Nestor's kingdom: 77

Kyparissos, town in Phokis: 76

Kyphos, home of Gouneus (A) in N.W. Greece: 81

Kypris, epithet of Aphrodite: 116, 118, 119, 126

Kythera, island off S. Peloponnese: 188, 265

Kytoros, town in Paphlagonia: 83

L

Laäs, town in Lakedaimon: 77

Laerkes, son of Haimon (3), father of Alkimedon (A): 277, 303

Laertes, father of Odysseus: 68 etc.

Lakedaimon, the kingdom of Menelaos, in S. Peloponnese: 77, 90, 93, 94

Lampos (1), son of Laomedon, 267, 339: Trojan elder, 88; father of Dolops (2) (T), 267

Lampos (2), one of Hektor's horses: 157

Laodamas (T), son of Antenor, killed by Aias (1): 267

Laodameia, daughter of Bellerophontes, mother of Sarpedon (T) by Zeus, killed by Artemis: 134

Laodike (1), daughter of Priam, wife of Helikaon (T): 87, 135

Laodike (2), one of Agamemnon's daughters: 169, 172

Laodokos (1) (T), son of Antenor, impersonated by Athene: 98

Laodokos (2) (A), charioteer of Antilochos: 308

Laogonos (1) (T), son of Onetor, killed by Meriones: 286

Laogonos (2) (T), son of Bias (3), killed by Achilleus: 344

Laomedon, father of Priam, 90, 339: son of Ilos, 339; father of Boukolion, 130; father of Lampos (1), 267, 339; father of Tithonos, Klytios (1), Hiketaon, 339

—employed Apollo and Poseidon, and cheated them: 152, 356

his folly in cheating Herakles: 123

his horses: 115, 123, 380, cf. 339

Laothoë, daughter of Altes, mother of Polydoros (1) (T) and Lykaon (2) (T) to Priam: 348, 361

Lapiths, tribe of people from Thessaly, led by Polypoites (A) and Leonteus (A), 81: 216, 217

Mykene, city in the Argolid, home of Agamemnon: 77, 104, 146, 167, 196, 270; loved by Hera, 97

Mynes (T), king of Lyrnessos, son of Euenos (1), killed by Achilleus: 80; husband of Briseïs (?), 330

Myrine, woman (Amazon?) after whom the gods named the mound in front of Troy called Batieia by men: 82

Myrmidons, the inhabitants of Phthia, led in war by Achilleus: 55 etc.; their amusements while idle, 81; brought under arms by Achilleus, 276–8; their five leaders, 276–7; their complaints of Achilleus, 277; led into battle, 278–9; mourn Patroklos, 315, 317, 324, 372, 374

Myrsinos, a town of the Epeians: 78

Mysians (1), Trojan allies, inhabitants of Mysia to S.E. of Troad: 83, 191, 255, 399

Mysians (2), Thracian tribe living near the Danube: 225

N

Nastes (T), son of Nomion, Trojan ally, joint leader of the Carians, killed by Achilleus: 83–4

Naubolos, father of Iphitos (1): 76

Neleus, father of Nestor: 65 etc.; 210–11

Nemertes, a Nereid: 311

Neoptolemos, son of Achilleus: 331

Nereids, sea-goddesses, daughters of Nereus: a list of them, 311

Nereus, sea-god, the old man of the sea, father of Thetis, 63, and the other Nereids: 311

Neriton, mountain in Ithaka: 78

Nesaia, a Nereid: 311

NESTOR (A), son of Neleus, father of Antilochos (A) and Thrasymedes (A), king of the Pylians: 56 etc.; leader of the Pylian contingent, 78

—addresses the Achaians: 66, 72–3, 74, 131, 144–6, 149, 167, 168, 186, 270

  charioteer: 155, 206

  chariot expert: 77, 379–80

  his cup: 209

  his prize for supremacy in advice (Hekamede): 209

  his shield: 157

  previous exploits: killed Ereuthalion, 103, 145; prowess in the war between Pylians and Epeians, 210–11

  reminiscences: 56–7, 103, 145, 209–11, 386

—Commended by Agamemnon, 73, 102–3; proposes building of wall,

171–2; reports on the embassy, 180; joins Diomedes on night expedition, 187–94; isolated by Trojans, kills six, wounded by Sokos, withdraws from the field, 204–6; rescued by Aias (1) and Menelaos, 205–6; urges food before battle, and formal reconciliation between Achilleus and Agamemnon, 327–9; competes in the wrestling-match, 388; competes in the foot-race, 389

Oichalia, city in Thessaly, home of king Eurytos (1): 77, 80

Oidipous, king of Thebes (1): 387

Oïleus (1), father of Aias (2) (A): 76 etc.; father of Medon (1) (A) by Rhene, 80, 240; husband of Eriopis, 240, 263

Oïleus (2) (T), killed by Agamemnon: 197

Oineus, king of Kalydon in Aitolia, son of Portheus, 246, father of Meleagros and Tydeus: 78, 127; entertained Bellerophontes, 134; punished by Artemis, 177; entreated Meleagros, 178

Oinomaos (1) (A), killed by Hektor: 124

Oinomaos (2) (T): 217; killed by Idomeneus, 236

Oinops, father of Helenos (1) (A): 124

Oitylos, town in Lakedaimon: 77

Okalea, town in Boiotia: 75

Olenos (1), rock of, landmark on border of Elis: 78, 211

Olenos (2), town in Aitolia: 78

Olizon, town in Thessaly: 80

Oloösson, town in Thessaly: 81

Olympos, mountain in N.E. Thessaly, home of the gods: 51 etc.; its gates kept by the Seasons, 125, 161

Onchestos, town in Boiotia: 76

Onetor, father of Laogonos (1) (T), priest of Idaian Zeus: 286

Ophelestes (1) (T), killed by Teukros: 159

Ophelestes (2) (T), Paionian killed by Achilleus: 350

Opheltios (1) (T), killed by Euryalos: 130

Opheltios (2) (A), killed by Hektor: 201

Opites (A), killed by Hektor: 201

Opoëis, town in Lokris, original home of Patroklos: 76, 317, 374

Orchomenos (1), city of the Minyans, in E. central Greece: 76; its wealth, 174

Orchomenos (2), town in Arcadia: 78

Oreithyia, a Nereid: 311

Oresbios (A), Boiotian killed by Hektor: 124

Orestes (1) (A), killed by Hektor: 124

Orestes (2), son of Agamemnon: 169, 172

Orestes (3) (T): 217; killed by Leonteus, 218

Orion, constellation: 320

P

Pelion, mountain in Magnesia, home of the Centaurs: 81, 276, 332

Pellene, town in Agamemnon's kingdom: 77

Pelops, father of Atreus and Thyestes: 67

Peneios, river in Thessaly: 81

Peneleos (A), leader of the Boiotians: 75, 227, 254–5, 280; wounded by Poulydamas, 306

Peraibians, people in N.W. Greece, led by Gouneus (A): 81

Pereia, place in Thessaly (?) where Apollo bred the horses of Admetos: 81

Pergamos, the citadel of Troy: 107, 119, 141, 142, 408

Pergasos, father of Deïkoön (T): 121

Periboia, daughter of Akessamenos, mother of Pelegon to Axios: 349

Perieres, father of Boros (2): 277

Perimedes, father of Schedios (2) (A): 267

Perimos (T), son of Megas, killed by Patroklos: 288

Periphas (1) (A), son of Ochesios, Aitolian killed by Ares: 127

Periphas (2) (T), son of Epytos, herald of Anchises, impersonated by Apollo: 300

Periphetes (1) (T), killed by Teukros: 255

Periphetes (2) (A), son of Kopreus, killed by Hektor: 270

Perkote, town to N.E. of Troy: 83, 130, 200, 202, 268

Persephone, wife of Hades, goddess of the underworld: 175, 178

Perseus, son of Zeus by Danaë: 251; father of Sthenelos (2), 326

Peteon, town in Boiotia: 75

Peteos, father of Menestheus (A): 77, 103, 221, 240

Phainops (1), father of Xanthos (1) (T) and Thoön (1) (T): 112

Phainops (2), father of Phorkys (T): 300

Phainops (3) (T), son of Asios (1) (T), impersonated by Apollo: 306

Phaistos (1), city in Crete: 79

Phaistos (2) (T), son of Boros (1), Maionian killed by Idomeneus: 110

Phalkes (T): 242; killed by Antilochos, 255

Pharis, town in Lakedaimon: 77

Phausias, father of Apisaon (1) (T): 207

Phegeus (T), son of Dares, killed by Diomedes: 109

Pheia, town in W. Peloponnese: 145

Pheidas (A), a leader of the Athenians: 240

Pheidippos (A), son of Thessalos, joint leader of the men from Kos, etc.: 79

Pheneos, town in Arcadia: 78

Pherai (1), city in Thessaly, home of Eumelos: 80

Pherai (2) or Phere, city in Messenia, S.W. Peloponnese: 121, 169, 172

Phere, see Pherai (2)

R

his gifts to men: 404

his horses and chariot: 154

his previous conquests catalogued: 250–51

his scales: 154, 287, 364

his will: 51, 156, 179, 196, 261, 269, 275, 288, 302, 305, 339

pities: Achilleus, 331; Agamemnon, 158; Hektor, 297, 363–4, 394; Achilleus' horses, 303; Aias (1), 307; Priam, 400

ponders the fate of men: Sarpedon, 282; Patroklos, 287; Hektor, 363–4

prophesies the future: 163, 257, 297

rains blood: 196, 283

sender of signs: 71–2, 97, 104, 154, 156, 158, 171, 182, 195, 196, 218, 220, 230, 264, 283, 305, 400

the source of kings' honour: 69, 298

violence or threats against gods: 63, 64, 153, 162, 249, 256, 258–9, 326–7

—Sends false Dream to Agamemnon, 65; glorifies Agamemnon, 75; prospered Rhodes under Tlepolemos (1), 79; sets Athene at Ares, 126; criticises Ares, 126; forbids gods to intervene on either side, 153; warns back Diomedes, 156; draws Hektor out of the fighting, 198–9; causes Aias (1) to retreat, 207; his seduction by Hera, 250–51; protects Hektor, 266; drives Hektor at the ships, 269–72; half grants Achilleus' prayer, 278; his favour for Patroklos, 299; blamed for Agamemnon's folly, 326; summons assembly, tells gods to take sides, 334–5; laughs to see the gods fight, 354; summons Thetis, to tell Achilleus to release Hektor's body, 394–5

Zeus of the underworld, Hades: 175